THE WORLD OF
ANIMALS

THE WORLD OF
ANIMALS

BACKPACKBOOKS

○

NEW YORK

Copyright © 2003 by Parragon Publishing

This 2005 edition published by Backpack Books,
by arrangement with Parragon Publishing.

Backpack Books
122 Fifth Avenue
New York, NY 10011

ISBN 0-7607-6819-6

Printed and bound in China

05 06 07 08 MCH 10 9 8 7 6 5 4 3 2 1

This edition created by Starry Dog Books.

Consultant Editor: Brian Williams

CONTENTS

A WORLD FULL OF ANIMALS

⬆ Boa constrictor

The world teems with animals. Almost everywhere we look, creatures are going about their daily lives. On a walk through the countryside we see birds high in the sky. Insects buzz around the flowers. Mice and voles scamper through the undergrowth. Rabbits race across fields. Worms burrow in the soil under our feet. Even in a busy city, pigeons flock and cockroaches scuttle.

These are a tiny selection of the kinds of animals that live on Earth. No one is sure exactly how many there are. Nearly two million kinds, or species, have been studied and identified by scientists. But many remote mountains, rainforests, coastlines and deep seas remain to be explored. The total number of animal species on Earth may be 10 million, 20 million, or even more. Most of them are likely to be small insects such as beetles.

◀ Mushroom

THE KINGDOMS OF LIVING THINGS

Scientists used to divide the living world into two main groups, or kingdoms: plants and animals. Today, most experts agree that there are five kingdoms. Two consist of microscopic life-forms, where each individual is just one living cell. One of these kingdoms is Monerans, including the germs known as bacteria.

⬆ Manta ray

The other kingdom is Protists. Some protists are like tiny, one-celled micro-animals. They move about and eat food. So they are included at the beginning of this book (pages 12–15). The third kingdom is Plants, such as flowers, trees, grasses, ferns, and seaweeds, and the fourth is Fungi, such as mushrooms, toadstools, and yeasts. The fifth kingdom, and the largest, is the Animals.

WHAT ARE ANIMALS?

Animals are multi-celled living things that get the energy they need for survival, and the nutrients they need for growth and repair, by feeding on other living things.

◀ Wild bees

EVOLUTION

Evolution is when living things change or adapt to their surroundings. The world is always changing, as weather and climate alter, seas rise and fall, volcanoes erupt, and earthquakes split the land. Living things change too, developing new bodily features and behavior, so they can survive better in the new and different conditions. But survival is a continuing struggle. It is as if nature chooses or selects which plants and animals will survive, and which will die. This is evolution by natural selection.

Evolution has been happening since life first appeared on Earth some 4 billion years ago. It has meant that some kinds of animals have died out, or become extinct, while others have evolved to take their place. All of this usually happens over a very long time scale, thousands or millions of years. But we have altered the world greatly in the last few hundred years. New types of living things can now be produced in a few weeks or months using the science of genetics. How this will affect nature in the future is very unclear.

◀ Tuatara

In this way they differ from plants, which capture their energy from sunlight.

Most animals feed by eating or ingesting their food. Carnivores such as wolves eat meat. Herbivores like deer feed on plant parts. Detritivores like worms and millipedes feed on dead and rotting bits of other living things. Omnivores eat almost anything.

❶ Caterpillars

Most animals have sense organs such as eyes and ears, so they can detect changes around them. They also have muscles so they can move about, react to changes, find food, and avoid danger. However very simple animals like sponges have few senses and cannot move. Some animals, like mussels and barnacles, fix themselves into position when young, and stay put for the rest of their lives.

HOW ANIMALS BREED
The key feature of all living things is that they breed—they produce more of their kind. Animals do this in a huge variety of ways. Many, from butterflies to birds, lay eggs. Some, such as mammals, certain snakes, and some fish, give birth to babies. A

❷ Horned grebe

few, like some flatworms, starfish, and jellyfish, can split and grow into two new individuals.

Animals care for their offspring in different ways. Monkeys and apes look after their babies for months, or even years. Most birds spend weeks tirelessly feeding the chicks that hatch from their eggs. Mouthbrooding fish shelter their young in their mouths. The gastric-brooding frog keeps its young tadpoles in its stomach! However, most animals lay or release their eggs, and have nothing more to do with the offspring.

❷ Puffin

Animals live in almost every type of surroundings, or habitat. A waterless desert, an icy glacier, a wave-battered coastline, a deep and pitch-black cave—they are all homes to animals of one kind or another. Each type of animal has features that enable it to survive in its habitat. Glacier grasshoppers can be frozen alive, yet come back to life when thawed out. Desert creatures escape the drought and heat by burrowing underground and staying still or dormant until it rains once more.

⬆ Frogs

⬆ Stinkbug

⬇ Penguins and chicks

⬆ Shrimp on a sea slug

HARMFUL, HELPFUL, AND USEFUL

Some animals have taken to living alongside people. We have covered much of the world with buildings, roads, factories, and garbage tips. These have become ideal habitats for animals such as cockroaches, rats, mice, and gulls. Some animals have become pests. Insects feed on cereal grains and destroy our crops. Some creatures, like flukes and mosquitoes, cause or spread disease.

But we have also found other animals helpful or useful. We have bred farm animals for meat, milk, fur, and skins. Working animals pull plows and carts or carry goods. Horses, dogs, camels, falcons, frogs, and others are used in sports and competitions. For some people, pets are their main companions.

EQUAL ANIMALS

When we talk about "animals and birds," some people think of furry mammals and fluffy chicks. But the animal kingdom contains a gigantic range of creatures— including insects, spiders, snakes, worms, slugs, snails, and other less appealing "creepy-crawlies." We may not want to pick them up, but they each have their role to play in nature.

Today, many animal species are in danger of extinction, due to our human activities.

⬆ Young male lion

GROUPING ANIMALS

To study and understand the animal kingdom, we need to have some method of grouping or classifying its creatures. Those with important similarities are put together in the same group. The main division is between vertebrates and invertebrates.

🅰 Hagfish

Vertebrates are animals with backbones and include fish, frogs and other amphibians, lizards and other reptiles, birds, and furry mammals. Invertebrates lack a backbone and include all other animals, from tiny flies to giant squid. This book is organized into sections using the standard system of classifying animals. It begins with simple invertebrates such as sponges and jellyfish. It ends with mammals that have complex behavior, such as solving problems and using tools. Classification panels give details of how many species are in the group, where they live, what they eat, and other information.

The classification system is broadly based on the idea of evolution. For example, all birds are classified together in the group called Aves. They are probably all descended from very early birds that first evolved millions of years ago. So all birds are related to each other. On a wider scale, the first birds probably evolved from reptiles such as the dinosaurs. In this way, relationships spread throughout the animal kingdom.

🅱 Backswimmer

It is tempting to see this system as a "ladder of evolution," with simple animals at the bottom, and apes, monkeys—and ourselves—at the top. But all animals have amazing adaptations. A penguin might not survive on its own in one of our large cities. But then, we would not survive on our own at the South Pole!

🅰 Sheep

We hunt them for "sport," kill them for collections, and eliminate them in case they are dangerous. Most of all, we take over their wild places so they no longer have anywhere to live. Habitat destruction is the major threat facing the natural world today. Without these animals, our world would be a far less exciting place.

▶ Horned owl

▶The man-o'-war is a cnidarian—
or rather, lots of cnidarians. It is a
floating group of cnidarian polyps
known as siphonophores.

SECTION 1
SIMPLE ANIMALS

THE SIMPLEST OF ALL LIFE FORMS ARE NOT ANIMALS. They are protists. Each is just a single living cell. Some are like microanimals, because they eat tiny bits of food. Others are like microplants, using the sun's light energy to live and grow. Protists number untold trillions and are the basic food for many tiny animals, especially in the sea, where they form much of the plankton.

A simple animal is a creature with few uncomplicated body parts. The simplest of the life forms we call animals are sponges. Each is little more than a collection of fairly similar cells, with no brain, heart, muscles, or similar body parts. Sponges live in rivers and lakes, and on seashores and ocean floors, around the world. Crawling and swimming among them are tiny animals smaller than pinheads, such as water bears and wheel animals. Floating above them in the sea are various creatures that resemble bags of jelly. They include comb jellies and jellyfish, all with long, stinging tentacles.

Close relatives of jellyfish are the sea anemones on the shore, and the anemones' similar but smaller cousins, coral polyps. All of these animals may have few and simple body parts. But they thrive in their millions. Indeed, coral polyps construct the largest animal-made structures on Earth—coral reefs.

THE MICRO-WORLD OF PROTISTS

PROTISTS ARE VERY SMALL. They are among the tiniest living things, and each is made of just one microscopic cell. An average protist is about 20 times smaller than the dot on this i. A very large protist might fit into this o. In the deep sea lives a gigantic kind of protist that grows to the size of your finger. Protists are living things, but they are not really animals or plants. They have a separate kingdom (major group) of their own, Protista. However some kinds, called protozoans, are like tiny animals (rather than tiny plants) because they can move around and they eat other living things—especially other protists! They are found in all watery or damp places, including seas, rivers, ponds, soil, and on and inside animals and plants. Some kinds cause diseases.

There are many different kinds of protists. Amebas are shaped like blobs and they can move around by changing shape as they ooze along like plastic bags of jelly. An ameba feeds by sending out armlike parts to surround a microparticle of food, and then merging the arms with its body to engulf the particle. After digesting what it can, the ameba simply oozes on and leaves the remains behind.

PLASMODIUM AND MALARIA

The protists that cause malaria grow through many stages in their lives. Some are in mosquitoes, some in humans. When a mosquito that does not have plasmodia bites a person who does have them, the mosquito sucks up plasmodia in its meal of blood. Then it bites another person and passes on the parasites.

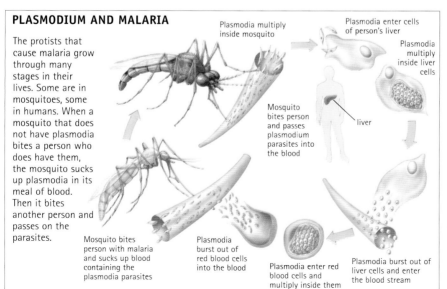

Plasmodia multiply inside mosquito

Plasmodia enter cells of person's liver

Plasmodia multiply inside liver cells

Mosquito bites person and passes plasmodium parasites into the blood

liver

Mosquito bites person with malaria and sucks up blood containing the plasmodia parasites

Plasmodia burst out of red blood cells into the blood

Plasmodia enter red blood cells and multiply inside them

Plasmodia burst out of liver cells and enter the blood stream

A few types of ameba are real giants, growing almost to the size of shirt buttons.

Another group of protists is the ciliates, such as stentors and parameciums (pages 16–17). They are known as ciliates because their bodies are covered by a "carpet" of miniature hairs called cilia.

The cilia beat regularly, like rows of miniature oars, to make the protist glide through the water. However, some ciliates, like stentor, cannot move about. They are attached by a stalk to the pond or stream bottom. They beat their cilia to make water currents that bring tiny bits of food to them.

THE AMAZING SLIME MOLDS

Sometimes a slimy, slug-shaped blob appears on an old tree. It looks like jelly, but gradually, over several minutes, it moves! This is a slime mold. It is not a single creature, but a collection of hundreds of single-celled living things resembling amebas. They normally live separately in the soil and among leaves. They gather together into a sluglike lump to breed. After creeping about for a while, the "slug" grows a stalk that releases tiny, dustlike particles called spores. These blow away and hatch into new amebas. A slime mold "slug" can weigh up to 2 pounds (900 g).

PROTISTS AND DISEASES

Many protists are parasites. They thrive on or in other living things, known as the hosts. The protist gains food and protection or shelter from its host. Some parasitic protists have hardly any effect on their hosts. Others cause great harm and serious diseases such as malaria and sleeping sickness. Malaria is common in many warm, tropical regions. The protists that cause it are known as plasmodia. They are spread by mosquitoes. When a mosquito bites a person, but before it sucks up blood, it passes a few thousand plasmodia protists into the person's body. These plasmodia parasites multiply inside the person's liver and blood. Eventually they produce the sweating, shivering, headaches, and other symptoms of the disease malaria. People who visit tropical places where malaria is common can take tablets or have injections to prevent them catching it.

⬛ Protists come in many shapes. Some are almost perfect spheres, like these diatoms. Others are shaped like bananas or commas.

PROTIST PARTS

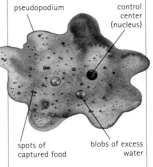

covering of cilia
oral groove (mouth)
stalk
holdfast

The protist called stentor is shaped like a microscopic mushroom. It lives in ponds, lakes, and slow-flowing streams, fixed to something solid by its holdfast. Every now and again it comes loose and wriggles to a new place.

An ameba is easily small enough to fit onto the head of a pin. It lives in water. It has no proper shape. It can spread out almost flat, extend armlike parts called pseudopodia, then form into a round ball and roll along.

pseudopodium
control center (nucleus)
spots of captured food
blobs of excess water

 World Watch

More than 200 million people around the world suffer from malaria. And more than two million people die from this disease each year—about one million of them in Africa. The name of the disease, *malaria*, means "bad air." This name came from the time when people thought the illness was spread by bad or stale air. Then it was discovered that malaria was caused by protists too small to see, carried by mosquitoes.

PROTISTS		
(Kingdom *Protista*) • more than 60,000 kinds or species • live in water, soil, other damp places, and inside creatures and plants • most are microscopic • single-celled (body made of only one cell)	Some main groups of protists: Amebas • 16,000 species • move about and feed by changing shape • some gather together and are known as "slime molds" Ciliates • 7,500 species • move and feed by tiny hairlike cilia	Euglenas • at least 1,000 species • mainly freshwater • have one long, whiplike flagellum • can capture the energy in sunlight, like tiny plants Parasitic protists • 5,000 species • live inside other animals • some cause diseases, such as malaria, sleeping sickness, and dysentery

FLOATING PROTISTS

MOST OCEAN CREATURES, EVEN GREAT WHALES,
DEPEND ON TINY PROTISTS. These protists live in the
upper layers of the sea. They form part of the plankton—
a "living soup" of all kinds of tiny plants, animals, and
other organisms, drifting with the currents. Trillions of
plantlike protists trap the sun's light energy and use it to
live, grow, and multiply. In turn, they are food for
millions of tiny animal-like protists. Both kinds of protists
are eaten by small sea creatures, such as tiny fish and shrimps, as well as the
larvae (young) of bigger animals. These are consumed by larger ocean
creatures, and so on, building up the ocean food chains to huge sharks and whales.

◳ In a drop of seawater, protists such as foraminiferans (pale and curled like spirals)
and radiolarians (blue and ball-shaped) teem in their thousands.

GREEN PLANKTON

Much of the plankton can make its own food
using sunlight energy. Like trees and other green
plants on land, the water-dwelling
protists have a green substance
called chlorophyll, which
absorbs light energy.

Spiroplecta
foraminiferan

Polykrikos
dinoflagellate

Miliota
foraminiferan

Gymnodinium
dinoflagellate

These members of the
green plankton are
sometimes called producers,
because they produce food for
themselves, rather than
consuming it as animals do. Because
strong sunlight can only shine down about 100
feet (30 m) into the sea, the green plankton
have to stay close to the surface to survive.

OILY! !

Crude oil, or petroleum, was
formed from the remains of
billions of tiny plankton
organisms that lived millions
of years ago. They sank
slowly to the seabed in
layers. The pressure of more
layers above eventually
turned them into oil.

Most live concentrated into the top 300 feet (90 m) of the ocean.
A few can make weak wriggling movements, but most are at the
mercy of ocean currents and they drift about in the endless
circulation of seawater.

DIATOMS

The diatoms are plantlike protists with beautifully
shaped, sculpted, and patterned shells. They float
in the upper levels of the sea, and also in lakes, as
part of the plankton. A diatom's shell is double-
layered and made of silica—the main mineral in
sand (and also in glass). Some diatoms have ringlike
flaps that help them float
near the surface.

RADIOLARIANS

These protists are
related to the amebas
shown on the previous
page. Like diatoms,
they have silica shells.

These are usually circular
or spherical, with lines and
patterns etched into the surface.
Some have silica rods sticking out,
like the spokes of a wheel.

Haplozoon
dinoflagellate

Noctiluca dinoflagellate

Ceratium
dinoflagellate

Rotalia
foraminiferan

△ Besides protists, the plankton contains eggs and
young forms (larvae) of larger animals such as
shrimps and crabs.

FORAMINIFERANS

Another group of amebalike protists, the foraminiferans, also live inside
shells. However, their shells are usually made of limestone or chalk
rather than silica. Foraminiferans are very common in sea plankton,
where they float about, feeding on even smaller organisms. A
foraminiferan sticks long, threadlike "arms" through the many holes,
called foramens, in its shell. It grabs food particles with these arms. A
few foraminiferans grow as large as a fingernail.

DINOFLAGELLATES

These plankton protists have long, spinelike projections, which probably
help to stop them sinking in the water, and which also deter predators.
Some can use the sun's light energy, like plants. Others grab tiny bits of
food. In certain conditions, especially a warm springtime, dinoflagellates
cause "red tides" along the seashore. They multiply in such huge
numbers that their bodies color the seawater bright red. Some kinds also
produce poisons that kill other forms of life, such as fish.

SOME KINDS OF
FLOATING PROTISTS

Diatoms
• 10,000 species
• live in the sea and in fresh water
• common in plankton
• have glassy, boxlike casings

Dinoflagellates
• 2,000 species
• live in the sea and in fresh water
• have two whiplike flagella
• some live inside other creatures,
  such as corals

Foraminiferans
• 3,000 species
• live in the sea and in fresh water
• have chalky shells with holes
• some capture food, others
  absorb sunlight

15

MOSS ANIMALS

MOSS ANIMALS OR BRYOZOANS, SOMETIMES CALLED SEA MOSSES, DO NOT LOOK LIKE ANIMALS AT ALL. As their name suggests, they live in the sea and look more like a patch of moss or a similar plant, or even like a doormat. This is because the tiny moss animals live together in a group or colony and extend their tentacles, like hundreds of miniature sea anemones (page 32). The tentacles wave in the water and filter floating bits of food, which the moss animals eat and digest.

Freshwater moss animals feed on protists such as paramecium, euglena, and volvox. Being single cells, these are far smaller than the moss animal. Sea-living moss-animals eat similar tiny food items such as floating scraps of seaweed, marine protists, and also the eggs and larvae (young) of larger animals such as crabs, starfish, and worms. The moss animal grabs its prey with its tentacles, which are covered with microscopic hairs called cilia.

Euglena

Paramecium

Tiny creatures such as moss animals, and the one-celled protists, eat the smallest living things—especially bacteria. Some bacteria hardly seem alive. They can be dried out, boiled, frozen, and even made into crystals in laboratory dishes (left). Yet they still become active when conditions are right.

In some ways, moss animals are similar to coral animals (page 36). Each one is tiny, only about half a pinhead across. It lives inside a hard, stony case and puts its tentacles into the water to catch floating pieces of food. Hundreds or thousands of individual moss animals are connected together into a flat, branching structure which spreads and grows over an underwater object. This object may be a rock or stone, a piece of wood, a large frond of seaweed, or even the shell of another animal like a clam or mussel. In some kinds of moss animal, the colony grows upward, like a plant, rooted at the base to a firm object. The cases of neighboring moss animals, known as zooids, are cemented to each other. The whole colony may widen like a fan or branch like a twig, and be brightly colored. It can have millions of individuals, resembling a piece of coral. But most moss animals are less spectacular. They live in small, flat, pale-looking colonies, rarely larger than coins.

FRESHWATER MOSS ANIMALS

Most types of moss animal live in the sea, but a few live in fresh water, especially if it is clean and unpolluted.

INSIDE A MOSS ANIMAL

A typical moss animal or bryozoan is about the size of a pinhead. It lives in a hard casing, shaped like a shoebox, that it makes around itself from hard, chalky minerals taken from the water. The bell-shaped ring of feathery tentacles surrounding its mouth filter tiny particles of food, like small algae (plants) and protists, from the water. These food particles are passed down into the mouth and digested in the baglike stomach. When danger threatens, strong strands of muscle pull the tentacles into the casing and then close and hold down the doorlike lid, the operculum.

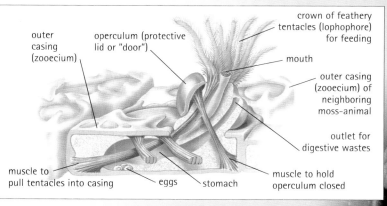

outer casing (zooecium)
operculum (protective lid or "door")
crown of feathery tentacles (lophophore) for feeding
mouth
outer casing (zooecium) of neighboring moss-animal
outlet for digestive wastes
muscle to pull tentacles into casing
eggs
stomach
muscle to hold operculum closed

In some kinds the protective case is flexible and jellylike, rather than hard and stony. In the late summer or fall, both sea and freshwater moss animal colonies produce hard, egglike structures. These survive through the winter and can resist freezing and drying out. The eggs may blow about in the wind, spreading the moss animals to new places. In the spring they develop into new colonies.

SEA MAT AND HORNWRACK

The sea mat is one common kind of moss animal. It grows on the fronds of kelps and similar brown seaweeds and forms flat, pale, lacy sheets that stand out well against the background of the seaweed frond. Another common type of moss animal is called hornwrack. It grows about as long as a human hand and is found in deeper water along rocky coasts. Sometimes colonies of hornwrack are washed up on the shore after a storm, and they look like pieces of pale, lacy seaweed.

ENTOPROCTS

Entoprocts are another group of tiny creatures, very similar to moss animals. The largest are only as big as rice grains. They live mainly in colonies and are fixed in one spot. Some grow on stones, others on seaweeds. A few live on other animals, including sponges, worms, crabs, and shellfish. Each entoproct has a horseshoe-shaped ring of about 40 tentacles for feeding, a cup-shaped body and a stalk fixing it to its host.

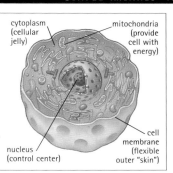

THE ANIMAL CELL

The bodies of all creatures, from moss animals to blue whales, are made of microscopic units known as cells. A typical animal cell is shown right. A protist is just one, all-purpose cell. A moss animal is about 5,000 cells. An elephant's body has 100 million million cells.

cytoplasm (cellular jelly)

mitochondria (provide cell with energy)

nucleus (control center)

cell membrane (flexible outer "skin")

Moss animals
(*Ectoprocts or Polyzoans*)
• about 4,000 species
• aquatic (live in water)
• mostly marine or sea-dwelling
• grow as rooted, branching colonies
• each animal has a bell-shaped ring of tentacles called the lophophore, for feeding
• most individuals are hermaphrodite (have both male and female sex parts)
• breed by releasing tough, egglike structures

Entoprocts
(*Endoprocts or Kamptozoans*)
• about 150 species
• aquatic (live in water)
• mostly marine or sea-dwelling
• grow as rooted, branching colonies
• each animal has a C-shaped ring of tentacles for feeding
• breed by releasing tiny, young forms or larvae

🔼 Volvox is the main kind of food for freshwater moss animals. It is a protist that lives like a plant, trapping the energy in sunlight to live and grow. Each floating ball is made up of hundreds of volvox protists.

🔼 In the warm waters along the coast of South Australia these *Celleporaria* sea mosses have formed colorful branching colonies on an old piece of wooden jetty.

WATER BEARS AND WHEEL ANIMALS

WATER BEARS ARE AMAZING TINY
CREATURES, WITH POWERS AS
STRANGE AS THEIR APPEARANCE.
A typical water bear has a plump body and
four pairs of stumpy, clawed legs. It also
has a faintly bearlike face, which might
make it look cuddly—if it were not so
tiny. Most water-bears are smaller
than the dot on this i. They creep about in the soil and
dead leaves, among plants such as mosses, in the fresh
water of ponds, streams, and lakes, and also in the sea.
They feed on the sap of plants, or on other creatures
even smaller than themselves. Another group of very
tiny creatures are wheel animals. Most look
like miniature cups on stalks. They take
their name from the ring of
microscopic hairs, cilia, around the
rim of what looks like the cup-
shaped body—which is actually the
creature's head. The cilia beat like
tiny oars to create water currents,
which bring tiny bits of floating
food to the animal's mouth.

▲ A water-bear has sharp claws
on its eight stubby legs, to grip
slippery plants or grains of mud and
sand. It has mouthparts like sharp
needles to pierce and suck food.

▲ This is a starlike
group or colony of
wheel animals as seen
under the microscope.

Collotheca wheel
animal

Filinia wheel
animal

Pedalia
wheel
animal

▲ There are many kinds of wheel animals
with different body shapes.

Kinorhynchs (below right) are tiny, 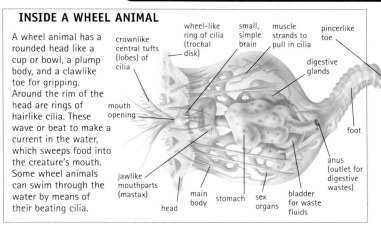 bristly, wormlike animals similar to hairybacks (left). They live in the sea.

◣ The hairs of a hairy back are really small knobbly outgrowths of the body, called papillae. The head is rounded and the tail forked.

INSIDE A WHEEL ANIMAL

A wheel animal has a rounded head like a cup or bowl, a plump body, and a clawlike toe for gripping. Around the rim of the head are rings of hairlike cilia. These wave or beat to make a current in the water, which sweeps food into the creature's mouth. Some wheel animals can swim through the water by means of their beating cilia.

Labels: crownlike central tufts (lobes) of cilia; wheel-like ring of cilia (trochal disk); small, simple brain; muscle strands to pull in cilia; pincerlike toe; digestive glands; mouth opening; foot; jawlike mouthparts (mastax); head; main body; stomach; sex organs; bladder for waste fluids; anus (outlet for digestive wastes)

Water bears are also known as tardigrades, a name that means "slow-steppers." They are very small—from one to 20 could fit on a pinhead. Some live in the sea, between particles of sand and mud. Others dwell in fresh water. But most live in places that are sometimes wet, and at other times dry—like muddy puddles, inside a moss plant, or in the rainwater gutters of buildings. They can survive here because, as the dampness dries out, the water bear turns into a special resting stage called a tun. It simply dries out, shrivels up to about one tenth its normal size, and becomes

◪ Pieces of food can be seen inside the mouth and stomach of this branchionus wheel animal. The small dark spot between the brownish food particles toward the center and the ring of hairs to the far left is the eye spot. This simple type of eye detects the difference between light and dark. A wheel animal is either male or female. This is a female. The male is only one third the size of the female. He has a shorter body, shaped like a collar. Most wheel animals swim by waving their cilia. Some can loop along like a caterpillar, attaching first the head and then the tail. Others stay fixed to a solid object by the clawed foot.

inactive, almost like an egg. This tun stage can survive for many months, even years. When the moisture returns, the water bear "hatches" out of its tun stage, and carries on living!

A WHEEL HEAD
Wheel animals are also called rotifers, which means "wheel-carriers." The wheel-like part is the head and mouth of the creature, with its tufts of hairlike cilia. The biggest wheel animals grow to about one eighth of an inch (3 mm) across, but most kinds are far tinier. Like water bears, they can survive drying out, and also being frozen or almost boiled, by shriveling up into a resting stage. The tough-cased, egglike resting stage of a wheel-animal is known as a cyst.

HAIRYBACKS
Yet another group of extremely tiny animals are the hairybacks, also called gastrotrichs. A typical hairyback has a round, bristly head and a streamlined body with a forked tail. It glides along the bottom of a pond or stream, nosing in the mud to feed on even smaller bits of food such as single-celled plants and tiny protists. Kinorhynchs are similar small animals, resembling worms. They live only in the mud and sand of the seabed.

Water bears *(Tardigrades)*
• about 400 species
• microscopic or nearly so
• four pairs of legs, with claws
• live in damp places, some in fresh water, a few in the sea

Wheel animals *(Rotifers)*
• about 1,800 species
• microscopic or nearly so
• wheel- or crown-like tufts of tiny hairs (cilia) on the head
• live mainly in fresh water, damp places, and in the sea

Hairy backs *(Gastrotrichs)*
• about 450 species
• live in fresh and salty water
• microscopic or small, up to 0.2 inch (4 mm)
• scaly or hairy body, forked tail

Kinorhynchs
• only about 120 species
• live in sea mud or sand
• small, up to 0.1 inch (2 mm)
• body divided into about 13 sections or segments

19

SPONGES

SPONGES LOOK MORE LIKE
PLANTS THAN ANIMALS. They
grow on underwater objects such as
rocks or plant stems. They cannot
move around, although a few types twitch slightly at the surface when
touched. They have no eyes or ears, brain or nerves, heart or blood. But they
do catch their own food, by filtering tiny particles
from water. The water enters the sponge
through thousands of tiny holes, or
pores, and then leaves through one
of the few big holes. Adult
sponges are fixed to the spot,
but when they breed, they
produce young ones or
larvae, which swim
actively. Eventually a
larva finds a suitable
place to settle down
and grow into the
adult colony of cells
we call a sponge.

◄ Tiny coral animals (polyps) grow around a sponge's oscule—the main exit hole for water. The tunnels are visible inside the sponge's main body cavity.

◄ A brittlestar climbs across an orange sponge.

◄ Breadcrumb sponges grow in several colors, including green (upper left). The hymenia sponge is usually blood-red (top right). Some solenia sponges are also red (top left). Column sponges can be purple or blue (center). Vase sponges are wider, with one large exit hole for water (lower left). The brain sponge is pink (lower right).

▶ Different types of cup sponge grow in fresh and salt water.

A typical full-grown sponge is not so much one single animal, more a collection or colony of animal-like cells. These form a flask-shaped body surrounding a central cavity. There are many tiny holes or channels in the body wall, linking the cavity inside with the sea water outside. Whiplike flagella on cells lining the cavity beat to make a current of water flow through the channels into the central cavity. The water brings with it tiny bits of food such as protists, tiny seaweeds, and animal eggs and larvae. The water, and the sponge's waste products, pass out through larger channels, oscules, usually at the top.

▼ These pink sponges, on an old jetty support, form a network of chambers and holes used by worms, fish, and other creatures.

BATH SPONGES

Most bath sponges are now made of plastic foam. But many years ago they were gathered from the sea. The common bath sponge lives on the seabed, in clear, warm water. It is rather slimy, and is a yellow or purple color. After it dies, its soft parts rot away to leave its flexible skeleton of fibers and spicules. This skeleton forms the sponge we use in the bath. Its thousands of tiny holes once let the living sponge suck in water. In some areas, such as parts of the Mediterranean Sea, so many bath sponges have been gathered that this animal is now very rare. It takes perhaps 20 years for a new bath sponge to grow.

HOW SPONGES BREED

Like many plants, sponges can reproduce by growing small extra parts, buds, which come away and grow into new sponges. Or they can breed sexually, like animals. Each sponge is both male and female, so it can make both sperm and eggs. An egg and sperm join, or fertilize, and develop into a tiny sponge larva which swims away. It lives in the open sea for a day or two, before settling on the seabed to grow into a new adult sponge.

HOW DO SPONGES SURVIVE?

Sponges have no obvious defenses. They cannot bite or sting. They cannot swim away. So how do they protect themselves? The bodies of many sponges are full of tiny, sharp spikes of hard minerals, such as lime, chalk, or silica (the same substance that glass is made from). These spikes, called spicules, make up the sponge's skeleton. They give its body firmness. They also help to deter animals who might try to eat the sponge. In addition, many types of sponges have an unpleasant smell or a horrible taste, which also puts off their predators.

PLACOZOANS

These tiny animals, which grow to the size of an ant, resemble giant amebas, but their bodies are made up of about 1,000 cells. Placozoans ooze and move like slugs. There are only a couple of species known and both live in the sea.

Sponges (Poriferans)
- about 10,000 species
- most live in the sea, a few in fresh water
- many have spiky inner skeletons
- body full of holes
- some grow to 14 feet (4 m) across

Placozoans
- only a few species
- live in the sea
- crawl along like slugs or giant amebas
- about one eighth of an inch (3 mm) long

COMB JELLIES

Comb jellies are strange, pale, ghostly sea animals that are similar in some ways to jellyfish. They have mainly see-through or transparent bodies, which are soft and squashy, and they drift or swim with the ocean currents. There are only about 100 different kinds, or species, of comb jelly, but some of these are amazingly common. They float in their thousands in the upper layers of the sea, as part of the surface plankton. In the twilight zone more than 1,500 feet (450 m) down, they are even more abundant and drift in huge swarms, millions strong. In fact, in the deep oceans, comb jellies are some of the most numerous of all animals.

🔺 Comb jellies vary in color depending on the angle of the sun, the color of the seawater, and also on what they have eaten.

Comb jellies range in size from smaller than a baked bean to as long as a human arm. Most are round and ball-shaped or long and slim like sausages. One of the most common kinds is known as the sea gooseberry. It has a pear-shaped body, about the size and shape of a grape, and is completely transparent.

ROWS OF COMBS

Running around the body of a comb jelly, like stripes, are eight bands or rows of what look like tiny combs—which is how these animals got their name. Each comb is made up of groups of minute hairs

known as cilia. These can beat in rhythm, like rows of oars. By beating its cilia, a comb jelly can swim through the water. Usually it swims straight up or down as part of its daily feeding routine, rising at night and sinking back to the depths by day. But, like many jellyfish, comb jellies are at the mercy of strong ocean currents.

STICKY TENTACLES

Trailing from the comb jelly's body are two long, sticky tentacles which dangle in the water. Smaller animals, including tiny shrimps and the young forms of crabs, starfish, and worms, become entangled in and stung by these tentacles. The sea gooseberry then brushes its tentacles across its mouth and swallows its prey.

GLOWING IN THE DARK

Although most comb jellies are transparent, if the sun catches them they shimmer in the water with iridescent rainbow colors. At night, some kinds can glow with multicolored lights. These come from lines of glowing spots inside the comb jelly, which shine through the transparent body, making the creature visible from a distance. It is possible that the

🔺 The lampea comb jelly is one of the sausage-shaped types. The comblike groups of tiny hairs are on ridges along the sides of the body. In some types of comb jelly the hairs are fused to each other to form one broad, flap-shaped surface. If a comb jelly is washed up on the beach, it loses its shape and soon dries out and dies.

▶ To catch food, a comb jelly lets its tentacles dangle in the water (right). They form a sticky drift net to catch small prey. When it is swimming or not feeding, it can pull or retract its two main tentacles into base pits or cavities in the sides of the body.

lights attract other animals toward the comb jelly, which then catches and eats them. (The ability of some creatures to make their own light is known as bioluminescence, page 14.)

VENUS' GIRDLE

Most comb jellies have rounded bodies. An exception is the remarkable Venus' girdle, which has a lacy, ribbonlike body about the size and shape of a yardstick. It is like a normal comb jelly that has been ironed flat! Venus' girdle swims by wriggling from side to side, rather like a snake.

Another unusual comb jelly is coeloplana, which looks like a slug with a tentacle at each end. It creeps over rocks and seaweeds in search of prey.

INSIDE A COMB JELLY

The comb jelly's see-through body contains various chambers and cavities. There are eight bands, each made of a row of tiny hairs or cilia, for swimming.

mouth

band of combs

digestive cavity

tentacle base pit

stomach

jellylike body

sticky, stinging tentacle

comb made of row of cilia

light-sensitive patch

Comb jellies *(Ctenophores)*
• about 100 species
• most have transparent, rounded bodies
• many have a pair of long tentacles
• live only in the sea
• range in size from 0.2 inch (5 mm) to more than 3 feet (90 cm)

▶ A comb jelly opens its mouth, which leads into the stomach region and the many-branched digestive cavities.

THE "NETTLE ANIMALS"

⬆ An underside view of a jellyfish reveals the billowing tentacles called oral arms that stick onto prey and pass it into the mouth.

JELLYFISH, SEA ANEMONES, AND CORAL POLYPS (THE TINY CREATURES THAT BUILD CORAL REEFS) ALL BELONG TO THE ANIMAL GROUP CALLED CNIDARIANS. This name means "nettle animals." It comes from the tiny stinging cells on the tentacles and other parts of these creatures. The stings are used to capture, paralyze, and kill prey; some are strong enough to give a painful sting to humans. However, a few cnidarians have such venomous stings that they can kill people. Cnidarians are also known as coelenterates, which means "hollow gut," because their bodies are almost all stomach, like a hollow bag. Most of these animals live in the sea, and have a circular body shape.

⬆ The branching stomach cavity and reproductive parts can be seen inside the body of this pencillate jellyfish.

The body of a jellyfish or other cnidarian has a single opening. This is both a mouth, to take in food, and an anus, to get rid of undigested leftovers. It is surrounded by the animal's tentacles. These are usually long and thin, and may number more than one hundred. They are coated with microscopic stinging cells.

Most cnidarians have soft, squashy, floppy bodies, containing a large, bag-like stomach or gut cavity. The body wall is made of a jellylike substance. Some types, like the corals, build hard, stony, cuplike skeletons around themselves for protection. Jellyfish have an extra-thick jelly layer which makes up the bulk of the body.

TWO BODY SHAPES

There are two basic types of body plan among the cnidarians. These are the medusa and the polyp. Some cnidarians spend most or all their lives as one form. The jellyfish, for example, are medusas, while coral animals and anemones are polyps. However, some cnidarians are first polyps, then change shape and become medusas—or the other way around.

◀ The soft body or bell of this doughnut jellyfish is buoyed up in the water.

▶ These purple striped jellyfish are hardly visible, as they drift like ghosts in the hazy waters of the sea.

THE POLYP

The typical polyp has a soft, cylinder-shaped body. The long lower part or stalk is attached at its base to a rock, seaweed or other object. At the top of the stalk is the polyp's mouth, surrounded by the ring of grasping, stinging tentacles waving upward. Sea anemones spend all their lives as polyps. They have no medusa form.

THE MEDUSA

A typical medusa is like a polyp that has had its stalk removed and then been turned upside down. Its body is shaped like an umbrella or bell, with the stinging tentacles dangling downward from the edges or rim. The mouth is in the middle of the tentacles. A medusa is usually the floating or free-living form, while the polyp is the attached or fixed form. Jellyfish spend most or all of their lives drifting slowly through the oceans, as medusas.

PALE OR COLORFUL

Some jellyfish, sea anemones, and corals are pale or milky white, especially in cooler seas. But many tropical types are beautifully colored, often in shades of pink, red, yellow, and orange.

When the tide is out, anemones on seashore rocks may look like dull blobs of jelly. But as the tide comes in they spread out their flowerlike tentacles, which resemble soft, waving plant petals. They are sometimes called "flowers of the sea." But of course, anemones are animals (page 32). Like all their cnidarian cousins, they may look harmless, but they are deadly predators.

INSIDE A JELLYFISH

A jellyfish is mostly a hollow stomach or gut cavity, where its meals are digested and dissolved. It has no proper eyes or ears. But it can detect touch, temperature, patches of light and dark, and water currents.

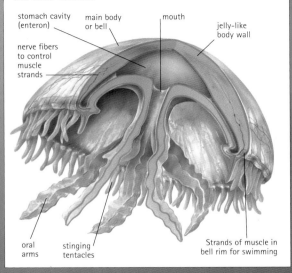

stomach cavity (enteron)
main body or bell
mouth
jelly-like body wall
nerve fibers to control muscle strands
oral arms
stinging tentacles
Strands of muscle in bell rim for swimming

Jellyfish and relatives
(Cnidarians or Coelenterates)

- about 10,000 species
- mostly sea-living, some dwell in fresh water
- have a circular body
- central mouth surrounded by tentacles
- most are soft-bodied, but some (like corals) make hard, stony, protective cases or skeletons

There are two main sub groups:

Anemones and corals   *(Anthozoans)*
- about 6,000 species
- live in the sea
- stalklike body attached at the base, with tentacles above (polyp form)

Jellyfish and hydroids
(Medusozoans)
- about 4,000 species
- most live in the sea, some (like hydras) live in fresh water
- both free-floating medusa and fixed polyps
- a few have stings that are dangerous to humans

JELLYFISH

JELLYFISH RANGE IN SIZE FROM SMALLER THAN THE TIP OF YOUR FINGER, TO GIANTS LARGER THAN A PATIO SUNSHADE UMBRELLA, MEASURING MORE THAN 6 FEET (1.8 m). But most are about the size and shape of a breakfast cereal bowl. Some types

▲ Haliclystus is a stalked jellyfish that lives in sheltered rock pools, clinging to seaweed.

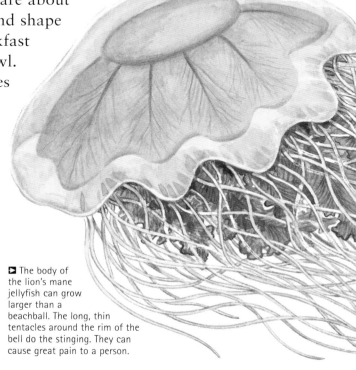

▶ The body of the lion's mane jellyfish can grow larger than a beachball. The long, thin tentacles around the rim of the bell do the stinging. They can cause great pain to a person.

can swim weakly by making pulsing movements of the main body or bell—like opening and closing your fingers. But these swimming motions are weak and most jellyfish are at the mercy of strong ocean currents. They are often washed up helpless onto the shore after a storm. Their floppy bodies collapse, and these creatures soon dry out and die.

▼ Stauromedusans, or stalked jellyfish, are jellyfish that think they are anemones. There is a stalk on the top of the bell with a sticky end that attaches to a piece of seaweed or sea grass.

SWIMMING JELLYFISH

Around the rim of the jellyfish's main body, or bell, is a ring of muscle fibers. These can be shortened or contracted to squeeze the bell like a purse-string and make pulsating movements, which propel water out of the bell and so push the jellyfish through the water. Usually a jellyfish swims upward, to rise closer to the surface. When it stops swimming, it sinks down again. Using these movements the jellyfish can follow its prey, the small animals of the plankton, as they rise near the surface at night and sink to mid water during the day.

HOW JELLYFISH BREED

Jellyfish reproduce by releasing tiny young forms, or larvae. These swim off and settle on the seabed, where they turn into small polyps. At this stage they resemble tiny see-through sea anemones, smaller than this o.

THE CNIDARIAN STING

A jellyfish has thousands of microscopic stinging cells, nematocysts, all along its tentacles. The cell "fires" a barbed dart that carries either a sticky, gluelike substance or a poison (venom). Each stinging cell has a lid covering the dart. Near the lid is a tiny trigger. When a prey animal touches the trigger, the lid springs open and the dart shoots out. Each stinging cell can only be used once, after which it breaks down, is absorbed into the jellyfish's body and replaced by a new stinging cell.

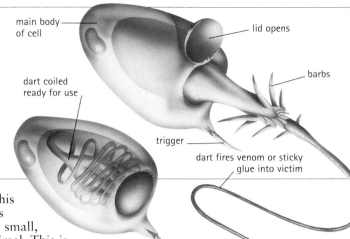

main body of cell

lid opens

dart coiled ready for use

barbs

trigger

dart fires venom or sticky glue into victim

Jellyfish polyps often spend winter in this form. In spring, each polyp form grows "buds." Each bud develops into a very small, star-shaped version of the adult animal. This is released and drifts away into the plankton.

BALANCING ACT

Jellyfish have no proper eyes. But they have special sense organs which can detect light or dark, and which also tell them which way is up or down. These pinhead-size sense organs are spaced around the edge of the bell. The animal uses them to tell the difference between day and night, and also to change its swimming direction according to the position of the sun.

PREDATORS

Even though jellyfish have poisonous stings, some animals eat them. Jellyfish predators include various kinds of fish, squid, and especially sea turtles. However, because many jellyfish are pale or transparent this probably makes them harder for predators to see and catch.

FLOATING MOON

The moon jellyfish, aurelia, grows to about 16 inches (40 cm) across and has a

◀ The moon jellyfish (aurelia) is one of the most common jellyfish, found in seas throughout the world.

bluish tinge. It is very numerous and can be seen in bays and estuaries close to shore, as well as in the open ocean far from land. Moon jellyfish feed on small members of the plankton, such as tiny shrimps and other crustaceans, and also on fish. These get stuck on the stinging cells, the lower surface of the bell, and the frilly oral arms, and are then transferred to the jellyfish's mouth. The moon jellyfish has a fringe of short stinging tentacles and four much longer feeding or oral tentacles. The pink horseshoe-shaped parts in the middle of its main body are its reproductive organs.

STALKED JELLYFISH

These unusual jellyfish live attached to rocks or seaweeds. They are small, growing only to the size of your little finger. They look like jellyfish that have turned upside down and become stuck by the top of the body, which is underneath. Stalked jellyfish can move to a different place by slowly cartwheeling along. They feed on tiny prey such as worms and copepods.

True jellyfish *(Scyphozoans)*
• about 200 species, all in the sea
• the main form or stage in the life cycle is the free-floating medusa
• the body is circular
• four-part symmetry, with four mouth or oral tentacles and four sets of reproductive organs
• sexes separate—a jellyfish is either female or male

MORE JELLYFISH

PROPER OR TRUE JELLYFISH ARE SHAPED LIKE FLOPPY BELLS OR
UMBRELLAS. There are other cnidarians that look like true jellyfish, but are
not, although they are close relatives. Some of these jellyfishlike cnidarians
have bodies with different shapes, such as boxes or
balls. Others, like the man-o'-war, look like
a single animal, but each body is really
lots of cnidarians all linked together
and living as one. These are
called colonial cnidarians.

PLASTIC !

The peculiar dried-out
bodies of the by-the-wind
sailor are sometimes found
on the beach, after strong
winds. Only the skeleton of
the disk-shaped float and
triangular sail remain. They
look and feel like
thin plastic.

In true or
proper jellyfish,
the body is rounded
and shaped like an umbrella, and
consists of a single cnidarian
animal. There are several kinds of
similar creatures which are often
called jellyfish, but they are not
true jellyfish. However, they are
still cnidarians, and so close
relatives of jellyfish.

BOX JELLYFISH

These jellyfish take their name from the boxlike shape of their
bodies, which have flat, square sides. Box jellyfish are found only
in warm, tropical seas. They have thin, trailing, stinging tentacles,
and they feed on small shrimps, fish and other animals floating
and swimming in the plankton. The stings of some box jellies are
especially powerful and can cause great pain to a person. Also,
box jellyfish sometimes gather together in huge swarms, as they
drift through the sea. If they are swept inshore by winds and
currents, these box jelly swarms can be very
dangerous to people swimming and wading.
Swimmers trapped in a swarm of these
cnidarians have been stung to death.

◀ ▲ True umbrella-
shaped jellyfish are
very different from the
man-o'-war (right)

▶ The man-o'-war
is a cnidarian—or
rather, lots of them.
It is a floating
group of cnidarian
polyps known as
siphonophores.

◀ This massive pink jellyfish floats in the warm waters of the Pacific Ocean, near the Philippines. It looks dangerous, but its venom is not harmful to humans.

▶ The innocent-looking box jellyfish can inflict extremely painful stings. It is known as the southern sea wasp, or jimble, and is common in Australian waters.

Even when box jellies are stranded on the shore and dead, their tentacles can still produce very painful stings. In some parts of Australia, box jellyfish are a particular hazard and beaches may be closed if a swarm drifts near.

FLOATING COLONIES

Some kinds of cnidarian live in floating colonies. From a distance, they look like a single animal—usually a jellyfish. But they are really hundreds of creatures, polyps, all living together. These jellyfish-like colonies of polyps are known as siphonophores. They usually float at the surface of the ocean.

FLOATING HOTEL

One of the best-known siphonophores, or colonial cnidarians, is the man-o'-war. It is also called the sea bluebottle. It consists of about 100–200 individual polyps, of different shapes and sizes, who all depend on each other.

▲ Box jellies such as the sea wasps have more angular, flat-sided bodies than true jellyfish.

The bluish-purple, gas-filled, balloonlike float at the top of the colony is one large individual polyp. It catches the breeze, like a sailing ship, to move the colony along. This float polyp buoys up the whole colony of other polyps beneath.

FOR THE GOOD OF THE GROUP

Each type of polyp in the man-o'-war is specialized to do a different job for the whole colony. Stinging polyps each have a single, very long tentacle trailing as far as 100 feet (30 m) down into the sea. The tentacles stick to and sting prey such as fish, squid, and shrimps. The venom is very strong and can seriously hurt a person. The paralyzed victim is then passed to the feeding polyps. These eat and digest the meal and share the nourishment through the whole colony. Another group of polyps does the job of reproduction, releasing eggs and sperm.

NATURAL SAILBOAT

The by-the-wind sailor, or velella, is another remarkable colony of cnidarians. Like the man-o'-war, it is a colony of polyps, acting together almost as a single animal. It too has a purplish gas-filled float, but above this is a hard skeleton which acts as a mast to support a thin sail. The sail catches the wind and moves the colony along. Short tentacles in rings beneath the float catch small items of food. By-the-wind-sailors grow as big as your hand and live in huge swarms, especially in the North Atlantic.

JELLYFISH-LIKE CNIDARIANS	
Colonial jellyfish (Siphonophores) • members of the hydroid group (see next page) • body looks like a single creature but is made of many individual cnidarian animals or polyps • some polyps sting and kill prey • some digest prey	• some act as floats • some carry out reproduction Box jellyfish (Cubomedusans) • resemble true jellyfish but have a more angular, box-shaped body • have four single or branched tentacles • extremely strong venom • include sea wasps

HYDROIDS

THE HYDROIDS ARE CNIDARIANS THAT MAINLY
RESEMBLE SEA ANEMONES. Each animal, or polyp,
has a stalk-shaped body and a flowerlike ring of
tentacles. However, some hydroids live as
colonies of polyps, almost like a single,
large "superanimal." Many of these
colonies branch and spread over any
solid surface. The man-o'-war and
the by-the-wind sailor (pages
28–29) are also hydroids.
However, they are unusual,
since they are floating
rather than fixed, and
they resemble jellyfish.

The typical hydroid is a colony
of small polyps, each less than
about 0.2 inch (5 mm) tall, all
connected and growing together.
They attach to and spread over a
rock, a frond of seaweed, or even
the shell of a larger animal. Such
hydroids are often known as sea
firs. They are most common on
sheltered, rocky seashores. At a glance,
they look very much like moss animals
or bryozoans (page 16). But the tentacles
of individual hydroid polyps are not covered
with tiny hairs or cilia.

🔽 The hydroid obelia
grows in many
branched groups. The
individual animals or
polyps are joined by
their stalks.

INSIDE A HYDROID

Most ponds and
streams are
home to
hundreds of the
tiny hydroids
called hydras.
Each has a
stalklike body
with new
individuals
branching from
it, like buds from
a plant stem. At
the top is a circle
of six or eight
tentacles around
the mouth.

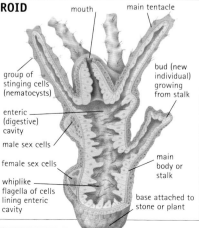

mouth

main tentacle

group of
stinging cells
(nematocysts)

enteric
(digestive)
cavity

male sex cells

female sex cells

whiplike
flagella of cells
lining enteric
cavity

bud (new
individual)
growing
from stalk

main
body or
stalk

base attached to
stone or plant

MINI SEA TREES

Some of the best-
known colonial hydroids
are obelias. Several different
species of obelia live along the coasts of the
Atlantic Ocean and Mediterranean Sea. Some
grow to more than 1 foot (30 cm) in height and
have zigzag stalks. Others have branching stems
and look like miniature trees.

TWO TYPES OF POLYP

There are two different kinds of polyp in each
obelia colony. The feeding polyps live inside
hard, protective cups. They stretch out from
these when active.

MORE! MORE!

The fresh water hydroid called hydra has amazing powers of recovery and regeneration. If it is sliced in two, each half can grow into a complete animal, regenerating all of its missing body parts. This helps when a piece of a hydra is nipped off by another animal such as a small fish. Hydras have even been turned inside out, yet they still recover and repair their bodies.

▶ Sea firs grow like tiny fir trees and ferns on rocks along the shore below the low-tide line. The branches of the colony bear feeding polyps with their stinging tentacles. Larger sea firs, known as sea ferns and sea hairs, are dried for flower decorations.

The polyp uses its stinging tentacles in the normal cnidarian way to catch tiny animals from the water. Because the polyps are all connected at their stalks or bases, food can easily pass around the colony.

The other kind of polyp is for reproduction. It is flask-shaped and has no tentacles. Tiny medusas, like miniature jellyfish, grow inside each reproductive polyp and are released to swim away in the sea. The medusas produce eggs and sperm, which float in the water. An egg and sperm join to form a tiny larva, which floats in the plankton and then settles and changes into a single polyp. This produces smaller versions of itself attached to its body, like plant buds. In this way the single polyp soon develops into a hydroid colony, and so the life cycle is complete.

IN FRESH WATER

In almost any pond or slow stream, on stones and among the leaves of water plants, live small green or pale brown animals that look like miniature sea anemones. These are hydras. They are not anemones, but hydroids that live in fresh rather than sea water. A hydra feeds in the typical cnidarian way, using its tentacles to catch tiny animals such as water fleas. It can grow buds on its stalk that turn into miniature versions of itself. These eventually separate from their parent and become new individual hydras. This type of reproduction is called asexual or vegetative, because it resembles the way that vegetables and other plants produce buds. Hydras can also reproduce in the usual animal way.

FIRE CORALS

These colonial hydroids resemble true corals (page 36). Each individual, or polyp, has a hard, chalky casing and a ring of stinging tentacles to catch prey. Fire corals can inflict painful stings on humans. The fire coral known as millepora can resist pounding by waves and often forms the highest parts of coral reefs. Millepora grows in various colors, from white and pink to yellow and orange. It is known as elk's-horn coral due to its antlerlike shape.

▲ Like corals, hydroids form colorful colonies on reef rocks in tropical and subtropical seas. Some grow over and around sponges and moss animals, forming crusty coverings with all creatures crammed together.

Hydroids (Hydrozoa)
• most are marine, living in the sea
• a few, like hydra, live in fresh water
• most live together in colonies, with connections for passing nutrients among themselves
• some, like hydras, live as individuals
• some colonies, like the man-o'-war, float at the surface of the sea (page 28)
• some, like obelias, live in stalked colonies
• many have powerful stings
• includes the fire corals

SEA ANEMONES

SEA ANEMONES AND CORALS ARE TOGETHER CALLED ANTHOZOANS, OR "FLOWERLIKE ANIMALS." They form the largest group of cnidarians, with some 6,000 species. Most of these are different kinds of coral, shown on the following pages. More familiar to many people are the sea anemones. These are mostly quite large (for cnidarians). They live singly, rather than in colonies, along coasts and in shallow water. They attach themselves to rocks, plants, shells or other firm surfaces, and usually stay put. Yet sea anemones can move around, by shuffling or gliding on the base of the stalk. If they are in a hurry, they may cartwheel or somersault. A few can even swim, by waving their tentacles or bending their bodies. But usually the only movements we notice are when the anemone's tentacles gently sway in the water—or when they sting and grab their prey.

◤ The dahlia anemone's short stalk is covered with lumps. Bits of gravel, shells and weed stick to these lumps. When the tide goes out and the anemone draws in its tentacles, it looks like a small pebble.

◤ The orange sea anemone has strong, sturdy tentacles around its central mouth.

OLD! ⚠

Some sea anemones have lived for as long as people. They have survived in large seawater tanks or marine aquaria, protected and well fed, and with clean unpolluted water, for 70 years or more.

Sea anemones are cnidarians but they have no medusa—the floating, jellyfishlike stage. Anemones live their entire lives as polyps. They resemble hydroids, but most anemones are larger and more heavily built, and they live alone rather than in groups. The stalk is fatter, and the tentacles around the central mouth are shorter and sturdier. Also, many sea anemones are brightly colored in shades of red, yellow, pink, brown, blue, and green. These colors may be warnings to other animals that the anemone is not good to eat and that it can sting with its tentacles.

MULTICOLORED BEADLETS

One of the most common types is the beadlet anemone. It lives on rocks between the low- and high-tide marks. It is usually bright red, but may be brown, orange, or green.

IN DEEPER WATER

Lower down the shore is the snakelocks anemone. It has as many as 200 long, coiling tentacles, usually bright green in color.

◨ Jewel anemones have pale knobbed tentacles. But their bright, shiny bodies glisten like gem stones in the water.

This type cannot stand being out of water at low tide for as long as the beadlet anemones. The dahlia anemone is another common type, named after the dahlia flower. It is patterned in pink, white, and red.

FEEDING AND FOOD

Most sea anemones feed by trapping small fish, shrimps, and similar animals in their tentacles. The stinging cells or nematocysts on the tentacles kill or paralyze the prey. Sea anemones have no eyes, but they can detect touch, and they shoot out their poison stings when their tentacles make contact. They can also detect substances released by the body of any animal they catch and injure. This makes more and more tentacles arch over, to help secure and disable the prey. The nematocyst barbed darts of most common anemones are not large or strong enough to pass into human skin.

◄ An anemone's tentacles are usually arranged in widening rings, based on the number six or eight.

▶ The orange ball anemone has bright, rounded, yellow-orange tips to its pale blue, see-through tentacles.

BIG MOUTH

The mouth of an anemone lies at the center of its tentacles. It can stretch so wide that the anemone is able to swallow prey almost as big as itself! The meal goes into the large stomach cavity in the stalk, where it is slowly dissolved and digested. Any leftovers are pushed back out later, through the way they came in.

Sea anemones make more of their kind in the same way as hydras, by budding off new individuals from their bodies. Or they can produce eggs and sperm in the usual animal way.

FIGHTING ANEMONES

Sea anemones may not look aggressive. But they try to get the best place in the rock pool. They push and shove against each other in slow-motion trials of strength. They may even try to tip rivals off the rocks into the mud or sand.

LARGEST... !

The biggest sea anemone is a type of discoma. It can reach 2 feet (60 cm) across. It lives among corals on the Great Barrier Reef in Australia.

Anemones and corals
(Anthozoans)
• about 6,000 species, all live in the sea (pages 24–25)
• stalklike body attached at the base, with tentacles above (polyp form only)
• circular body with tentacles, sex organs, and other parts based on the numbers six or eight

33

ANEMONES AND PARTNERS

SEA ANEMONES ARE SIMPLE CREATURES. They have no proper brain, only a few nerves to control the movements of their tentacles and stalk. They can only do the simplest actions, such as detecting and eating prey, and gliding along the rocks to a new place. Yet anemones have many "friends" on the seashore. They live in partnerships with other creatures such as fish, shrimps, crabs, and worms. These other creatures have thick shells or coatings of body mucus (slime) that protect them from the anemone's stings. Usually, both partners benefit from being together. For example, the anemone feeds on leftovers from the food of its fish friend, while the fish is safe hiding in the anemone's tentacles. This type of helpful partnership in nature is called symbiosis.

△ Shrimps are at home among anemones

Symbiosis happens between many types of creatures, such as cleaner fish and bigger fish, and oxpecker birds and cattle. But it is especially common among sea anemones. It has probably evolved gradually, over millions of years.

TOLERANT PARTNERS
As a result, the anemone has become used to the presence of another creature in its tentacles. It can detect this partner by the chemical substances that

△ This tiny porcelain crab is safe among the tentacles of an anemone. It scavenges small bits of food and keeps the anemone clean.

the partner gives off, and so rarely tries to sting it. At the same time, the partner has evolved some kind of protection against the anemone's stings, and is hardly ever hurt.

TYPES OF PARTNERS
Clown or anemone fish, usually striped orange and white, form symbiotic partnerships with anemones. So do various kinds of banded shrimps, and crabs. Some hermit crabs allow calliactis sea anemones to live on the large sea snail shell that the crab uses as a mobile home. The anemone gets carried around and probably has more chance of finding prey. Meanwhile the crab is protected by the stinging partner attached to its shell.

△ The sunstar above is not an anemone friend, but a victim. The large dahlia anemone is slowly pulling the sunstar, a type of starfish, into its mouth.

PLUMOSE ANEMONE

This type of sea anemone can stretch itself tall and thin, or pull down its stalk or column to be shorter and fatter. The anemone pictured here is halfway between these two positions. Plumose anemones occur in many colors, from almost perfect white through cream, yellow, and brown to orange and red. They live in seashore pools, especially under rocky overhangs, and on and under breakwaters, piers, and jetties. They can catch larger prey, but they mainly feed on tiny bits of floating food filtered from the water by the feathery tentacles.

fine stinging tentacles

group (plume) of tentacles

mouth

stalk or column

slimy covering to stalk

muscle strands in stalk

adhesive (sticky) base

When one catches food, the other can share the leftover bits and pieces. The calliactis anemone is sometimes called the parasitic anemone. But it is not really a parasite, since it rarely does the hermit crab any harm. The two are usually equal partners, so a better name for it would be the symbiotic anemone.

MORE PARTNERSHIPS

Other crabs may grab anemones in their pincers, like underwater flaming torches. The crab waves the anemone, to scare away enemies or to try and sting possible prey. Again, both crab and anemone benefit from the relationship.

▷ Clownfish and their anemone partners are popular in tropical saltwater aquaria. The fish's thick coating of slime protects it against the anemone's stings.

CORALS

THERE ARE MORE THAN 5,000 DIFFERENT KINDS OF CORAL. A coral animal or polyp is usually less than 0.4 inch (1 cm) tall, and looks like a miniature sea anemone. In fact, corals are very close cousins of anemones (pages 32–33). Most types are found in tropical seas. Some coral polyps live singly, but most live with others of their kind, linked or connected into huge groups or colonies. Some build stony protective casings around themselves. This is how the rocks of a coral reef gradually build up. Sea fans are coral polyps that make tough, horny skeletons which branch into a tree or fanlike shape. The protective cases of soft corals are more like spongy, rubbery jelly.

🔺 Red-tipped soft coral

🔺 Some soft corals form colorful, branching, fingerlike structures that are tough and leathery.

🔽 The reef rocks made by coral polyps have many holes, crevices, caves, and overhangs. These are ideal places for larger animals to hide.

Coral animals are cnidarians. They catch their prey with sticky or stinging tentacles, like sea anemones and jellyfish. But, unlike jellyfish, corals do not have a medusa or floating stage in their lives. Like anemones, all coral animals are polyps. In a coral colony, each polyp is connected to its neighbor by living tissue, usually at its base. So the whole colony is joined, almost like one giant multi-animal.

Each polyp can catch its own tiny victims, but the food may then be shared among the nearby members of the colony. This is important because in some corals, certain polyps cannot feed for themselves. Instead, they help to protect or support the colony, by building cases or outer skeletons.

HIDING FROM ENEMIES

In stony corals, each polyp makes a cup-shaped skeleton beneath itself, from rock minerals that it takes out of the sea water. When danger threatens, such as a polyp-eating fish or starfish, the polyp retreats into this protective cup. It emerges again later when the danger is past.

HOW CORALS EAT

A feeding polyp spreads its little tentacles in the sea water. It relies on currents and waves to bring fresh supplies of food, usually with each tide. It catches tiny protists and animals as they drift past. These stick to the tentacles and are then passed to the mouth at the center, just as in the larger anemones. Many coral polyps come out to feed only at night. This is when sea plankton rise nearer the surface. The polyps wave their shiny tentacles and make a patch of coral rock look like a glistening, multicolored, living carpet.

BREEDING

When conditions are right, usually on a calm night when the moon is full, all the corals in one area release their eggs and sperm into the sea. These float near the surface in great clouds.

⬧ At breeding time, coral animals release clouds of eggs and sperm that drift away in the seawater.

Each sperm joins with, or fertilizes, an egg. The fertilized egg develops into a tiny coral larva that floats in the sea for a short time. Then it swims down to the seabed to find a resting place. The larva sticks itself firmly onto a rock, and grows into a tiny coral polyp, complete with a ring of tentacles. After several weeks, if the single original polyp survives, it has sprouted or budded several new polyps. These remain joined together. As their numbers increase and spread, they gradually form a new coral colony.

⬧ This bright, nighttime coral reef scene shows various kinds of coral, anemones, sponges, and fish such as seahorses and wrasses. By day, most coral polyps withdraw into their protective cases.

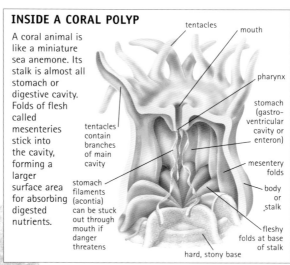

INSIDE A CORAL POLYP

A coral animal is like a miniature sea anemone. Its stalk is almost all stomach or digestive cavity. Folds of flesh called mesenteries stick into the cavity, forming a larger surface area for absorbing digested nutrients.

tentacles

mouth

pharynx

stomach (gastro-ventricular cavity or enteron)

tentacles contain branches of main cavity

stomach filaments (acontia) can be stuck out through mouth if danger threatens

mesentery folds

body or stalk

fleshy folds at base of stalk

hard, stony base

TYPES OF CORAL

• stony or hard corals, usually colonial—some are reef-builders
• soft corals
• gorgonian corals, also called sea fans and sea whips (types of soft coral)

37

CORAL REEFS

A CORAL REEF IS A HUGE LUMP OF ROCK MADE BY MILLIONS OF TINY ANIMALS—CORAL POLYPS, AS SHOWN ON THE PREVIOUS PAGE. Reef-building coral polyps make small protective cases, or skeletons, for their soft bodies from chalky minerals they take out of sea water. These cases are shaped like cups, disks, or boxes. Each group or colony of coral polyps grows and spreads in its own pattern or shape, as the older polyps form "buds" that grow into new ones. As the older polyp animals die, they leave their empty, stony cases. But more polyps grow above and beside them. In this way, over years and centuries, thousands of rock-hard polyp cases build up to form the stony, strange and beautiful shapes of the coral reef.

⬀ A colony of soft coral polyps extend their frilly red-tinged tentacles to grasp bits of food.

Reef-building coral polyps make the hardest, strongest most massive structures formed by any animals. But they are delicate little creatures. They can only thrive in warm, clear, clean, shallow, sunlit seawater. This is partly because each polyp contains, inside its body, hundreds of microscopic living things called dinoflagellates. These are protists (pages 14–15) and they need sunlight to grow. They live in partnership with the coral polyps.

⬇ Coral reefs grow only in shallow tropical or subtropical seas, where the average water temperature is more than about 68°F (20°C).

The polyp provides shelter, minerals and raw materials for its protists. In return the protists use the sun's light energy to make food for themselves, which they share with their polyp. So coral polyps need sunlight to survive. This type of helpful partnership is known as symbiosis (page 34).

DIVERSE REEFS

Coral reefs are some of the richest wildlife habitats on Earth. The front of the reef slopes down steeply into the sea, and this is where the wave action is fiercest, especially during storms. But behind the reef ridge or crest, there is usually a shallower, calmer area, protected from the biggest ocean waves. This is the reef flat, or lagoon. The crevices and caves in the reef rocks provide homes for a multitude of fish, shellfish, worms, crabs, shrimp and other animals, and also for plants such as seaweeds.

◢ Corals are usually named after the shapes formed by their thousands of empty skeletons. These build up in patterns according to how the polyps grow and reproduce. The bulges and wrinkles of brain coral look like a human brain!

◀ ▼ Gorgonian corals form delicate, lacy, fernlike shapes (left). Finger coral looks like a human hand (below left). There are many different shapes of mushroom corals (below).

PROBLEMS ON THE REEF

Coral animals are quickly affected by any changes to their surroundings. Pollution in the sea, such as oil spills from ships, kills the coral polyps and the many animals that eat them. Another threat is mud and silt from worn-out farm fields and cut-down forests far inland. This is washed into rivers and carried to the sea. The mud makes the water cloudy, so sunlight cannot reach the plantlike protists on which the coral polyps depend.

Also, in many parts of the world, the rock-hard coral shapes and patterns are cut away by people, and sold to tourists. This trade is destroying some reefs at an alarming rate.

> ### LARGEST... !
> The Great Barrier Reef stretches more than 1,250 miles (2,000 km) along the coast of Queensland, northeast Australia. It has taken millions of years to reach this size. The Great Barrier Reef is by far the largest structure built by living things (including us!). Many of its 3,000 smaller reefs are now marine parks, where the coral environments are protected.

THE REEF-EATING STARFISH

Another natural enemy of coral, especially in the Indian and Pacific Oceans, is the crown-of-thorns starfish, which eats polyps. One of these large predators can destroy 50 square feet (4.6 sq m) of coral in one year. In some reefs, these starfish have increased hugely in numbers—either as part of a natural cycle, or due to changes made by people.

◀ Corals grow in all colors of the rainbow, like this blue coral from the Caribbean.

39

▶ The octopus trails
its tentacles behind
it as it jets through
the water.

SECTION 2
WORMS, SNAILS, & STARFISH

MANY LONG, THIN, SOFT, SLIMY, WRIGGLY CREATURES ARE CALLED WORMS. They are not very appealing to most people. Yet worms are some of the most varied and important members of the animal kingdom. There are at least 20 major groups of worm, ranging from common earthworms that keep the soil fertile, to tiny parasitic worms that cause horrible diseases, to giant tubeworms as thick as your arm living in pitch blackness at the bottom of the sea.

The mollusk group is not well known to many people. Yet it is second only to insects, in the number of different species. Most mollusks have a hard protective shell around the soft body. The group includes limpets and whelks on the seashore, snails in gardens, and water snails in ponds. Some mollusks are eaten as food, such as oysters, mussels, scallops, and clams. A few, like cone shells, are deadly poisonous. And one of the largest of all animals, the giant squid of the ocean depths, is a mollusk.

Yet another enormous group of sea-dwelling animals is the echinoderms, meaning "spiny-skinned." Starfish, urchins, brittlestars, featherstars, and sea lilies are all echinoderms. One of the strangest is the sea cucumber. It looks like an animated sausage eating slimy ooze on the sea bed. If it is attacked, it sicks up sticky threads from its stomach and squirts them out of its mouth!

EARTHWORMS AND LEECHES

◗ The horse leech grows to 12 inches (30 cm) long. It swallows tiny animals whole.

THERE ARE AT LEAST 30 DIFFERENT GROUPS OF WORMLIKE CREATURES. The main group is the annelids or segmented worms, also called true worms. An annelid worm has a body divided into lots of similar ringlike sections called segments. There are 12,000 species of annelid worms, including familiar earthworms, lugworms, and ragworms on the seashore, and leeches. Although these animals are amazingly numerous, we rarely see them because most worms live only in water or under the ground in damp mud, sand, or soil. This is because worms absorb oxygen through their thin, moist skin. If the skin dries out, the worm dies. Worms are also soft, slow-moving and vulnerable, so they gain some protection from living in tubes and tunnels.

◪ Most of these tropical fanworms (page 44) are hidden in purple-tinged tubes. Two have spread their spiral yellow feeding tentacles.

DELICIOUS WORMS

Worms have few defenses against predators, except their underground lifestyle and ability to breed in great numbers. Birds such as thrushes and blackbirds depend on plentiful supplies of worms for themselves and their chicks. Some birds even trample on the soil to mimic the patter of raindrops, which brings the worms to the surface.

◗ A spiral fanworm's feathery tentacles are covered with sticky mucus, which traps tiny bits of food and flows slowly into its mouth.

earthworms spend nearly all their lives underground, burrowing in the soil. They push aside some earth and swallow the rest. The earth passes through the worm's gut and nutritious bits like pieces of dead leaves are digested. The remains pass out of the worm's rear end as fine-grained droppings. These are left as curly worm casts at the surface. Millions of earthworms keep soil fertile. They break down and recycle plant and animal remains. Their burrows allow air and moisture into the soil, for plant roots to use, and to help water drain away.

▲ Two earthworms partly emerge from their tunnels on a damp night, to mate. They lay side by side and exchange sperm.

MATING IN THE GRASS

An earthworm has no obvious head. The front or mouth end is slightly more pointed than the rear end, and it has simple detectors that can distinguish between light and dark, but which cannot form an image like proper eyes. One obvious feature of the earthworm is a part called the saddle or clitellum, where several segments seem to be enlarged and fused together. When two worms meet to mate, they put their saddles next to each other. Each earthworm is an hermaphrodite—it has both male and female parts. So each passes sperm to the other, to fertilize its eggs. Each then forms a cocoon of eggs around the saddle. The cocoon slips off and is left in the soil, and baby worms hatch from it.

◢ A leech moves by "looping." It stretches forward while anchored by its back sucker, and sticks down the front one. Then it detaches the rear sucker, shortens its body, attaches the rear sucker again, and so on.

WATER WORMS

The bright red tubifex or sludge worm is a cousin of the earthworm. It lives in fresh water, and is sometimes called the bloodworm because of its color. The bright red is due to a pigment (colored substance) that is specialized to take in oxygen from the water, through the skin into the worm's body. The pigment is so plentiful that this worm can live in stagnant water that is very low in oxygen. Hundreds of sludge worms build tubes of sticky mucus in the mud and wave their tails in the water to obtain oxygen.

THE BLOODSUCKERS

Leeches are like flattened types of worms. They have muscular bodies which can shorten or lengthen, and a sucker at each end. Some leeches prey on smaller worms, insect grubs, and similar creatures. Others are parasites, sucking the blood of fish or other animals, including people. The hungry leech clamps itself onto an animal as it passes, perhaps while coming to water to drink. It then rubs its way into the skin with three sets of tiny teeth and gorges itself, sucking in five times its own weight of blood and fluids. The leech can survive for weeks before needing another meal.

▼ Sludge worms can survive in stagnant ponds and ditches.

ANNELID WORMS

• about 12,000 species
• tube-shaped soft body
• divided into segments

Three main subgroups:
Earthworms
• 3,000 species
• most live in soil or fresh water
• hermaphrodite (each individual is both male and female)
• includes most earthworms, also sludge worms (bloodworms)

Leeches
• 500 species
• many are leaf-shaped
• mostly freshwater, some in the sea or on land
• some are bloodsuckers
• hermaphrodite

Bristleworms
Described on page 44

43

BRISTLEWORMS

BRISTLEWORMS ARE NAMED FROM THE STIFF BRISTLELIKE HAIRS, KNOWN AS CHAETAE, STICKING OUT ALL OVER THEIR BODIES. More than half of the types of segmented worms (page 42) belong to the

⬧ Feeding fanworm

bristleworm group, also called polychaetes. In some types the bristles are attached to paddlelike flaps. Bristleworms live mainly in the sea, and use these flaps as oars, to paddle over the bottom or dig into sand and mud. Some kinds live inside tubes.

⬧ Ragworm

Compared to earthworms, most bristleworms have an obvious head and tail end. The head usually has tentacles, which may look like thin fingers, or be arranged as a frilly ring or a feathery crown. Some types of bristleworms also have simple types of eyes that can pick out shapes. There may be a pair of long threadlike feelers at the tail end.

Bristleworms on the shore include ragworms and lugworms. Ragworms often live in burrows lined with their own hardened mucus (slime), in the muddy silt that collects at the bottom of a rock pool. When the tide is out, the ragworm stays hidden. When the tide comes in, the ragworm emerges from its burrow to feed on the surface of the mud. It can wriggle like a snake, or swim by rowing with its paddlelike flaps.

Ragworms eat a range of food, from dead animals and small creatures such as shrimps to seaweeds. Their strong jaws can easily bite chunks of flesh from a carcass—and even draw blood through human skin. They can also shed their slimy body covering and eat it, to take in the microbes in the slime.

FAN-FEEDERS

The main body of a fanworm stays hidden inside a protective tube set into the sea bed, which it builds from mud or sand particles glued together with its own slimy mucus. Fanworms are named for their stiff, feathery feeding tentacles, which they stick out from the top of the tube and spread out like a fan. One of the most beautiful fanworms is the peacock worm. Its tube may be 10 inches (25 cm) long. When safe, it extends the tentacles and waves them in the water. The tentacles are coated with a thin layer of sticky mucus that catches any bits of food floating past. They also work as gills for breathing.

If a fish or other predator swims nearby, the peacock worm whisks in its tentacles and pulls itself down into the safety of its tube. Sometimes peacock worms and other fanworms live in groups, looking like a carpet of flowers. When danger appears, they are gone in a flash, leaving the seabed looking bare and lifeless.

▶ Lugworms hide under the sand in U-shaped burrows. The worm wriggles to make water flow through its burrow, so it can breathe.

THE MOUSE WORM

The sea mouse is not a mouse at all, but a type of bristleworm. It grows about 8 inches (20 cm) long. Its plump, humped body is covered with gray-brown, hairy flaps, almost like the fur of a real mouse. Sea mice live mainly on muddy or sandy seabeds, in the Atlantic Ocean and Mediterranean Sea.

◼ At the bottom of the sea, giant white tubeworms live near vents that pour out scalding, sulfur-rich water. They are 10 feet (3 m) long and as thick as your arm. They take in the sulfur chemicals, and bacteria in their bodies use the chemicals to make food, which they share with the worm.

HARD TUBES

Some bristleworms build much tougher, more rigid tubes from chalky minerals, either in the sand or on rocks. The hard, white, wiggly tubes on seashore weeds and boulders belong to bristleworms called keelworms. When the tide is in, the keelworm pushes its tiny crown of feeding tentacles from the end of the tube, to gather food.

SAND CASTS

Little mounds of sand or mud on the shore are the casts of lugworms. These worms are 6-8 inches (15–20 cm) long, soft, and thicker at the front end. They feed like earthworms, by eating the sand or mud, digesting any nutrients, and then passing out the remains as the familiar worm cast.

◼ The tubes of peacock worms partly stick up from the seabed.

(continued from page 43):

Bristleworms
• 8,500 species
• most live in the sea
• body has bristles or flaps
• sexes separate (male or female)
• includes lugworms, ragworms, fanworms, peacock worms, sea mice, scaleworms, catworms

FLATWORMS

FLATWORMS ARE THE SIMPLEST OF ALL WORMS.
They are indeed flat and smooth, resembling leaves or
ribbons. They lack the ringlike body sections or
segments of annelid worms (page 42). There are more
than 13,000 species of flatworms. But they are less
familiar than earthworms, because most are too
small to see easily, while others live in water, and
some are parasites inside other animals. Most free-
living flatworms are found in the sea, among
weeds, or the pebbles on the shore. Some live in
fresh water and a few in damp soil.

◄ Free-living
flatworms c
turbellarians ofte
look like leave
They live as predator
hunting even smalle
creatures, or scavengin
on corpses. The many
branched intestine and th
mouth area under the cente
of the body are visibl
through the thin skir

Flatworms that can move around freely, rather than being parasites
inside animals, are called turbellarians. The freshwater
turbellarians, or planarians, are streamlined animals, with
an obvious head and tail end. Some species even have
several small eyes around the front end, while
others have two larger eyes on top of the head.
Some also have a pair of feelers on the head,
to help them feel objects and detect
scents as they move about.The
underside of a flatworm is
covered in tiny hairs, cilia,
which wave smoothly to
and fro to glide the
worm along.

SHRINK! ⚠

Some flatworms can
reproduce by splitting
themselves into two. Each
half then regrows the
missing portion and two
separate flatworms result.
They can also feed on
themselves if food is in
short supply, absorbing
their own bodies and
gradually shrinking in
the process.

▼ Flatworms in the sea ar
larger and more varied than th
freshwater species. Some ar
brightly patterned or colore

◄ Many freshwater planarians have an obvious head end with eyes.

Flatworms can also move by rippling their muscular undersides. Many feed on smaller animals, or on the dead bodies of other creatures. When some flatworms find food, they push part of their gut out from the body, then slowly suck the food and gut inside again.

FLATWORMS OF POND AND STREAM

Planarians are common in ponds and streams all round the world. They hide among pebbles and weeds by day, and are mostly only fingernail-sized or smaller, so are seldom seen. They are active mainly at night. In the dark water, they glide smoothly along the surfaces of plants, or slither across submerged logs and stones. Sometimes they slip upside down along the underside of the water's surface, feeding on creatures trapped by the surface film.

Different types of these free-living flatworms are suited to particular freshwater habitats. The crenobia planarian lives in cold upland streams. It has earlike feelers and a pair of large eyes. The polycelis planarian is also found in running streams. It has many tiny eyes around the edges of its head. The dugesia planarian has a triangular head with two large eyes on the top. It lives in ponds and streams, but cannot cope well with fast currents.

◄ Large tropical flatworms crawl through dead leaves in rain forests.

INSIDE A FLATWORM

Flatworms have very simple bodies. On the outside is a layer of cells called the epidermis. On the inside there is another layer of cells, the endodermis, arranged in tubes to form the intestine (gut or digestive tract). The only way in and out of the intestine is the mouth, which may be at the head end, the tail end, or part way along the underside. In between the epidermis and the intestine are masses of cells called the parenchyma. These make up the flatworm's muscles, glands, nerves, and reproductive organs.

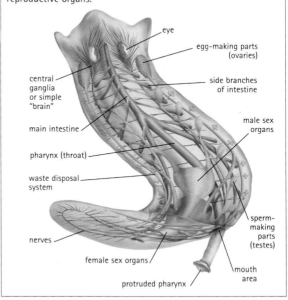

- eye
- egg-making parts (ovaries)
- central ganglia or simple "brain"
- side branches of intestine
- main intestine
- male sex organs
- pharynx (throat)
- waste disposal system
- nerves
- sperm-making parts (testes)
- female sex organs
- mouth area
- protruded pharynx

HOW FLATWORMS BREED

Most flatworms are hermaphrodites. This means each has both male and female sex organs. So any two flatworms can come together and mate, each passing on sperm to the other. Each of the pair then goes on to develop and lay its eggs.

The eggs are sticky when first laid, and are attached beneath stones or underwater logs. After a few weeks, the eggs hatch out into tiny baby flatworms that gradually grow into adults. This is quite different to parasitic flatworms (page 48), where the young forms or larvae often differ in shape from the adults.

Flatworms (Platyhelminthes)
- 25,000 species
- live in water or damp places, or inside other animals
- soft, flattened, leaflike body
- no body sections or segments
- most are hermaphrodite (male and female)
- some free-living, some parasitic

Divided into three groups:

Flukes and Tapeworms
Described on pages 48–49

Free-living flatworms (Turbellaria)
- most in the sea, some in fresh water, a few on land
- most less than 1 inch (2 cm) long
- head end has dark eyes

Gnathostomulans
- 100 species
- live in the sea
- small (up to 0.04 inch/1mm)
- tiny and wormlike

FLUKES AND TAPEWORMS

FLUKES AND TAPEWORMS ARE FLATWORMS (PAGE 46) THAT MOSTLY
LIVE AS PARASITES, ON OR INSIDE OTHER ANIMALS AND PEOPLE.
Many flukes can live both inside their host—in its intestine, liver, or heart—and
on or under its skin, gripping by special leechlike suckers. Tapeworms live right
inside their host's gut, for months at a time. The host is not
always aware of the worm's presence, but it may feel ill
since the worm steals its nutrition or
damages its body parts. Tapeworms
tend to live in larger mammals.
Flukes live in nearly every kind of
animal, from insects and crabs to
fish, reptiles, birds, and mammals.

Most flukes are leaf-shaped and about
1 inch (2.5 cm) long, although some are
more rounded, like other worms. At the
front end, the adult fluke has a sucker
which it uses to hang on to its host.
There may be another sucker
farther down its body, to give
the fluke extra sticking power.

The outside of an adult fluke is
covered with slimy mucus. This
protects it from the host's body
fluids and digestive juices, which
would otherwise attack and kill it.
The adult fluke feeds by sucking up
the blood and other fluids from its host
animal. One kind of fluke lives inside the
bodies of frogs and toads. When the host
returns to water to breed, the flukes
release their eggs into the water as
well. Then the tiny fluke larvae
attach themselves to the frog's
tadpoles, infecting the next
generation of amphibians.

LONG! !

Tapeworms can grow very long.
One kind found in whales may reach
66 feet (20 m) in length. Tapeworms
have been a problem for people as
long as there have been people.
Ancient Egyptians suffered from
these parasites.

⬆ A tapeworm
has a head called
the scolex, with tiny
hooks for clinging to the
inside of the host's gut. The
body grows in baglike parts behind the
head. These are not proper segments, but sacs
containing sex organs with their eggs and sperm.

The liver fluke is a flatworm that burrows into the livers of animals such as sheep.

A COMPLICATED LIFE

Many kinds of flukes have complicated life cycles. They live on or in different hosts at different stages of their lives. Some flukes even move from one host to another four times. Typically, a fluke would spend most of its adult life in the body of a large vertebrate animal such as a fish, reptile, bird, or mammal. But it transfers its eggs or larvae to the body of an invertebrate, such as a snail or a slug, when it breeds.

FLUKE DISEASES

Liver flukes infest the livers of sheep and cattle, and cause disease. As an adult, the liver fluke feeds on blood in the sheep's liver. Its eggs pass out with the sheep's droppings and lie in the pasture. They only develop further if they hatch near a water snail. When the young or larval fluke finds a snail, it burrows in and lives there for a while. Then it leaves the snail and attaches itself to plants at the water's edge. If a sheep eats a plant with one of these larvae on it, the sheep becomes infected, the fluke larva grows into an adult, and the cycle is complete.

TROPICAL DISEASE FLUKES

Bilharzia or schistosomiasis is a tropical disease caused by a blood fluke called schistosoma. These flukes live inside the veins near the host person's intestine or bladder. The eggs are released near the gut, and some pass out of the host's body with the feces. If they get into water, they can infect the second host, a type of water snail. After developing inside the snail, the next stage of fluke larva escapes into the water. If these larvae end up on a human, they burrow into the skin and enter the blood.

TAPELIKE WORMS

Tapeworms get their name from the tape- or ribbon-like bodies of the adult worms. The body is flat and can be very long—30 feet (9 m) or more, looped back and forth several times inside the host's intestine.

LIFE CYCLES OF FLUKES AND TAPEWORMS

Many flukes infest two, three, or four hosts during the different stages in their lives. For example, certain kinds of flukes live inside a person, in the intestine, liver, or bladder. They produce tiny eggs, which pass out in the host person's urine or feces. Only if the eggs find their way into a host (such as the correct type of snail) do they develop into larvae. Then this host must be eaten by the right type of fish, for the next stage to happen. Finally a person eats the poorly cooked fish and takes in the fluke larvae, which mature into adults.

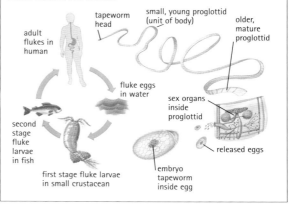

adult flukes in human

tapeworm head

small, young proglottid (unit of body)

older, mature proglottid

fluke eggs in water

sex organs inside proglottid

released eggs

second stage fluke larvae in fish

first stage fluke larva in small crustacean

embryo tapeworm inside egg

Most tapeworms live as parasites inside the intestines of large carnivorous animals, including people. At the front end, the tapeworm secures itself to the gut wall of its host with hooks and suckers. The tapeworm has no mouth or gut of its own. It feeds by absorbing nutrients through all the surfaces of its body. It has plenty of food all around it, provided by its host.

This fluke is less than 0.04 inch (1 mm) long. It lives in the blood of many animals.

People badly affected by tapeworms become very thin, even though they eat normally. This is because the worms "steal" their food. One kind of human tapeworm has the pig as a second host. Another species infects cattle. If someone eats pork or beef infected with tapeworm larvae, he or she may become infected. In the past, the pork tapeworm was a common human parasite due to eating raw or under-cooked pork. Cooking or curing the meat kills any tapeworm eggs or larvae.

FLATWORMS (continued from page 47):

Flukes (Trematoda)
• parasites, some causing diseases in animals and people
• most small, less than 2 inches (5 cm)
• leaf-shaped body

Tapeworms (Cestoda)
• parasites in animals and people
• long, 30 feet (9 m) or more
• ribbon-shaped
• tiny head with hooks
• no mouth or intestine
• egg bags look like segments

ROUNDWORMS

ROUNDWORMS ARE FOUND ALMOST EVERYWHERE, IN VAST NUMBERS. Most are tiny and live in water or soil, so we rarely notice them. Others are parasites and cause disease and suffering. They include eelworms, hookworms, threadworms, filarial worms, and a host of other species. A typical roundworm has a long body that tapers toward each end, is round like a tube, and does not have sections or segments. Roundworms are also known as nematode worms.

The strongyloides roundworm is a parasite in sheep. It bores through the skin into the blood and ends up in the intestine.

About 20,000 different kinds of roundworms or nematodes have been discovered. But the true number is probably far higher—perhaps half a million. Because they are so plentiful, roundworms are very important in the balance of nature. By feeding on dead and decaying animals and plants, they help to break these down and return the goodness to the soil, recycling vital nutrients. Tiny roundworms living between grains of sand at the seaside feed on bacteria, and by doing so, help to keep the beaches clean!

The pig roundworm, ascaris, has the typical roundworm body—long and thin, pointed at both ends, with no obvious head or tail.

EVERYWHERE
Roundworms live in just about every habitat on the planet. Most are so small that we cannot see them. Free-living (nonparasitic) roundworms are usually less than 0.04–0.08 inch (1–2 mm) long. A single spadeful of garden soil may contain 0.5 million.

When we do notice roundworms is when they are parasites in plants and animals, and cause enormous damage. Roundworms not only do damage themselves. They may also carry viruses that infect the host. A common plant parasite is the eelworm, which attacks the roots of several crops, notably potatoes, tomatoes, and sugar beet. A single potato plant may have 40,000 eelworms infesting its roots.

◖ The threadworm (pinworm) is a common human parasite. It is harmful in large numbers.

◖ Some types of roundworms colonize plants and ruin crops. Certain kinds cause hard swellings known as galls. Others puncture plant cells and suck out the sap. Still others infest animals of all kinds. No creature is safe, even other worms. These tiny roundworms are eating their way into an earthworm.

THE DREADED HOOKWORM

Hookworms are particularly harmful parasitic nematodes. They are among the most common causes of human illness, affecting more than 1,000 million people, especially in tropical Asia. Newly hatched hookworms burrow through the skin of a person and get into the bloodstream. They then travel around the body and settle in the intestine, where they feed and grow. They have a very weakening effect on people. Children, especially, suffer from anemia (shortage of red blood cells). An infected person becomes pale and weak, and the legs and abdomen swell. If not treated quickly with drugs that kill the worms, death may result.

FILARIAL WORMS

Another unpleasant tropical parasite in humans is the filaria roundworm, wucheria. It gets into the body's lymph tubes and glands, which carry fluids around the body and fight germs. As the worms grow and multiply, they block the lymph system and cause terrible swellings, especially in the limbs, known as elephantiasis.

The filiaria roundworm is spread by flies and mosquitoes. The worm's young are released by the mother and make their way to the surface blood vessels. When a mosquito bites the person's skin, it takes up the filaria with the blood. The worm grows inside the mosquito's head. Then, when the mosquito bites another person or animal, the worm enters through the wound and infects the new host. Some roundworms have several hosts in their lives, as flukes do (page 48).

GIANT ROUNDWORM

The Guinea worm, another tropical parasite, lives in humans and may grow more than 3 feet (90 cm) long. It causes pain and disfigurement, and ulcers develop when the worms release their eggs through the skin.

Roundworms *(nematodes)*
• 20,000-plus species
• all habitats
• most are free-living, some are parasites
• body rounded, but without segments
• many are tiny
• largest are up to 3 feet (90 cm)

THE LIVES OF PARASITES

Many kinds of roundworms, flukes, tapeworms, and other worms live as internal or endo-parasites. They obtain shelter and nutrients from their hosts, and usually cause harm in return. The life of a schistosoma parasite (a fluke, page 48) is shown here. Worms are suited to the parasitic way of life. Their thin, flexible bodies can squeeze through the host's blood vessels, intestines, and other parts. A worm can also absorb nutrients and oxygen easily through its thin skin.

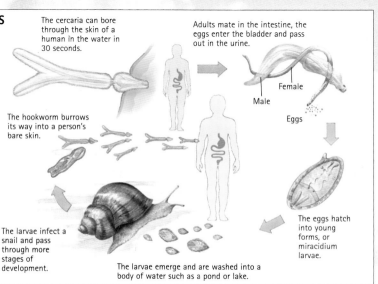

The cercaria can bore through the skin of a human in the water in 30 seconds.

Adults mate in the intestine, the eggs enter the bladder and pass out in the urine.

Female

Male

Eggs

The hookworm burrows its way into a person's bare skin.

The eggs hatch into young forms, or miracidium larvae.

The larvae infect a snail and pass through more stages of development.

The larvae emerge and are washed into a body of water such as a pond or lake.

51

OTHER WORMS

BESIDES THE MAIN GROUPS OF
WORMS (SEGMENTED WORMS,
FLATWORMS, AND ROUNDWORMS),
THERE ARE MANY OTHER TYPES OF
WORMS. They include ribbon worms,
spoon worms, arrow worms, and acorn
worms. They are not necessarily close
relatives of the main worms, or of each
other. But all have the main worm
feature—a long, wriggling body.

🔻 Peanut worm

Peanut worms are cylinder-shaped, with a flexible
stalk-like proboscis at the top that can be
extended or pulled back inside the body. The
proboscis has frilly tentacles at the end, which are
used for feeding. Peanut worms range from
pinhead size to more than 28 inches
(70 cm) long.

🔻 Ribbon worms live among rocks and
stones on the shore and under the sea.
They hunt tiny animals for food.

Ribbon worms or nemerteans live mostly in the
sea. They have soft, slimy bodies that are slightly
flattened toward the head, and range in length
from 0.02 inch to 30 feet (0.5 mm to 9 m). Some
ribbon worms are black or dark, others are
brightly striped or banded. Most are predators.

Horsehair worms or hair worms often live in
groups and look like a mass of living, writhing
hair. They often coil themselves almost into knots.
Adults live in damp soil or water and do not feed
at all. They just reproduce their kind. The young
horsehair worms live as parasites, inside the
bodies of insects and similar hosts.

SPOON WORMS

Spoon worms include
some of the strangest
of all animals. Most
have pear-shaped
bodies, with hooks
and a proboscis at
the head end. They
live in the sea, either
in mud burrows or
crevices in the rocks. In
one kind, the bonellia
spoon worm, the female
has a body about 6 inches
(15 cm) long. But her
enormous proboscis is 3 feet
(90 cm) in length, and is
forked at the end. She is vivid
green in color. Yet the male is
almost microscopically small
compared to the giant female.
Bonellias are quite common
in the Mediterranean Sea.

🔺 Arrow worms
live in the tropical
oceans in huge
numbers. They feed
mainly on smaller
animals of plankton,
including fish fry.

LONGEST! ⚠

The longest known animal is
a type of ribbon worm—the
bootlace worm. It often
grows to 15 feet
(4.5 m) long, but lengths of
100 feet (30 m) have
been recorded.

SPINY-HEADED AND
PEANUT WORMS

Spiny-headed worms
are all parasites and
live inside larger
animals, especially fish.
Their mouthparts are
equipped with spiny
hooks, which they use
to attach themselves to
their hosts.

🔻 Spiny-headed
worms

Arrow worms

BEARD WORMS

Beard worms live in the ocean depths, in tubes almost buried in the mud. They have long, thin bodies, just a "matchhead" wide, but 3 feet (90 cm) or more long. At the front is a beardlike tuft of 100 or so tentacles. They have no stomach or intestine, absorbing nutrients through the body surface.

PRIAPULID AND HORSESHOE WORMS

Priapulid worms burrow in the mud on the seabed or shore. They resemble the peanut worms, but the stalklike proboscis at the head end has a ring of teeth rather than tentacles. Priapulid worms have frilly appendages on the tail. These probably work as gills for breathing. This is one of the smallest of all animal groups, with only about ten known species.

Horseshoe worms are another very small group in terms of numbers of species. But the worms themselves can be very abundant in muddy sand. They live in tubes which they make for themselves. Some kinds burrow into limestone rocks. The animal itself is long and wormlike, but at its top or head end it has a fanlike swirl of tentacles. When feeding, only the spreading tentacles can be seen at the top of the tube.

TONGUE WORMS

Tongue worms are parasites, living inside the nose passages and lungs of mammals, birds, and reptiles. The tongue worm has no obvious features except for its head end, which has five fingerlike parts sticking out. The middle one of the five has the tongue worm's mouth at its tip.

Horsehair worm

ARROW WORMS

Arrow worms are transparent, arrow-shaped animals about 1 inch (2.5 cm) long, with small "fins" at the sides and tail. They live in the upper layers of the sea and hunt small fish and animal plankton such as copepods, using spines near the mouth to grasp their prey.

Priapulid worm

ACORN WORMS

Acorn worms live in burrows in mud and sand on the seabed. They are found mainly in shallow water near the coast. They range in size from about 1 to 20 inches (2.5 to 50 cm) long. Between the proboscis and the rest of the body is a distinct collar. In some, the proboscis is short and looks like an oak tree's acorn. Acorn worms are very fragile creatures, and out of their burrows, they easily fall to pieces!

Ribbon worms (Nemertea)
• 900 species
• most are marine
• long and ribbon-shaped
• sexes separate in most species

Horsehair worms (Nematomorpha)
• 250 species
• water or damp soil, some marine
• long and hairlike
• sexes separate

Spiny-headed worms (Acanthocephala)
• 1,000 species
• parasitic
• spiny mouthparts

Peanut worms (Sipuncula)
• 350 species
• marine, in sand and mud
• cylinder-shaped
• mouth with frilly tentacles

Spoon worms (Echiura)
• 150 species
• marine, in burrows in mud or sand
• sausage- or pear-shaped
• long, fingerlike proboscis

Beard worms (Pogonophora)
• 100 species
• marine, in the deep sea

• beardlike tentacles on head
• sexes separate

Arrow worms (Chaetognatha)
• 70 species
• marine, in plankton
• long, transparent body, with flaps or fins
• most are transparent
• extremely numerous

Priapulid worms (Priapula)
• 10 species
• marine, live on the sea floor
• tube-shaped

Horseshoe worms (Phorona)
• 20 species
• marine
• live in hard tubes
• have head tentacles

Tongue worms (Pentastoma)
• 100 species
• mainly parasites of reptiles, mammals, and birds
• four short tentacles around head end

Acorn worms (Hemichordata)
• 100 speciess
• marine, on the sea floor, mostly in burrows
• fingerlike proboscis on head

THE RANGE OF MOLLUSKS

SNAILS AND SLUGS, AND SEA CREATURES SUCH AS WHELKS, COCKLES, CLAMS, AND MUSSELS, ARE ALL MOLLUSKS. So are octopuses, squid, and cuttlefish. Indeed, there are nearly 100,000 species of mollusk, making up the second largest group of animals after insects and other arthropods. They vary greatly in size and shape, but all have soft bodies, and many have hard shells. Most mollusks move about on a large, flat pad, called the foot. The head of a mollusk often has soft, bendy tentacles, used for feeling its way about or grasping food. The main mollusk groups are described on the following pages.

◩ The bright colors and pattern of tropical sea slugs warn tha they are bad to eat. The knob and frills help in breathing

◩ The octopus trails its tentacle behind i as it jets through the wate

◪ Sea slugs look like multicolored snails without their shells. They crawl around on the seabed looking for food.

Most mollusks live in the sea. Only certain species of two groups, the bivalves and the snails, live in fresh water. Some snails are even able to live in damp conditions on land. There are seven main groups of mollusks. The three most familiar are the gastropods such as snails, limpets, and winkles, the bivalves such as mussels, clams, oysters, and razorshells, and the cephalopods such as octopuses, cuttlefish, nautiluses, and squid.

All mollusks have a large, cloaklike part around the main body, called the mantle. In many mollusks, this makes a hard, protective shell on the outside, which the creature can withdraw into, to avoid danger. The shell grows as the edges of the mantle ooze a mineral-rich, liquid substance. Thi hardens, and the shell grows with its owner.

The shells of some mollusks are round and smooth. Some are coiled into tight spirals, or spread out like fans. A bivalve's shel is two flaplike shell halves, called valves, hinged together. In mollusks such as slugs and cuttlefish, the shell is inside the body. If there is no shell, the mantle forms a leathery cover around the body.

Many mollusks look like little more than squishy blobs. But the body is quite complicated inside, containing many of the usual important parts such as a brain, heart, and kidney. Muscles can pull and squeeze the body into almost any shape.

◪ Scallops are bivalve molluscs, which means they have two shell parts. The scallop can snap its shell shut to swim jerkily.

THE MOLLUSK'S RADULA

One special feature of mollusks is a filelike "tongue" called a radula, covered in rows of hard teeth. The mollusk uses this to scrape away at its food, perhaps tiny seaweeds covering a rock, or lettuces in the garden. Not all mollusks feed in this way, however. Squid and octopuses are active predators, tearing up their prey with a beaklike mouth.

▶ Tusk shells have long, curving, tapering shells that look like elephants' tusks. The shell is open at both ends. The tusk shell lives half buried, head-down in the sand. It feeds by spreading its threadlike tentacles into the sand.

THE MOLLUSK'S FOOT

The mollusk's large, muscular, padlike foot is used for many tasks. Squid and octopuses have developed the foot into tentacles to catch prey. A limpet uses its sucker foot to cling to rocks. A snail slides about on its foot. A clam's foot is like a strong finger that pokes and digs into the sand or mud. A razorshell's foot is so powerful, it can dig the animal down into the seashore mud, almost as fast as a person could dig with a shovel.

◀ Chitons are oval in shape and have a shell divided into eight arched plates, making them look as if they are protected by chain-mail armor. The alternative name for this group is "coat-of-mail shells." They graze on the film of seaweed covering rocks in shallow water along the coast. Chitons can curl up tightly if dislodged from their rocks.

FOOD FROM MOLLUSKS

All over the world, people like to eat mollusks—favorites include oysters, clams, cockles, mussels, scallops, abalones, winkles, octopus, and squid. They are usually an important source of food in coastal places and on islands. Some mollusks have become rare or even endangered as a result of being over-collected for food.

▲ Many mollusk shells are incredibly beautiful, especially when wet from the sea. The tropical conch shell is especially attractive. Empty, it has been used as a trumpet to make sounds for thousands of years. However, the souvenir trade in mollusk shells endangers many species (page 60).

▷ Mussels are fixed to seashore rocks by strong, stringy byssus threads.

MOLLUSKS

- up to 100,000 species
- most live in the sea, some in fresh water, a few on land
- soft body in cloaklike mantle
- many have hard shell around body
- many have large, muscular base or foot
- some have flexible tentacles

Main groups of mollusks:
Tusk shells
- 350 species
- marine
- burrow into sand
- single shell shaped like elephant's tusk

Slugs and snails
- 70,000 species
- marine, freshwater and land-living
- most have a single shell, often coiled
- head has tentacles
- glide on muscular foot

Bivalves
- 20,000 species
- most are marine, some freshwater
- hinged shell of two parts (valves)
- foot rounded, not flattened
- most burrow, or live attached to rocks

Squid and octopuses
- 650 species
- live in the sea
- long tentacles around mouth
- large eyes, big brains
- hide in rocks or swim in the sea

Chitons
- 550 species
- live in the sea, on rocks on the shore, or in shallow water
- body oval and domed (like a woodlouse), with eight plates
- no eyes

SLUGS AND SNAILS

LAND SNAILS AND SEA SNAILS, LAND SLUGS AND SEA SLUGS, ALONG WITH LIMPETS AND WHELKS, ARE ALL GASTROPODS—MOLLUSKS WITH SOFT, SQUIDGY BODIES. The name gastropod means "stomach-foot," because these mollusks seem to slide along on their stomachs. But it is really the same muscular foot possessed by all mollusks. Many snails and limpets have a hard shell, so gastropods are sometimes called univalves (meaning "one shell"). A slug's soft body is exposed.

◄ Some sea slugs have large hairlike tentacles on their backs. These can carry stings or horrible-tasting fluid.

◄ Few mollusks are more familiar than the common garden snail. After a heavy rainstorm, snails emerge as if from nowhere in the damp conditions. They rasp their way through many kinds of leaves and plant bits on the ground.

When a gastropod slides along the ground, its large, flat stomach-foot spreads out underneath. Muscles in the foot ripple backward and forward. As they move, land snails and slugs ooze a trail of slime to ease the way forward and reduce friction.

THE SHELL'S TRAPDOOR
On the back of the foot, most sea snails and some land snails have a flap called an operculum. When danger threatens, the snail retreats into its shell and pulls the operculum over the opening, like closing a trapdoor, for protection.

Many gastropods have four tentacles on the head. Two are feelers that help them to find their way by touch.

The other two are often stalks with eyes at the tip. But many gastropods have no eyes at all.

SHELLS AND SURVIVAL
Snails seem to live everywhere, not only in all parts of the oceans, but in almost all habitats on land. Like all mollusks, the snail needs plenty of moisture to survive. So land snails stay in or near moist places. If the weather is too cold or too dry, the snail makes a seal of slime over its shell entrance. This hardens into a kind of temporary door. In the fall, in temperate regions, many snails settle down for the winter in this state. As it gets warmer in the spring, the snail breaks open the seal and emerges again. In hot, dry weather, snails also seal themselves in their shells and wait for cooler, moister conditions. Surviving heat or dryness like this is called estivation.

MALE AND FEMALE
Snails are hermaphrodite, which means that each animal is both male and female at the same time. When they mate, each snail passes sperm into the body of the other snail. Each partner goes on to develop and lay a clutch of leathery eggs. There may be dozens of eggs in a single clutch.

LARGEST... !
The biggest snail is the African giant snail, whose shell can be almost 10 inches (25 cm) across.

JELLY BABIES !
Water and pond snails lay their eggs in a string or blob of jelly, usually stuck to the stem of a water plant or stone. The jelly helps to protect the eggs from being eaten, and also stops them drying out if the water level in the pond or stream changes. In an aquarium tank water snails often lay their eggs on the glass. This allows a clear view of the tiny baby snails developing inside.

◄ Slugs like this keeled slug have a great appetite for all kinds of plants, including potatoes. The keeled slug often burrows under the soil, especially to eat plant roots and to hide during the day.

Eventually many tiny snails hatch. Except for their size, they look very like the adults, each with its tiny shell. It takes about two years for a snail to reach maturity.

SLUGS

Slugs are like snails that have lost their protective shells, although some slugs do have small shells inside their bodies, just under the skin of the back. Some even have a tiny shell on the back. To protect themselves, slugs produce large quantities of very sticky slime, which puts off many predators. The slime also helps to stop the slugs from drying out. However, some birds, such as thrushes, and some mammals, including hedgehogs, can cope with this slime. They eat large numbers of slugs. Song thrushes can even tackle snails. They bash the snail against a hard object, like a stone, until its shell breaks open. Then they quickly eat the tasty flesh inside.

◿ This Indonesian sea slug can swim by undulating its capelike foot. The gills are tall, yellow, and spiky. Sea slugs eat seaweeds and small animals such as sea mats and corals that coat rocks.

SLUGS AT SEA

The marine relatives of snails and slugs include some of the most beautiful of all sea creatures. Like land slugs, sea slugs are mostly without shells. Many of them have feathery gills and bodies covered with amazingly bright, almost glowing patterns and colors. There are sea slugs in shades of orange, pink, or blue, and with tufts of vividly brilliant gills on their backs. The bright colors warn predators that they should be left alone. Sea slugs taste horrible, and some even have poisonous stings on their backs.

◿ Most snails are little bigger than cherries. But a few, such as the giant ram's-horn snail of ponds and lakes, can be 4 to 6 inches (10 to 15 cm) across.

> GROUPS OF SLUGS
> (continued from page 55):
>
> Land and freshwater snails, slugs
> • 20,500 species
> • on land and in fresh water
> • spiral or coiled shell (not in slugs)
>
> Sea slugs
> • 1,250 species
> • mostly sluglike, lacking shells
> • bright colors
> • frilly gills

◿ Sea slugs are also called nudibranchs. This yellow-spotted red nudibranch is from the seas around the Philippines.

SEA SNAILS AND LIMPETS

MANY KINDS OF SNAILS LIVE IN THE OCEANS.
In fact, there are more than twice as many sea-living snail
species as there are land and freshwater species combined.
These sea snails include whelks, limpets, top shells,
winkles (periwinkles), cowries, cone shells, and many
others, especially in tropical seas.
All of these have a one-piece, usually
coiled, shell, and are gastropods
(page 56). Also included in this large
group are the sea hares, which look
more like a combination of a slug
with a hare's long ears.

❷ Slipper limpets tend to
attach themselves to their own
kind. They also change sex
with age. The oldest, near the
base of the pile, are females.
The uppermost are males.

❷ Cowrie shells have been
trinkets since prehistoric times.
They may have been an early
form of money.

❷ The chocolate-lined top shell
is one of many top shells with
very fine lines on the shell.

There are about 55,000 kinds of sea snails. Many land snails are drab gray
or brown, but many sea snails are stunningly colorful, although their
brightness fades after death. Some sea snails live along the coast, in the
rock pools and shallows. Others live on the very
deepest ocean floor in pitch darkness. Land
snails have lungs to breathe air. Sea snails
have gills to breathe in water, like fish.

❷ Marbled cone
shell

LIMPETS AND ABALONES

When the tide goes out,
limpets can be seen
clinging to rocks or
other surfaces, where
they graze on
seaweeds. The
limpet's soft body is
completely protected from predators
such as birds and fish by its hard,
cone-shaped shell, which it pulls
down tight onto the rock. The
muscular foot clamps down
hard, with such force that it is
very difficult to pull a
limpet from its resting
place. When the tide
comes in again, the
limpet lifts its shell
slightly and slides
over the rocks,
searching for
seaweeds.

The common spider conch from the Indian and Pacific region s long shell projections like the legs of a spider.

scrapes and pulls these into its mouth with its othed tongue. When the tide begins to fall, the mpet returns to its "home base" on the rock.

BALONES

balones are like big limpets. They live among eds of kelp seaweed in South Africa and California, and grow up to 8 inches (20 cm) cross. They are a great seafood delicacy, ot only with people, but also with nimals such as sea otters, eabirds, seals, and sea lions.

WINKLES AND WHELKS

Winkles or periwinkles are among the commonest of the sea snails, visible on seashores all over the world. When a winkle retreats inside its shell, it closes the "door"—a plate called the operculum.

Whelks are larger than winkles, with a sturdy, spiral shell that can grow up to 4 inches (10 cm) ong. A whelk is a carnivore. Its sharp-toothed ongue or radula is on a flexible stalk, the roboscis. The whelk uses this to probe and rub ts way through the shell of a victim, such as an oyster or mussel, to get at the flesh.

MORE TYPES OF SNAILS
(continued from page 55):

• Top shells, turban shells, limpets, violet sea snails, winkles, spire shells, conches, necklace shells, moon shells, whelks, oyster drills, turret shells, cone shells, augers

Whelks are also known for their egg cases. These are the spongy, papery objects found washed up on the beach, and sometimes called seawash balls. Each compartment is an egg about 0.5 inch (1 cm) across. The female glues the eggs into a fist-sized mass as she lays them in shallow water. The first young to hatch feed on the others!

SEA HARES

These odd creatures look like land slugs with large "ears." But like sea slugs, they have feathery gills, and bright patterns and colors. Like their namesakes on land, they graze on plants. If in danger, they release a colored substance or dye into the water.

🔺 Limpets cling tightly to rocks at low tide.

🔻 Green sea hare

DEADLY! ⚠️

Cone shells in the Indian and Pacific Oceans have radula teeth which are like tiny, hard "darts." These are fired like miniature harpoons at the prey. The dart injects an incredibly powerful venom that can kill a fish—or even a human.

🔻 The dog whelk eats other mollusks, such as mussels, especially when they are dead. It uses its sensitive breathing tube or siphon to detect the smell of rotting flesh in the water.

SEASHELLS

THE VARIETY OF SHAPES AND COLORS IN SEASHELLS FROM AROUND THE WORLD IS AMAZING, MAKING THESE SOME OF NATURE'S MOST BEAUTIFUL AND INTRICATE OBJECTS. Most seashells are the hard homes made by various kinds of mollusks (mainly sea snails) when they were alive. After the sea snail has died, all that remains is its shell, and this may get washed up on the beach. But most shells are fairly brittle, and get broken by the action of the waves. Even on a beach, wind, waves, rain, and sand gradually crack and wear the shells into fragments. Finally they are ground up and the chalky minerals are recycled.

World Watch

Should people collect seashells? Taking one or two that have been washed up on the beach may seem to do no harm, since the original animals have passed away. But collecting the living animals for their shells is having devastating effects on many species. Abalones are some of the many mollusks that have been over-collected in certain parts of the world. The very survival of this beautiful creature is threatened.

⬥ The abalone or ear shell is valued for its pearly lining and as a food.

⬥ Strawberry topshell

Some shells, such as scallops, cockles, mussels, oysters, and razorshells, belong to bivalved mollusks. In life, these shell parts are joined in pairs, at a hinge, but they often get washed up as single items on the shore. The insides of some shells, especially those of some bivalves, are lined with mother-of-pearl. This is a smooth, shiny substance that shines with a pearly sheen.

TOWER SHELLS
Tower shells are long, tapering spirals. A common species on the European coast is the auger shell, which can grow to 2 inches (5 cm) in length.

TOP SHELLS
Some of the most colorful sea snail shells are top shells. European top shells are quite small, from about 1 inch (2.5 cm) in height. But many are patterned with glorious streaks or zigzag markings.

⬥ Venus's comb is the shell of a sea snail from the Pacific Ocean. The shell has delicate spines, like the teeth of a comb. The spines are longer in females of the species than in males.

Their colored backgrounds may be cream, orange, red, or gray-green, depending on the species. Some tropical top shells are much larger, reaching well over 6 inches (15 cm) in height, and are even more colorful in bright hues of red and pink or vivid green and blue.

COWRIES

Cowries have perhaps been prized for longer than any other seashells. Cowrie necklaces have been found in the tombs of Ancient Egypt.

The largest and most impressive cowries live in the warm seas of the tropics. The tiger cowrie of the Indian and Pacific Oceans, for example, grows to 4 inches (10 cm) or longer. Its shell is beautifully blotched in orange or brown on a cream background. Cowries are smaller and much less common in temperate regions such as northern Atlantic shores. The spotted cowrie shell can sometimes be found on sandy beaches.

CONCHES

The conches are some of the largest of all sea snails. In North America, a "conch" is usually a queen conch, common off the coast of Florida. Queen conches are valued not only for their shells but also as seafood and fish bait.

Conch shells are among the most prized of all shells with collectors, because of their delicate patterns and colors and their glossy sheen.

◪ Lampshell shells look like bivalve mollusks, but belong to a different animal group, the brachiopods.

◪ Spider conch shell

◁ Screw shell

◪ Harp shells have intricate ridges, grooves, and stripes.

Like other seashells, they may be burned to make lime minerals, or ground up to make porcelain. Sadly, queen conches have been collected in such numbers that they have become quite scarce.

The largest sea snail shell is that of the trumpet conch of Australia, which can be over 30 inches (75 cm) long and 3 feet (90 cm) across the spines. The smallest seashells are almost microscopic, even when the animal is fully grown.

BIVALVE MOLLUSKS

BIVALVE MEANS "WITH TWO VALVES." Bivalve mollusks have a shell in two halves, called valves. The valves are usually joined together by a flexible hinge, so that in most species, the animal can open and shut them rather like a small suitcase. The soft, fleshy body of the bivalve mollusk is inside, protected by the hard shell, which few predators can lever or crack open. Most of the creatures we call "shellfish" belong to this group. They are shelled, but are not fish! They are well known because they are eaten as seafood. Examples are cockles, mussels, oysters, scallops, and clams.

◢ The breathing tubes or siphons of a giant clam are cone shaped.

Most bivalve mollusks cannot move around easily, and some are stuck to their rocks. So they let the water bring food to them, by filtering out edible particles. The water is sucked into the body through a tube called a siphon. Inside, food is filtered by the comblike or feathery gills, which also take in oxygen. The water leaves through another siphon.

◢ The file shell's tentacles filter food from the water.

BIVALVES GALORE

Cockles have pale, rather rounded shells, with furrows radiating outward. They live in sand and mud on the lower shore, using the muscular foot to burrow down below the surface. Mussels stick themselves to rocks and breakwaters (groynes) with strong threads called byssus threads. This means they are not rolled around and damaged by the waves. At low tide they are exposed to the air, but they keep their shells tightly shut and are soon covered again as the tide returns. Oysters have gray shells, which are irregular and flaky or scaly. They are highly prized as seafood in many parts of the world. They are farmed on boards or fences in some estuaries, so that natural populations can be left alone.

◢ Scallops can swim away from danger by quick opening and closing their shells, and squirting o[ut] water. The tiny dots around the mantle are eye[s]

Scallops are among the few bivalves that can mov[e] fast. They swim by flapping the two valves of the shell open and shut. As in many bivalves, the mantle forms a fleshy covering to the edges of the valves. It may have waving tentacles and tiny eyes.

Razor or pod shells often turn up on the beach. They are named after the old-fashioned barber's "cut-throat" razor, because of their narrow, rectangular shape, up to 8 inches (20 cm) long. They burrow into the lower shore.

BORING INTO WOOD AND ROCK

Some bivalves use their hard shells to make holes, even drilling into wood or soft rock. Piddocks and shipworms have shells with rough surfaces, which they use to rub and grind away at rock or wood. Eventually, the mollusk has dug a small burrow for itself, where it can live unmolested by predators. A colony of shipworms (left) can cause great damage to wooden boats and breakwaters.

The cockscomb oyster is a [r]ed oyster that looks like a [c]ockerel's (rooster's) comb.

FRESHWATER BIVALVES

Although most bivalves live in the sea, some have adapted to life in fresh water, mostly in rivers or lakes. One of the largest is the swan mussel, which can grow to more than 8 inches (20 cm) long. It is common in muddy lakes or slow rivers. The pearl mussel is another large species, and is famous for its pearls. Pearl mussels prefer large, fast, sandy rivers, with soft water.

The pea mussel really is the size of a pea, and is very common in rivers. Most bivalves are either male or female, and breed by casting their eggs [a]nd sperm into the water, to mix and develop. Pea mussels are [h]ermaphrodite (both male and female). The tiny young develop inside [t]he mother-father, and are born fully formed.

WHAT ARE PEARLS?

[I]n oysters and many other mollusks, the fleshy, shell-forming mantle makes [a] special substance called nacre, which lines the inside of the shell. It forms [a] smooth, white, mother-of-pearl lining called the nacreous layer. A foreign [s]ubstance, such as a bit of grit or a tiny parasite, may enter the shell. If the mollusk cannot get rid of it, it is gradually covered in nacre. This builds up in thin layers until the grit is completely wrapped in a ball of shiny white nacre—a pearl. The finest pearls come from pinctada pearl oysters, which live in the Pacific Ocean. The world's largest pearl came out of a giant clam. It was 5 inches (12 cm) across.

LARGEST... !

The giant clam, tridacna, lives in the Pacific Ocean. It is the world's largest bivalve. Its shells can be over 4 feet (120 cm) in length and it weighs as much as 725 pounds (330 kg).

The razor [s]hell (razor [cl]am) uses its [m]uscular foot to [b]urrow into the [s]eabed. It pushes the [f]oot, like a pink finger, down [in]to mud. The foot tip swells to [a]nchor itself, then the razor shell shortens [t]he rest of the foot to drag itself and its [n]arrow shell deeper.

Like all bivalves, giant clams [u]sually stay open to feed—clamping [sh]ut when danger threatens.

ANOTHER GROUP OF MOLLUSKS:

Bivalves
• 20,000 species
• most are marine, some freshwater
• hinged shell of two parts, called valves
• fingerlike foot
• most burrow, or live attached to rocks

SQUID, OCTOPUSES, AND CUTTLEFISH

◿ Octopus tentacles are covered in suckers, which they use to hold their prey and to move over the rocks.

◿ The pearly nautilus may sit a rock to rest (top), or float slowly in mid water with its tentacles pulled in (above).

THE MOST FASCINATING OF ALL MOLLUSKS ARE SQUID AND OCTOPUSES. They are called cephalopods, a name that means "head-footed," because their molluskan foot is at the head end and has lots of long tentacles. They have the typical mollusk's soft body, but only the squid has a shell, which is small and rod-shaped, and inside the body. These creatures are fierce predators. Squid swim very fast, and octopuses hide away in caves and holes in the rocks. Squid and octopuses can squirt out an ink-like liquid if they are attacked. This makes the water cloudy, allowing the mollusk to escape to safety.

▷ The paper nautilus or argonaut looks like the pearly nautilus, but it is really a type of octopus. The female makes a thin, papery shell to shelter herself and her eggs, and sometimes her much smaller male partner.

quid are narrow and streamlined, with flaplike
ns at one end to keep them steady in the water.
hey have large eyes and good vision, to track
eir prey in the ocean. To catch food, they use a
ng pair of tentacles, which have adhesive suckers
the end. They have eight shorter tentacles too,
so with suckers. Squid move slowly by rippling
eir fins, or dart suddenly using a kind of jet-
ropulsion, squirting water rapidly out of the
phon (breathing tube).

▲ Some kinds of squid can produce lights inside their bodies.
They have special body parts to create the light, and some can
even direct the light like a flashlight. This is very useful in the
dark depths of the sea.

UTTLEFISH

uttlefish are like small, flattened squid, with a fin
nning around all sides of the body. Even more
an squid, they are the chameleons of the sea,
ble to change color and pattern in a split second.

◄ A cuttlefish holds its tentacles together for streamlining as it swims.

he skin of a cuttlefish is patterned with tiny spots of
ifferent colors—yellow, red, brown, and black. The animal
  can control the size of these by muscles, and make many
  different shades by mixing the amounts of each color.

LARGEST... !

The giant squid of the ocean depths is the
largest mollusk, and also the largest animal
without a backbone. It reaches a maximum
length of about 56 feet (17 m) from the tip
of its outstretched tentacles to its tail end.
Its eyes are the largest in the animal
kingdom, at more than 16 inches (40 cm)
across. The smallest squid are only about
0.4 inch (1 cm) long.

OCTOPUSES

An octopus has a sacklike body, large eyes, and eight long
  tentacles used for catching prey. Like other cephalopods, its
  beaklike mouth is hidden in the middle of the ring of tentacles,
  where they join the body. Octopuses have complicated behavior
  and are often said to be the most intelligent invertebrates. They
  can recognize different shapes, choosing the correct one to
  obtain food. They can also remember simple tasks, such as how
  to open a food box.

▲ The blue-ringed octopus of
the Indian and Pacific region is
only small, but has a very
poisonous bite. The rings on its
body glow bright blue if it is
threatened.

The common octopus of the Atlantic varies in size, but can reach
  about 3 feet (90 cm) in body length, with a tentacle spread of 10 feet
(3 m). Octopuses are rarely seen. They spend most of the day holed up
in crevices in the rocks. They come out mainly at night, to hunt for
other mollusks, crabs, and similar prey. They also scavenge for dead meat.

HE NAUTILUS

Only one kind of cephalopod has a proper external shell like other
ollusks. This is the nautilus, which has a shiny shell curled over its body.
t swims along the seabed, using its 35 or so tentacles to find prey. Unlike
ts cousins, it cannot squirt ink to hide and escape danger.

CEPHALOPOD MOLLUSKS

Octopuses, squid, and cuttlefish
• 650 species
• marine
• streamlined shape (squid and
  cuttlefish)
• ten tentacles in squid and
  cuttlefish, eight in octopus

Nautiluses
• 6 species
• marine
• large spiral shell
• many tentacles

STARFISH AND SEASTARS

STARFISH AND THEIR RELATIVES ARE CALLED ECHINODERMS. This means "hedgehog skin," and many of them are indeed very spiny. These creatures are numerous and widespread, but they all live in the sea, so many are unfamiliar. They have a body built around a radial plan, like the spokes of wheel, rather than the bilateral or two-sided bodies of other animals. They also have tiny, flexible tube feet that end in suckers, for walking and feeding. As well as starfish, this group includes feather stars, sea lilies, sea urchins, and sea cucumbers.

🔺 Sun star

🔺 Sea lily (crino

Most groups of sea animals have a few species adapted to life in fresh water or even dry land. Echinoderms do not. These creatures are quite large, and many are brightly colored and easy to see, especially as they are slow-moving.

MANY ARMS

Many species of starfish have five arms, but some have seven, and others as many as 14. The upper side of the body usually has small, hard plates or spines embedded in the skin, for protection. Underneath, each arm has rows of tiny tube feet, like miniature sucker-ended fingers. The arms bend so that the starfish can glide across the seabed.

🔲 Starfish are flat, and have arms that spread out from the center in a starlike pattern.

ARMED! ⚠

If a starfish is damaged and loses part of an arm, it can re-grow the missing piece again. The new part is often slightly smaller. Sometimes it branches into two, giving a six-armed starfish!

The crown-of-thorns starfish
eats small coral animals called
polyps. Sometimes these
starfish gather in such large
numbers that they eat away
an entire coral reef. They are
covered with sharp, poisonous
spines as defense.

▶ The Pacific blue star has
five arms. Like its relatives,
it is a slow-motion but very
effective predator.

Starfish are very strong
and can prise open the
shells of clams and
other bivalve mollusks.
When attacking its
victim, the starfish
arches over it and
clamps a couple of
arms onto each side.
It then pulls with great
strength and stamina.
As the two parts of the
mollusk's shell begin to
gape, the starfish turns
its stomach inside out,
through its mouth and
into the gap in the shell. It then begins to digest
the prey's flesh. Eventually, the shell opens wide
and the starfish completes its meal.

SOME TYPES OF STARFISH

Common starfish are indeed common. They
sometimes gather in huge numbers over about
a square mile (2.5 sq km) of seabed, all moving
slowly as they feed on bivalves and other
mollusks, worms, crabs, and also other
echinoderms. These vast marauding columns of
starfish leave a trail of
dead and dying seabed
animals in their wake.

▲ Starfish look harmless, but
they are all predators.

The sand star lives
on fine sand,
where it often
lurks, half
buried. It has a
beautiful star
shape, and its
five arms are
edged with spines. The common sun
star is bright red, with as many as 14
short arms, spreading out sunlike
from its large central disk. Its prey
includes the common starfish.

WRITHING ARMS

The brittlestar (shown on page 20)
is indeed brittle. Parts of its long,
delicate arms often break off.
The five arms spread out from
a small central disk, and can
loop back on themselves as
the creature writhes speedily
across the seabed.

Most brittlestars live below the tide zone, in
deeper water. They can sometimes be found piled
up in huge heaps, with as many as 1,000
individuals on just a few square feet of the seabed.
Most brittlestars feed by gathering up small edible
items from the mud, or by filtering them from the
water. The common brittlestar of the Atlantic and
Mediterranean regions is a filter-feeder. It lives in
dense colonies, with each animal waving its spiny
arms to catch anything edible that may float past.

FEATHERY ARMS

Feather stars are similar to starfish and have
feathery arms, used for both feeding and
swimming. Many have ten arms, but some species
may have almost 200! Feather stars grasp onto
rocks or seaweeds and can also creep about. They
feed by waving their arms in the water to filter
out edible particles.

LILIES IN THE SEA

Sea lilies are close
relatives of feather stars
and feed in a similar
way. Each animal is
attached by a stalk to
the seabed, usually deep
in the ocean. The stalk
may be more than 3 feet
(90 cm) long. They look
like flowers on stalks,
hence their name.

▲ This starfish is humped
over its prey, dissolving
and absorbing its flesh.

ECHINODERMS	

• 6,250 species
• live in the sea
• five-rayed (spoked) body plan
• inner skeleton, often spiny
• tiny tubelike feet
 	
Three of the main groups:
 	
Starfish
• 1,500 species
• flat and star-shaped
• usually five arms (sometimes more)
	Brittlestars
	• 2,000 species
	• flat and star-shaped
	• usually five arms (sometimes six,
	  or branched)
	• arms long and brittle
	
	Feather stars and sea lilies
	• 625 species (mostly feather stars)
	• either swimming (feather stars) or
	  stalked (sea lilies)
	• feed by filtering seawater

67

SEA URCHINS AND SEA CUCUMBERS

⬆ Sand dollars take their name from their resemblance to coins, being round and flat or disk-shaped. They move around just below the surface of the sand.

SEA URCHINS, SAND DOLLARS, AND SEA CUCUMBERS ARE ECHINODERMS, LIKE STARFISH (PAGE 66). They have the same echinoderm feature of tiny tube feet, and many species bristle with spines. These are for protection, but sea urchins also tilt their spines to move along, as if on stilts. Some types of urchins have poison-tipped spines.

⬆ These sea squirts are barrel-shaped, with jellylike bodies. They feed by filtering tiny creatures from the water as it flows through them. Other type are shaped like tiny tadpoles ar live inside a "house" that they build from jellylike material.

Sea urchins and sand dollars have rounded bodies, either ball-shaped, or flattened. The scientific name for their group is the echinoids, which means "hedgehog-like." It refers to the spiny covering of many species. Echinoids, like starfish, have a five-rayed body plan. But the arms are curled up and over and joined at the top to make the ball-like body. Urchins use their spines to lever themselves along slowly, and they can also climb by using their very long and flexible tube feet.

Sea urchins feed by grazing on seaweeds and small animals, such as moss animals, that grow on the surfaces of underwater rocks. Some urchins, known as heart urchins, have a more streamlined and almost heartlike shape. This helps them to burrow beneath the sand. One type is known as the sea potato. Its brownish, potato-shaped empty shell, known as a test, is sometimes washed up on beaches.

SEA CUCUMBERS
Sea cucumbers are named after their warty, sausage-shaped bodies, which look similar to a cucumber. Unlike most other echinoderms, sea cucumbers have soft bodies, although the skin is tough and leathery. The mouth is surrounded by tentacles, which can be pulled back inside the animal. Sea cucumbers have three rows of tube feet and crawl slowly along the seabed.

When disturbed or attacked, some sea cucumbers can shoot out parts of their insides, including their stomach and intestine. This sticky mass entangles and puts off most predators, even lobsters. The sea cucumber then regrows the missing parts.

SQUIRTS IN THE SEA
Sea squirts are not echinoderms, but members of a group called the tunicates. They resemble blobs of jelly, and live stuck to rocks or seaweeds along the tide zone and in the shallows. They are called sea squirts because, when the tide has gone out to leave them exposed on the shore, they sometimes squirt out jets of water.

⬆ The rosy feather star (near right) waves its filter-feeding arms to catch tiny bits of food. The sea potato or sand urchin (on the sand) is a hairy-looking urchin that lives in a burrow under the beach. Lancelets (below) are long, pale creatures that filter-feed in seabed sand and gravel.

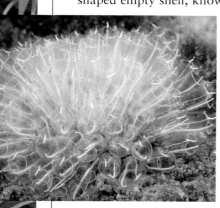

◀ Sea squirts or tunicates have very special features. These include a main nerve or nerve-cord, and a stiff tube called a notochord—a very simple version of our own backbone.

The largest kind of sea cucumber, the stichopus sea cucumber, lives in seas around the Philippines. It can grow more than 3 feet (90 cm) long and nearly 6 inches (15 cm) wide.

These creatures may bridge the gap between the two great groups of animals, the invertebrates (animals without backbones) and the vertebrates. A sea squirt larva looks like a tadpole and has a very simple rodlike version of the backbone, called a notochord, inside its body. But this breaks down as the larva grows into an adult.

Lancelets are fishlike creatures that also possess a notochord. However, unlike fish, they have no proper backbone, jaws, eyes, or fins. They live half-buried in sand or gravel, filtering food from the water. Lancelets grow to about 4 inches (10 cm) long, and can swim weakly if they need to escape from a predator. They live in shallow water, in temperate and tropical seas.

MORE ECHINODERMS
(continued from page 67):

Sea urchins and sand dollars
• 950 species
• ball-shaped body, may be spiny
• no arms

Sea cucumbers
• 1,150 species
• body long and sausage-shaped
• no arms
• tentacles around mouth

Other sea creatures:

Tunicates (sea squirts)
• 1,400 species
• attached to rocks or swimming
• tadpolelike young or larvae

Lancelets
• 25 species
• small, about 4 inches (10 cm)
• fish-shaped body
• no eyes or fins

◘ Sessile sea squirts look like see-through bottles attached to the rocks (below). Flask-shaped planktonic sea squirts swim and drift along (below right). Some sea cucumbers have frills and flaps along the body (bottom, in the sand).

▲ Moths usually hold their wings
out sideways at rest.

SECTION 3

INSECTS & OTHER ARTHROPODS

THERE ARE AT LEAST 5 MILLION DIFFERENT KINDS, OR SPECIES, OF ANIMALS. And at least 80 out of every 100 species are insects. They range from tiny gnats and fairy flies, almost too small to see, to fist-sized beetles, and moths with wings as long as your hands. Three key features of insects help to make them so successful, widespread, and diverse. These are: a hard outer body casing (exoskeleton), wings for flying, and six legs with flexible joints for fast running.

Other animals have a tough outer body casing and jointed limbs, too. They include eight-legged spiders and scorpions (arachnids), and multilegged centipedes and millipedes. Most insects do not live in the sea. But another huge group of joint-limbed creatures does—crustaceans such as crabs, lobsters, prawns, shrimps, and krill. Most people are not familiar with creatures of the open ocean. So they rarely see one of the world's most numerous kinds of animal—the small flealike crustaceans known as copepods.

All of the above creatures belong to the animal group known as arthropods. This name means "jointed legs." The arthropod's body casing and limb design have allowed this group to conquer all the Earth's habitats—from high mountains, hot springs, and salty lakes, to dark caves and the deepest seas.

THE WORLD OF BUGS

THERE ARE PROBABLY MORE THAN TEN MILLION
DIFFERENT KINDS, OR SPECIES, OF ANIMALS.
Of these, possibly nine out of ten are bugs and
other insects. The insects belong to a larger
animal group known as the arthropods,
which means "jointed limbs." The
leg has rigid sections linked by
flexible joints—similar to our
own arms and legs. Insects
and other arthropods also
share another main
feature—a hard outer covering to the body,
called the cuticle. It forms a protective casing
known as an exoskeleton, which covers the
arthropod's body like a suit of armor. Ants,
beetles, bugs, cockroaches, flies, fleas, bees,
and other insects, which all have six legs, are
arthropods. So are the eight-legged
arachnids such as spiders
and scorpions, the multi-
legged centipedes
and millipedes,
and crustaceans such
as crabs, lobsters, and
shrimps. For every human
being alive today, there are
probably at least one million insects
and other arthropods.

◿ Social insects live in groups,
often in huge nests like this
termite mound. Other social
insects are ants, bees, and wasps.

◿ Dragonflies
are the biggest
flying insects.

Arthropods are mostly small. But they affect
people the world over. Some are harmful.
Termites eat away wooden buildings and
bridges. Locusts devastate vast areas of crops.
Wasps annoy us with their stings, and lice with
their blood-sucking bites. Poisonous spiders and
scorpions can cause great pain, even death.
Serious diseases are spread by some arthropods,
such as malaria by mosquitoes, plague by fleas,
and Lyme's disease by ticks.

INSIDE AN INSECT

An insect's body is
divided into three main
sections—head, thorax
(chest), and abdomen.
Most insects have
three pairs of legs and
one or two pairs of
wings, all attached to
the thorax. (The worker
ant, as shown here,
lacks wings.)

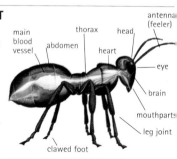

main
blood
vessel · abdomen · thorax · heart · head · antenna (feeler) · eye · brain · mouthparts · leg joint · clawed foot

Mites are tiny arthropods related to spiders. Some live in soil. Others are parasites and suck blood from animals.

USEFUL ARTHROPODS

Some arthropods are useful to both people and plants. Bees make honey and carry pollen for flowers. Predatory insects such as lacewings eat plant pests such as aphids (which are also arthropods). Silkworms are really moth caterpillars that spin silk. Dung beetles help to recycle animal droppings. Small flies called fruit flies, drosophila, have been used as insect "guinea pigs" to unlock the secrets of how genes work.

SENSES

Most arthropods have keen senses, especially sight, smell, and touch. Each eye is made of a cluster of separate units, each with its own lens. This design is called a compound eye. Arthropods cannot see as much detail as we can, but most are excellent at detecting small movements, and many insects can see different colors.

Arthropods use their feelers or antennae to smell and even "taste" the air or water around them, detecting tiny particles of scents and odors. The antennae and the tiny hairlike bristles on the body and legs can also detect the slightest touch and movements such as wind or water currents.

THE CUTICLE

An arthropod's cuticle is like a thick, stiff outermost layer of the skin. It forms a rigid casing, the exoskeleton, to support the soft inner parts of the body.

▶ Grasshoppers and crickets have powerful chewing "jaws." In most insects these move from side to side rather than up and down.

WHERE INSECTS LIVE

Insects are found in almost every corner of the Earth, on land and in the air—in forests and grasslands, deserts, marshes and wetlands, streams and lakes, even high on mountains and glaciers, and deep in pitch-dark caves. Our parks and gardens, and even our houses, also buzz and crawl with insects. They include houseflies and ants, fleas on pets, and silverfish in dark cupboards. Insects have not colonized the sea itself, although they live on coastal land.

OTHER ARTHROPOD HABITATS

Spiders, scorpions, centipedes, and millipedes thrive mainly in warmer countries, especially among the dead leaves of the tropical forest floor and high above among the tree leaves. Most crustaceans, from tiny copepods to huge crabs and lobsters, live in the sea. Some, like crayfish and water fleas, dwell in fresh water. A few, like woodlice, can survive in damp places on land.

AN ARTHROPOD'S COVERING

The arthropod's body is covered by the cuticle, which is thin and light, yet strong and tough. It is made mainly from a substance called chitin. In land arthropods such as insects, the cuticle has a waxy, waterproof covering. In order to grow, an arthropod must shed its cuticle, and grow a new, bigger one underneath. This process is known as moulting or ecdysis.

Cuticle diagram labels: touch-sensitive bristle, waxy coating, pore (hole) for wax, outer cuticle, inner cuticle, skin, nerve fiber, wax gland

Insects
• more than one million species
• body divided into three main parts
• three pairs of legs
• most have two pairs of wings
• live on land and in fresh water

Crustaceans
• 43,000 species
• body divided into three main parts
• many have a hard, shell-like casing
• several pairs of legs
• two pairs of feelers
• most live in the sea

King Crabs
• 5 species
• heavy, rounded outer shell
• long tail spine
• large eyes
• live in the sea

Arachnids
• 80,000 species
• body divided into two main parts
• four pairs of legs
• jaws with fangs
• most are land-living

Centipedes
• 3,000 species
• body long and flattened
• one pair of legs per body segment
• long feelers
• jaws with fangs
• run fast
• live on land

Millipedes
• 10,000 species
• body long and rounded
• two pairs of legs per body segment
• short feelers
• walk slowly
• live on land

BEETLES AND WEEVILS

BEETLES AND THEIR SMALLER COUSINS, WEEVILS, MAKE UP THE LARGEST SUB-GROUP OF INSECTS. They are called the Coleoptera. There are almost half a million known kinds, or species, of coleopterans, making up about one third of all animal species. And hundreds of new species are found each year. Most insects have two pairs of wings, but in beetles the front two have become hard and strong, like a shield over the top of the body. They are called wing cases, or elytra. Th wing cases form a protective covering for the delicate second pair of wings. These are folded under the wing cases when the beetle is at rest. As it takes off, the beetle lifts the hard wing cases and then unfurls its thin wings, which it flaps to fly away. Beetles are the most widespread of all insects. They live in almost every habitat and region o our planet except the sea. Som are almost microscopic, others are nearly as big as a fist.

△ The great diving beetle must come to the surface every few minutes to gather air to breathe. It has strong mouthparts and can bite hard.

STRONGEST... !

The strongest insect is the rhinoceros beetle, also called the hercules beetle. It can lift and support more than 800 times its own weight.

◨ A typical weevil has a long trunklike snout. Some weevils are pests, eating wheat and flour, or crops such as apples, carrots, nuts, and clover.

Beetles are not only incredibly numerous, they are also extremely varied. The familiar red spotted ladybugs that we see in parks and gardens are brightly colored to warn other animals that they taste horrible. Predators such as birds soon learn to avoid these small beetles.

Tiger and ground beetles are active hunters, with large eyes for seeing prey and long legs for racing after it. One kind of green ground beetle, the bombardier, can squirt a spray of stinging chemicals from its rear end at an attacker.

WEEVILS
Weevils form the largest sub-group of beetles, with more than 60,000 species. They feed on seeds, fruits, and flowers. A weevil has a long, curved snout (called the rostrum), which looks like a tiny elephant's trunk.

◘ Dung, scarab, and minotaur beetles feed on detritus—animal droppings and bits of dead animals and plants. Many dung beetles roll the dung into large balls and lay their eggs in it. The larvae hatch out and eat it, helping to recycle minerals and nutrients.

◖ Green tiger beetles are truly the tigers of the insect world. They stalk and then rush after victims, killing them with a bite from the strong, fanglike jaws.

The surface of the wood is marked with their small, round flight holes, and inside is a network of tunnels and powdered wood. The larvae of longhorn and deathwatch beetles also tunnel through wood, eating and weakening it as they go.

NIGHT LIGHTS
On hot summer nights, flashes of pale green or yellow light can sometimes be seen among trees, or on the forest floor. These are fireflies and glow worms. They are not flies or worms, but kinds of beetle. Fireflies flash to attract each other in the mating season. Their wormlike larvae also give off light, to warn predators such as shrews that they have a nasty taste and should be left alone.

Old beams and other wooden objects often have round holes we call woodworm. These are the work of the furniture beetle. The adult beetles lay their eggs on wood (trees or furniture). When the larvae hatch from the eggs, they tunnel into the wood, feeding on it as they go. These larvae change into adults, which eat their way out and fly away.

▶ Female fireflies and glow worms have no wings and small wing cases, showing the segmented main body or abdomen underneath. The males are much smaller and fly to the females.

NATURE'S UNDERTAKERS
Sexton or burying beetles are the undertakers of the natural world. They have a keen sense of smell and are attracted to rotting bodies, such as dead birds or small mammals such as mice and rats. First the beetles mate, then they set to work to bury the corpse, by digging out the soil beneath it. They then lay their eggs in a chamber dug into the soil next to the body. When the larvae hatch, they feed on the decaying flesh of the corpse.

WATER BEETLES
Some beetles live in fresh water. Diving beetles use their hairy legs as oars to row themselves through the water. The larva of the great diving beetle is a fierce predator, catching tadpoles and small fish with its sharp, curved jaws. Whirligig beetles swirl about like tiny wind-up toys on the surface of a pond. Each eye is divided into two parts. One part looks up into the air, the other down into the water.

HEAVIEST... !
The heaviest insect is a kind of beetle, the goliath beetle of Africa. It can weigh up to 4 ounces (108 g), which is almost as heavy as two ordinary hen's eggs.

Beetles and weevils
(Coleoptera)
• almost 500,000 species
• front wings are hard wing cases
• biting mouthparts to eat small animals or plant food
• most are active, fast runners

75

BUTTERFLIES AND MOTHS

AFTER THE BEETLES, THE SECOND LARGEST SUB-GROUP OF INSECTS IS THE BUTTERFLIES AND MOTHS, WITH ABOUT 175,000 SPECIES. They live wherever there are trees and flowers, being most numerous in tropical parts of the world. They are known as Lepidoptera, a name that means "scaly winged," because their large, papery wings are covered with tiny scales. The bright patterns on the wings are made by different colors and patterns of scales, like a living mosaic. There are a number of differences between moths and butterflies. Most moths are active at night; butterflies usually fly by day. Most moths are dull browns and grays; many butterflies are brightly colored. Most moths have feathery feelers (antennae); butterflies have thin, club-ended feelers.

◪ The peacock butterfly has large patches on its wings that look like eyes and are called "eye spots." When the butterfly is in danger, it opens its wings to reveal the eyes, which frighten away predators.

◪ Clearwings are day-flying moths. They look more like butterflies, with their bright colors and slim bodies.

▣ Blue morpho butterfly

Butterflies and moths are insects which go through a drastic change in body shape as they grow up. This is called complete metamorphosis. The life cycle begins when an adult male and female mate, often flitting about in a courtship flight. The female usually lays her eggs on the food plant—the plant that the caterpillars will eat when they hatch. She places them carefully, either in groups or singly, on the undersides of leaves. For the brimstone butterfly (see the box, opposite), the caterpillars' food plant is buckthorn. In fact, caterpillars do little else except eat. After growing and molting its skin several times, each caterpillar changes into an inactive, hard-cased chrysalis. This seems to rest for a few weeks, or even through the winter.

▣ A butterfly or moth, like this large white butterfly, has a long, tube-shaped mouth. This is normally coiled up under the head. To sip nectar from deep in a flower the butterfly straightens its mouth and uses it like a drinking straw to sip up the sugary fluid.

▶ Moths usually have hairy, plump bodies. The feathery antennae of a male moth can pick up the female's scent from more than 600 yards (1 km) away.

The outside of the chrysalis doesn't appear to change, but inside the body breaks up into a kind of thick, living soup. This re-forms into the wings, legs, feelers, and other parts of an adult butterfly or moth. The adult emerges from the chrysalis case and flies away to search for its own food, usually the sweet, sugary fluid called nectar in flowers.

Some butterflies and moths migrate long distances as adults, to avoid dry or cold seasons and find more sheltered places. In North America, monarch or milkweed butterflies fly south in late summer from Canada to Mexico. This journey of more than 2,000 miles (3,200 km) can take up to four months. In southeast Australia, bogong moths shelter in caves in the cool uplands during the hot, dry summer, and return to the lowlands to breed in the fall.

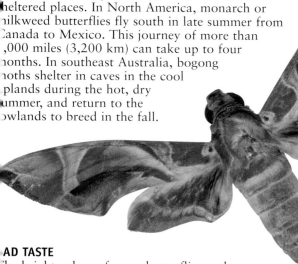

BAD TASTE

The bright colors of some butterflies and moths, especially in the caterpillar stage, warn animals who might try to eat them that they taste horrible. Others are brightly colored to attract mates.

▲ Moths usually hold their wings out sideways at rest.

LARGEST... !

The giant agrippa moth has the biggest wingspan of any insect, up to 12 inches (30 cm) from tip to tip. The birdwing butterfly of New Guinea is second. Its wingspan is about 11 inches (28 cm).

Butterflies and moths (Lepidoptera)
- 175,000 species
- adults have four wings, often colorful
- adult has long, tubular mouth
- most feed on flowers
- larvae are leaf-eating caterpillars

▲ The hawkmoths, like this elephant hawkmoth, are fast and powerful fliers with narrow, V-shaped wings.

THE LIFE CYCLE OF A BUTTERFLY

When a young butterfly or moth hatches from its egg, like this brimstone, it is a long, worm-shaped creature called a caterpillar, grub, or larva. This crawls, eats, and grows, molts its skin, eats and grows again, and so on, molting perhaps seven times. Then it sheds its last skin, forms a hard case around itself, and becomes an inactive chrysalis or pupa. Inside this case the creature's body undergoes amazing changes. Finally the adult butterfly emerges from the case, stretches its crumpled wings and flies away. These changes in body shape while growing up are called complete metamorphosis.

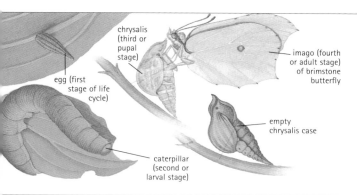

chrysalis (third or pupal stage)

imago (fourth or adult stage) of brimstone butterfly

egg (first stage of life cycle)

empty chrysalis case

caterpillar (second or larval stage)

BEES, WASPS, AND ANTS

BEES, WASPS, AND ANTS MAKE UP THE THIRD
LARGEST SUBGROUP OF INSECTS. They are
known as Hymenopterans. They include the
familiar honeybees and bumblebees, as well as
carpenter bees, many kinds of wasps and hornets
with their dangerous stings, black and red ants,
and army ants, which march through tropical forests in
columns. They also include more than 100,000 species of tiny
parasitic wasps that live on and in plants or other animals.

◢ The lacewings a
large-winged insects th
prey on smaller, sof
bodied bugs such as aphi

Ants, wasps, and bees are the main kinds of
social insects. They live together in colonies or
nests, helping each other
by doing different tasks
such as fetching and
distributing food,
cleaning, or
defending the
colony from attack.
Some bumblebees
live in colonies of
only a few individuals,
perhaps four or five. A
typical wasps' nest
numbers 2,000
individuals. A
honeybees' nest or hive
has up to 50,000
members.

◀ Ants follow a
invisible trail of scen
or pheromone, as the
forage for foo

Driver ants and army ants have
no permanent nests. They
march through the
forest in columns half a
million strong, killing and
eating anything in their path
and setting up a bivouac camp
for their overnight stop.

◀ The female great woo
wasp has a long, sharp "stin
which is really an egg-laying tu
or ovipositor. She drills throu
tree bark to the grub of a woo
boring wasp within, and lays a
egg in it. When this egg hatch
the wasp larva feeds on the ho
larva, slowly killing it and fina
emerging as an adult wood was

◢ This sphinx moth
caterpillar is host to maggot-
like parasitic wasp larvae,
which will eat it alive.

QUEEN AND WORKERS

In a typical wasps' or bees' nest, there is just one
female who lays eggs. She is the queen. A queen
honeybee lays up to 1,500 eggs each day. She is
looked after by female workers. Some of these
workers, called forager workers, fly off to collect
food, mainly pollen and nectar, from flowers.

As well as laying eggs, the queen bee also contro
the colony by preventing workers from developin
into queens themselves. Her mouthparts produce
special chemical called queen substance, which
spreads through the nest. If she dies, the queen
substance fades away. Then some of the grubs,
developing in their six-sided compartments, or
cells, in the nest, develop into young queens.
Others develop into male bees or drones.

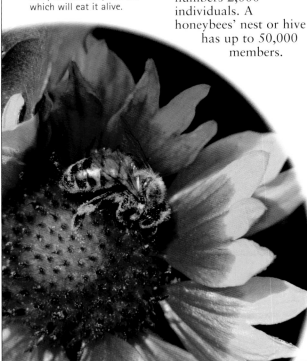

◀ Bees gather nectar and pollen from flowers, chew and
predigest it, and "sick" it back up as honey. This feeds the
grubs (larvae) in the nest.

The young queens and drones mate. One new queen takes over the existing colony. The others fly off to found fresh colonies elsewhere. Wild bees nest in holes in trees and rocks. Honeybees have been domesticated in hives for more than 3,000 years.

INSECTS WITHIN INSECTS

Some parasitic wasps lay their tiny eggs on or inside the bodies of other insects. Even the eggs of insects are not safe from attack by these tiny wasps. The smallest of all insects are called fairy flies. About ten would fit on a pinhead. But they are not flies; they are minute wasps. They lay their eggs inside the eggs of other insects. When the grubs hatch out, they are surrounded by the nutritious contents of the egg, which they consume before emerging.

◀ Bees and wasps like this common wasp have four wings. But the two wings on each side are hooked together so they flap up and down as one.

TERMITES

Termites have the largest and most complicated colonies of any insect. There may be more than five million in one nest, all controlled by a king and queen. Worker termites fetch and carry food, and special soldier termites with large jaws guard the colony. The queen termite lays 30,000 eggs each day, and she can live for 15 years!

LACEWINGS AND ANT LIONS

Lacewings take their name from their delicate wings. The adults have a weak, fluttery flight and are often attracted to lighted windows at night. They and their pincer-jawed larvae eat smaller creatures such as bugs. Adult ant lions look similar to lacewings and are found mainly in warm countries. The ant lion larva digs a cone-shaped pit in loose soil or sand and waits at the bottom. When a small insect tumbles into the pit, the ant lion slides the sand, and the prey, down into its huge jaws.

▶ Bees, wasps, and hornets make their nests from chewed wood, which dries as thin paper.

◀ These bumblebees have opened a cell in their nest to clean the pupa. Like butterflies, hymenopterans go through four stages in their lives—egg, grub, or larva, the pupa in its cocoon or case, and the adult.

Bees, wasps, and ants (Hymenoptera)
• at least 130,000 species
• four thin wings, joined on each side
• chewing mouthparts
• ants mainly wingless
• many can sting
• many feed from flowers

Termites (Isoptera)
• 2,250 species
• live in large colonies

• workers are wingless
• feed on rotting wood
• live mainly in warm countries

Lacewings and ant-lions (Neuroptera)
• 5,000 species
• lacelike veins in the large wings
• larvae and adults catch and eat other insects
• live mainly in warm countries

79

FLIES

THE COMMON HOUSEFLY IS A WELL-KNOWN, BUZZING NUISANCE IN THE KITCHEN OR AT A PICNIC. It is a member of the insect subgroup called the true or two-winged flies, Diptera. The group has more than 90,000 species around the world. It includes gnats, midges and mosquitoes, craneflies, horseflies, botflies, hoverflies, fruitflies, bluebottles, greenbottles, and dungflies. The main feature of all these flies is that they have just one pair of proper wings, rather than the usual two pairs of most insects. The second or rear pair are small, thin, and club-shaped. Called halteres, they help the insect to balance as it flies.

◘ Dungflies roll animal droppings into balls and lay their eggs in it, so the maggots (larvae) can feed on it when they hatch.

TWO-WINGED OR TRUE FLIES

The two-winged or true flies are the supreme aerobats of the insect world. Not only can a hoverfly hover in midair, it can also fly sideways and backward. The wing of a fly or similar insect is a thin flap that contains no muscles. The fly moves its wings by changing the shape of its thorax, the part of the body where the wings are attached. It does this by using muscles inside its thorax to make the wings click up and down. The wings are attached to the body by rubbery hinges, which make them bounce back up at the end of each down stroke. Using this method, most insects can beat their wings more than 300 times a second. Some midges and hoverflies flap them more than 1,000 times a second. The speed of the flapping creates a droning, buzzing, or whining sound.

◘ Different types of biting midges suck the blood of many animals, especially mammals and birds, but also amphibians and even insects.

adult stage. Hoverflies are expert flower-feeders. They especially like the flat flowers of plants in carrot family. Yet their larvae eat aphids and other bugs, or dung, or even survive as "guests" in the nests of ants and wasps, feeding on the debris and rubbish.

Midges and mosquitoes bite to suck our blood. They can a great nuisance and spread diseases such as malaria and yellow fever (pages 12–13), especially in wet and marshy areas where they breed. They lay their eggs on the surface of ponds and pools.

WHAT FLIES EAT

Many flies eat very different foods in their young or larval stage than they do in the

he clusters of tiny, waxy eggs stick together and
oat on the surface like miniature rafts. Then the
omma-shaped larvae hatch out and swim down
to the water by wriggling, to feed on
ny plants and animals.

he five species of tsetse fly
Glossina) live in Africa. They
ed by sucking the blood of
eople and animals such as
attle, but as they feed they
pread microscopic protists
alled trypanosomes. These breed
the blood of a person and cause a
rious disease called sleeping sickness.

A mosquito has a long,
needlelike mouth to
suck blood.

ORSEFLIES

he large, powerful horseflies can inflict painful
ites on people, cattle, and horses with their
ladelike mouthparts. The wounds itch, bleed,
nd swell up, but horseflies rarely spread disease.
heir larvae also bite fiercely and suck the body
ices from worms, grubs, and other small, soft-
odied animals.

Several kinds of flies are attracted by a rotting
t carcass. A tiny gnat, with feathery antennae
t the far left of the scene) watches a buzzing
een-eyed horsefly (center). The tsetse fly
bove left), with blue eyes,
reads the disease
eping sickness. Stages
the fly life cycle are
gs (on the rat's
es), larvae or
aggots (in its
dy), and
pae or
coons (just
low the
rsefly).

FLESH-EATING GRUBS

Some kinds of fly, such as the botfly of tropical
America and the tumbu fly of Africa, lay their eggs
on the skin of large animals, including
people. The maggots or larvae of some
species burrow through the skin and
eat the living flesh beneath. They
can cause serious infections.

The sheep nostril fly really does
lay its eggs inside the nose of a
sheep. Its larvae live and feed in
the nose passages, and can bore their
way through to its eyes and brain.

DRIBBLING ONTO ITS FOOD

The housefly buzzing around the kitchen may have
fed last on rotting garbage or animal droppings. It
dribbles saliva (spit) from its spongelike
mouthparts onto its food to make it dissolve into a
liquid. Then it paddles around in and sucks up this
"soup." Germs stick onto its legs and mouthparts.
Then it buzzes off—and may land
on your meal! Houseflies can
spread various illnesses,
including diarrhea and
food poisoning.

Craneflies (left)
are also called daddy-
longlegs. The fruit fly
(right) has red eyes.
The three dung
flies (below right)
have distinctive
red faces.

FLIES
• at least 90,000 species
• worldwide, especially tropical
• one pair of transparent wings
• larvae are legless maggots

DRAGONFLIES AND DAMSELFLIES

❏ A dragonfly has its legs together in a basketlike trap to catch prey in flight.

❏ Adult mayfly

WITH WHIRRING WINGS, A DRAGONFLY DARTS FROM ITS PERCH NEAR THE PON GRABS A TINY GNAT IN MIDAIR, AND RETURNS TO THE TWIG TO EAT. There are some 5,000 species of dragonfly and damselfly, known as Orthopterans. Each has a long, slender body, two pairs o long, large, vein-patterned wings, and very big eyes for seeing prey. Damselflie are usually smaller and slimmer than dragonflies, and their flight is slower an less direct. The dragonfly is one of the champion insect fliers, able to cruise at around 3 miles per hour (5 km/h), dart ten times faster in a short burst, then stop almost at once and hover. Dragonflies and damselflies usually hunt over ponds, swamps, and slow rivers. In fact, these are the places where they grow up. The young stages of these insects, called larvae or nymphs, live underwate They grow and develop for up to five years in the water, depending on the species, before climbing out, shedding their skins, and becoming adults.

❏ Damselflies hold their wings over their backs at rest. Males and females link together at breeding time to form a "mating chain" that may be five or six damselflies long!

All the insects shown here have one feature in common. Their young, or larvae, live in fresh water—often for two years or more. The larvae are usually brown or gray and creep around in ponds, lakes, streams, and swamps. Dragonfly larvae are large, and like their parents they are very strong hunters. They feed by grabbing other water creatures, such as tadpoles and even small fish, with their enormous pincerlike jaws. The larva sheds or molts its skin many times. Finally it climbs up a reec or plant stem, and the adult crawls out of its last larval skin. Its wings spread and harden, and its body becomes slim and colorful. Then the adult dragonfly dashes off to catch its first victim, in the air rather than in the water.

KEEP OUT!

An adult male dragonfly takes over a length of riverbank or lakeside as his breeding territory He defends it fiercely by chasing off other males that stray nearby. He may even fly at people walking past to get a good look and make sure they are not rivals.

The stonefly has two long
elers on its head and two
ng tail filaments. It is a weak
er and usually crawls over
ants and rocks
ar water.

The emperor dragonfly has a
ue patterned body and wings
inches (10 cm) across. It
lds them out to the sides
hile resting.

When a female appears,
he holds her behind her
head using his tail
claspers, and she swings
her abdomen forward to
mate with him.

MAYFLIES
A mayfly lives for a year
or more as a larva in a
stream or river, eating
tiny plants and other
bits of food. It sheds its
skin up to 25 times—a
record for an insect.
Then it crawls up a
plant stem into the air
and sheds its skin twice,
first becoming a winged
sub-adult, and then a
proper adult, able
to breed. Yet
after all this,
the adult
mayfly lives
for only a few
hours. It has just
enough time to breed
before it dies. Adult
ayflies often emerge in swarms on the same day.
hey "dance" over the water as they mate, and
e females lay eggs by dipping their rear ends
elow the water's surface. Some adult mayflies
ave such tiny mouths that they could not feed
ven if they had time!

TONEFLIES
toneflies also have short lives as adults,
sually just a week or two. Yet they also
pend a year or more as water-dwelling larvae.
tonefly nymphs dwell in clear, rocky, fast-
owing streams.

A mayfly larva has three tail
filaments, which help it swim.
It has small, non-flapping wings.

Stoneflies grip the stony
stream bed with their
strong hooked legs, to
prevent themselves
being swept away in the
current. Adult stoneflies
resemble adult mayflies,
but they have two tail
filaments rather than
three, and when at rest,
they hold their thin,
veined wings flat over
their bodies.

CADDISFLIES
Adult caddisflies have
slightly hairy wings and
bodies, like some moths. They are seldom seen
far from water, where their larvae live
inside tube-shaped cases built from
whatever is common in the pond
or stream. Some caddis
larvae even use tiny
empty snail shells as
mobile homes.

Dragonflies and damselflies
(Orthoptera)
• about 5,000 species
• two pairs of large, long,
  transparent, veined wings
• big eyes
• young (nymphs) live in water
• adults often fly near water

Mayflies (Ephemeroptera)
• about 2,000 species
• delicate veined wings, usually
  two pairs
• three thin or fan-shaped tail
  filaments
• young (nymphs) live in water
• adults very short-lived

Stoneflies (Plecoptera)
• about 3,000 species
• flattened body
• two thin or fan-shaped tail
  filaments
• young (nymphs) live in water
• adults live along river banks

Caddisflies (Trichoptera)
• about 6,000 species
• young (nymphs) live in water,
  often in protective cases
• adults hairy, with four wings
• live near fresh water

Caddisflies are usually
active at night.

Some caddisfly nymphs make their body cases
from snipped-off lengths of plant stems (top).
Others use bits of water plant leaves (center) or
tiny pieces of gravel (bottom).

Like dragonflies, damselflies have
thin, delicate wings strengthened by
veins. These tubes contain blood as the
new adult spreads its wings. But then
they become hard, dry, and empty.

BUGS

◮ In certain seasons, usually summer, female aphids do not lay eggs, but give birth to fully formed babies, or nymphs. This allows them to reproduce very quickly.

THE WORD "BUG" IS OFTEN USED FOR ANY TYPE OF INSECT, OR FOR ANY OTHER KIND OF CRAWLING CREATURE. However, bugs are really a distinct subgroup of insects, known as Hemipterans. There are some 70,000 species of bug. They all share the usual insect features of six legs, a three-part body, and four flapping wings, but they also have a feature unique to the group—a mouth like a needle, specialized for piercing and sucking liquids and juices. Some bugs are predators. Assassin bugs and bedbugs, and water bugs such as pondskaters and backswimmers, feed on the blood and body fluids of other animals. Other bugs are plant-feeders, such as leafbugs, cicadas, and aphids.

◮ Leaf hoppers and frog hoppers are small bugs that suck sap from plant stems and buds. The nymphs surround themselves with a bubbly froth called "snake spit," for protection from the hot sun and predators.

Several kinds of bug live on or under the water. Pondskaters skim around on the surface, hunting for flies and other insects that have fallen in. The pondskater senses the ripples made by the struggling prey and speeds over to bite and suck out its body juices. Backswimmers and water boatmen row themselves through the water using their hairy legs. They have very strong mouthparts for catching tiny pond creatures and can even give a person a painful bite. The water scorpion is a large bug that captures prey with its pincers. The long tail is not a sting, but a snorkel—a tube through which the water scorpion breathes as it hangs just below the surface.

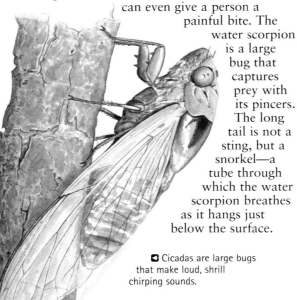

◮ Cicadas are large bugs that make loud, shrill chirping sounds.

CALLING TO ATTRACT A MATE

Some insects use sounds to attract mates. And some of the loudest insect sounds are made by male cicadas. Their piercing, high-pitched calls are heard in many of the warmer parts of the world. The noise comes from the sides of the cicada's thorax or body, which flick in and out, like shaking a metal sheet to and fro very rapidly. Adult cicadas live and feed in trees. But their young, or nymphs, develop in the soil, feeding on the sap of plant roots. They are among the longest-lived of all insects. Some cicada nymphs stay underground for more than 20 years, before emerging and shedding their skins to become adults.

◮ The backswimmer's front four legs touch the water's surface, to detect tiny ripples made by prey.

◮ The earwig's tail pincers, or cerci, are used to capture prey, fend off enemies, and hold the partner when mating. They are curved in males (right) and straight in females.

◮ Green leaf bug

After crawling from its old it skin, the cicada's crumpled ngs soon expand.

This tropical cockroach is mouflaged to resemble dead aves on the forest floor. ckroaches were one of the st kinds of insect to appear Earth, more than 300 million ars ago.

INSIDE AN INSECT'S LEG

The leg of an insect or other arthropod is like a long, slim tube made of several sections. The casing, or exoskeleton (page 72), is thin between the sections to allow the leg to bend, moved by several muscles inside.

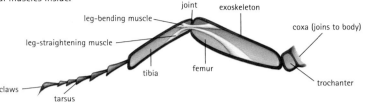

joint · exoskeleton · leg-bending muscle · leg-straightening muscle · coxa (joins to body) · tibia · femur · trochanter · claws · tarsus

APHIDS

The greenflies and blackflies that become pests in the garden during summer are bugs called aphids. They are mostly small, just fractions of an inch long. They suck sap from flowers such as roses, fruits such as currants, vegetables such as cabbages and lima beans, and many other plants.

Aphids have amazing powers of reproduction. They spend the winter s eggs. The first aphids to hatch in spring are emales. They can produce young without having o mate with a male first. This method of reeding is known as "parthenogenesis." It llows aphids to reproduce very quickly and uild up large swarms. In late summer, females roduce some male babies, too. hese mate with the females, which lay eggs to live hrough the winter.

COCKROACHES

Cockroaches look like bugs, but belong in their own insect subgroup. They are among the toughest of all insects, and with their strong chewing mouthparts can survive on almost any scraps of food. They also reproduce quickly and may become serious pests. Cockroaches live in almost all land habitats, from icy mountains to deep caves or the dead leaves and soil of tropical forests.

EARWIGS

Earwigs will hide in any dark hole or crevice, and will burrow in soil or crawl under tree bark. They eat a range of plant and animal foods, including harmful grubs. The female is a caring parent. She cleans her eggs and protects her young.

True bugs *(Hemiptera)*
- about 70,000 species
- beaklike mouthparts for piercing and sucking
- many have narrow or flattened bodies

Cockroaches *(Blattodea)*
- 3,700 species
- long, low, flattened body
- long feelers
- hard front wings protect rear wings underneath
- fast-running

Earwigs *(Dermaptera)*
- 1,200 species
- flattened body
- pincer-like tail

Many bugs, like these ackspot leaf bugs, are olored or camouflaged to atch their surroundings.

Some bugs show arental behavior, which is re among insects. This male shieldbug guards her ggs against predators.

CRICKETS AND GRASSHOPPERS

CRICKETS AND GRASSHOPPERS HAVE LONG,
POWERFUL BACK LEGS FOR LEAPING AND
JUMPING, USUALLY TO ESCAPE PREDATORS.
They belong to the insect subgroup known as
Orthopterans. Most have camouflaged bodies,
colored and patterned to blend in with their surroundings. As they leap, they

⬛ Crickets, like this green bush cricket, and mantids usually live singly.

⬛ Grasshoppers have large, fanlike rear wings. When these are not in use they are folded and protected by the smaller, harder front wings.

may spread their two rear wings in a flash of whirring
color. The young or larvae of crickets and grasshoppers
look like small versions of the adult, except that they do
not have wings. The wings grow gradually, each time the
larva sheds its skin. This type of development is known
incomplete metamorphosis, and the larvae are called
nymphs. There is no pupa or chrysalis stage
(page 77). Other insects that grow like this
include cockroaches, bugs, dragonflies,
termites, mantids, earwigs, and stoneflies.

The rasping and chirping of crickets and grasshoppers are familiar
sounds in hot weather. The male insects "sing" to warn others off
their territory or to attract a mate. Crickets and the similar katydids
rub the comblike front wing veins together to make the noise.
Grasshoppers and locusts rub their back legs against the front
wing veins. Each leg has a row of hard pegs that make the
wing vibrate. One kind of cricket, the mole cricket, lives
in a burrow rather than on grass stems and plants like
most crickets and grasshoppers. To make its song
even louder, it digs a mating burrow with the
entrance shaped like a double funnel.

⬛ A leap
desert loc
straighte
each
section in tu

The mole cricket's burrow entrance acts as a
kind of loudspeaker. On a still night, its song
can be heard more than 1 mile (1.6 km) away.

STICK AND LEAF INSECTS
The stick and leaf insects, or phasmids, live mainly
in tropical regions. They avoid birds and other
predators with their amazing camouflage. Their
bodies look like thin sticks or twigs, or like flat leaves.

◖ A stick insect spreads its large, fanlike rear wings.

Most of them are green or brown, to match the plants on which they feed. Some leaf insects even have V-shaped patterns on their bodies resembling the veins or ribs of a leaf. Others have brown edges, patches or blotches, so that they look like old or damaged leaves.

NO MALES NEEDED
Some kinds of female stick insect do not need to mate with a male before laying eggs. In some species males are hardly ever found. This kind of breeding is called parthenogenesis.

▢ Leaf insects (shown here on the leaves) are extremely well camouflaged in both appearance and behavior. They move and sway to mimic a leaf being blown by the wind. Stick insects (at the top) hold out their legs at the same angles as the twigs around them.

◖ A grasshopper (left) has shorter antennae or feelers than a cricket (below).

LONGEST... !
The longest insects are some kinds of stick insect. They grow to 14 inches (35 cm) from head to tail.

MANTIDS
Mantids are fierce hunters. They catch and eat other small animals, such as large insects and spiders, grabbing them with their spiny, pincerlike front legs. The mantis has large eyes and excellent vision. It sits patiently on a plant or flower, waiting for a suitable victim to come near. Then it strikes, too fast for us to see, and grabs the prey in its spiny "arms." When some kinds of mantid breed, the female eats the male just after they mate, or even while mating. In other species there are no males. The females reproduce by parthenogenesis.

▷ The praying mantis is named for its waiting-to-pounce posture, with front legs folded as if in prayer.

Crickets, locusts and grasshoppers (Orthoptera)
• 20,500 species
• long, strong hind legs for jumping
• small, hard front wings
• large, fanlike rear wings
• feed on plants

Stick and leaf insects (Phasmatoidea)
• 2,500 species
• live mainly in the tropics
• resemble leaves, twigs or sticks

• even the eggs are camouflaged, to resemble plant seeds
• large, fanlike rear wings
• eat plants

Mantids (Mantodea)
• 1,800 species
• live mainly in warmer countries
• triangular head with big eyes
• large front legs with pincerlike claws
• eat mainly other insects

87

FLEAS, LICE, AND OTHER INSECTS

FLEAS AND LICE ARE TINY, WINGLESS INSECTS THAT ARE PARASITES. They feed on other animals, called their hosts, either by sucking their blood or by chewing their skin or feathers. Fleas have sideways-flattened bodies and can slip easily among fur or feathers. They pierce the flesh of the host using their sharp, needle-like mouthparts. Most fleas are parasites of mammals. Humans, rats, cats, dogs, rabbits, bears, porcupines, beavers, and many others each have their own particular flea species. Other fleas are parasites of birds especially those that live in burrows, such as puffins, where the flea larvae can develop in warm safety. A flea escapes danger by leaping with its long, powerful back legs. These have a special click mechanism that stores energy and then releases it suddenly, like a spring-loaded lever. The average flea measures just a few pinheads across, but it can jump more than 12 inches (30 cm)—about 100 times its own length. For its size, the flea is the world's greatest animal athlete!

▲ The louse has hook-shaped, gripping legs with very strong claws. It clings to the skin or hair and resists being brushed off or washed away. In tropical regions, lice spread diseases such as typhus and relapsing fever.

▲ The springtail has a long, leverlike tail. This is normally hooked under the main body. When released, it springs downward and flicks the insect into the air.

◄ A human louse sucks the blood of its host. The blood gradually fills the front of the louse's abdomen, turning it dark red.

OLDEST... !
The first insects were probably springtails. Fossils in 400 million-year-old rocks have been found.

A louse clings on to its host using its sharp claws. Its flattened body lies close to the skin, making it very difficult to remove. Like fleas, there are different kinds of lice for different animals, including humans, dogs, guinea pigs, elephants, seals, warthogs, and hummingbirds! The human louse is about 0.1 inch (2 mm) long and its bite causes an itchy lump. The female glues her eggs to human hairs. The eggs look like tiny grains of salt and are called "nits."

BARKLICE AND BOOKLICE

In addition to the lice described above, which are sometimes known as sucking or parasitic lice, there are two other groups of lice. Barklice are small and active, living on the bark of trees, among leaves or in birds' nests. They feed mainly on tiny plants and molds.

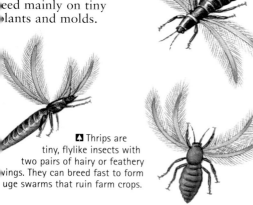

◩ Thrips are tiny, flylike insects with two pairs of hairy or feathery wings. They can breed fast to form huge swarms that ruin farm crops.

Booklice are similar and are sometimes found in old houses and buildings. They usually feed on mold, but they also eat the starchy paste used in the glue that binds the pages of old books.

THRIPS

The thrips are among the smallest of all insects. They have feathery or fluffy wings and can fly quite well. Most feed on plants, and especially on the flowers. They can multiply quickly and eat the flowers of wheat, onions, carrots, and fruits such as apples and oranges. In warm, thundery weather they may take to the air in great swarms, crawling on our skin and in our hair and eyes. They are sometimes known as thunderflies or thunderbugs.

SPRINGY TAIL

Springtails are also very small insects, none being longer than a fourth of an inch (5 mm). They are named after the springlike structure on the tail. They flick this down to jump away when disturbed. They are so different from other insects that they have their own major subgroup (subclass), Collembola.

SILVERFISH

This is one of the simplest or most primitive of all insects. It has no wings, but very long antennae and a three-forked tail. It is found in kitchens and food stores, coming out at night to feed on scraps. The silverfish is named for its silvery color and its bendy, fishlike movements.

abdomen with 11 segments or sections

side tail fork (cercus)

antenna

small eye

central tail filament (telson)

leg

◩ A flea's back legs are more than twice as long as its front and middle legs. The needlelike mouthparts are between the front legs.

Springtails are among the most abundant and widespread of all insects. They live in their millions in the soil, among dead leaves and moss, and in rotting wood. Some kinds are pests because they eat farm crops such as cereals and clover. Others live on sandy beaches, around rock pools on the shore, and even at the surface of the stagnant, polluted water in ditches.

Fleas (Siphonaptera)
- 1,800 species
- very small
- wingless
- body flattened sideways
- powerful jumpers
- blood-sucking parasites of mammals and birds

Lice (Phthiraptera)
- 3,500 species
- very small
- wingless
- parasites of other animals

Booklice and barklice (Psocoptera)
- 2,000 species
- resemble lice but more active
- some eat paper and book bindings

Thrips (Thysanoptera)
- 5,000 species
- tiny
- resemble flies with hairy wings

Bristletails and silverfish (Thysanura)
- 600 species
- wingless
- shiny flat body, long antennae
- bristly two- or three-pronged tail

Springtails (Collembola)
- 2,000 species
- very small
- wingless
- spring-lever tail for leaping
- live in damp habitats, including surfaces of ponds and streams

89

CRABS, LOBSTERS, AND SHRIMPS

INSECTS ARE THE MOST COMMON ANIMALS ON LAND. But they do not live in salty water. Instead, another group of arthropods occupies the oceans—the crustaceans. They include crabs, lobsters, shrimps, and barnacles. The shrimplike krill eate by great whales are crustaceans. So are the small creature called copepods, which teem in such vast swarms that the are the most numerous animals in the sea. Some crustaceans, such as water fleas and crayfish, live in fresh water. A few, like woodlice, live on land.

▲ Common shore crab

▲ Like all crustaceans, the slipper lobster grows by shedding or molting its old carapace (shell). The new one underneath enlarges and then hardens.

For many people, the most familiar crustaceans are crabs. There are thousands of crab species, from giant spider crabs with pincers as long as your arm, to tiny porcelain and pea crabs that would fit in this o. A typical crab has a flattened body covered by the hard, shell-like carapace. The abdomen (rear part of the body) is small and tucked under the shell at the back. There are ten limbs—one pair of large pincers and four pairs of walking legs. Most crabs live in the sea, but a few dwell in rivers and lakes. The common shore crab is very hardy and can live in both salt and fresh water, and even out of water for a few hours.

THE HERMIT'S HOME

The front end of a hermit crab has the typical hard crab carapace and pincers, and two pairs of large walking legs. But the rear of its body is soft and twisted. This is because a hermit crab lives in the abandoned shell of a sea snail, such as a whelk. It holds the shell from inside with its two pairs of smaller rear legs. When the hermit crab grows too big for its shell, it has to "move house." It finds a larger shell, and quickly slides its body backward into the new home.

CRAYFISH AND LOBSTERS

Crayfish and lobsters are like elongated crabs with the rear body part, the abdomen, held out straight at the rear like a tail, rather than tucked underneath.

◄ The red-banded cleaner shrimp lives on coral reefs. Its bright colors advertise the service it provides—picking tiny parasites and pests off larger animals such as fish. The shrimp gets a meal and the fish gets cleaned

The middle body part of crayfish and lobsters, the thorax, has four pairs of walking legs with a pair of very large, strong pincers or claws at the front. In some types of lobster one pincer is bigger and designed for crushing, while the smaller one is sharper for cutting and snipping.

▲ Krill live in cool oceans, in swarms several miles long, numbering many millions. They are cousins of shrimps and feed by filtering the tiny plants and animals of the plankton from seawater.

The lobster's head has two pairs of antennae. The larger pair curl out in front and may be longer than the whole body. The lobster uses these to feel among rocks for food such as shellfish, which it crushes with its pincers. A lobster is well protected. Its head and thorax are covered by a thick, rigid carapace. The abdomen has a series of jointed plates, one for each segment. It can also defend itself with its powerful pincers.

◀ Crayfish are the largest freshwater crustaceans. Like their cousins, lobsters, they feed at night. By day they hide in a lair, in a hole or under stone.

SHRIMPS AND PRAWNS

Shrimps and prawns are like small, lightly built lobsters. Shrimps can crawl well but prawns usually swim by rowing with the five pairs of paddle-shaped limbs under the abdomen. The shrimp has a body flattened from top to bottom, while the prawn is flattened from side to side. They eat anything they can find, including dead animals. When alive they are almost transparent and well camouflaged against the rocks and sand. They only turn pink when cooked!

BIGGEST... !
The Japanese giant spider crab is the largest crustacean and the largest living arthropod. Its body is the size of a dinner plate, and it can measure 11.5 feet (3.5 m) across its outstretched claws.

◢ Some crabs, like the robber crab, live partly on land. This powerful crustacean can even climb up trees near the shore.

◀ Prawns use their delicate pincers to search through mud and sand for anything small and edible.

◀ Shrimps are similar to prawns, but lack the long, pointed snout or rostrum at the front of the head.

CRUSTACEANS

Main groups include:

Crabs
• 5,700 species
• most live in the sea
• round, flattened body, hard shell
• four pairs of walking legs
• one pair of pincers

Lobsters and crayfish
• 400 species
• most live in the sea
• long body
• four pairs of walking legs
• one pair of pincers

Shrimps and prawns
• 2,000 species
• most live in the sea
• long body
• swim and crawl well

All of the above are in the main crustacean group Decapoda, meaning "ten-limbed."

Krill
• 90 species
• swim in the open sea
• resemble shrimps
• live in gigantic shoals

BARNACLES AND OTHER CRUSTACEANS

WHEN THE TIDE IS OUT, AN ACORN BARNACLE HARDLY LOOKS LIKE AN ANIMAL AT ALL. Its pyramid-shaped shell, cemented firmly to a rock, has a tightly shut door at the top. But when the tide comes in, the door opens and the barnacle extends its long, feathery, fanlike limbs into the water. These beat regularly with a grasping motion to pull tiny bits of food toward the barnacle's mouth. Many other kinds of small crustaceans live along seashores and in the open oceans. The adults look very different, resembling shrimps, fleas, or mussels. But their young forms or larvae are all very similar. These billions of small crustaceans make up much of the ocean plankton.

Acorn barnacles coat roc along the seashore and shallow water. They are prey on by whelks, starfish, and fi Some species can survive abo the high-tide level, with t occasional spray from wav

A barnacle begins life as a tiny egg which hatches into a vaguely shrimplike larva. This drifts and swims as part of the plankton for a few days. In shallow water, it finds a firm place like a rock where the waves break at low tide. The larva sticks its head to the rock with its own natural glue and grows several hard, chalky plates around its body. Finally it changes into the adult barnacle, which feeds by kicking its feathery limbs to create water currents that draw food particles into its shell. Sometimes barnacles cause problems when they settle to live on a ship's hull, a buoy, or an undersea cable. They also attach to large sea animals such as whales, sharks, and turtles. They may live there for 20 years or more.

Woodlice (sowbugs) can on survive in damp places, such a among dead leaves or under tree bark. This is because the covering, or cuticle, over the jointed body shell is not waterproof. If a woodlouse is exposed to the hot sun, it drie out and dies.

Goose barnacles have shell-like plates around the body for protection, like their cousins the acorn barnacles. They also have a fleshy stalk, or peduncle, which attaches to a floating piece of debris such as a lump of driftwood (or a boat).

INSIDE A WATER FLEA

The common water flea, daphnia, is about the size of this O. It swims jerkily by rowing with its long feelers (antennae), and feeds by filtering microscopic plants and animals from the water with its feathery legs. Although it is called a water "flea," it is not a true flea—it is a crustacean. There are thousands of daphnia in even the smallest pond. They are important food for small worms, fish, and shellfish.

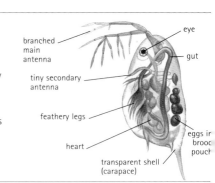

branched main antenna

tiny secondary antenna

feathery legs

heart

transparent shell (carapace)

eye

gut

eggs ir brooc pouc

▷ Brine shrimps are food for crabs and flamingoes.

[MO]VING UPSIDE DOWN

[F]airy shrimps and brine [sh]rimps have rows of [fe]athery or brushlike [li]mbs along each side of [th]e body. They swim [sl]owly—and upside down— [b]y waving these limbs. These [d]elicate-looking crustaceans rarely [gr]ow bigger than your finger, and most [ar]e much shorter.

[F]airy shrimps have no defenses against predators, [p]artly because they live in places where predators [ar]e uncommon. They inhabit temporary pools, [su]ch as puddles of rainwater, where animals like [fi]sh cannot survive. When the pool dries out, the [ad]ult fairy shrimps die, [bu]t they leave very [to]ugh eggs in the mud. [Th]ese hatch when the [po]ol fills again. Brine [sh]rimps can survive in [th]e extremely warm and [sa]lty water of salt lakes [an]d coastal lagoons.

[TH]E MOST COMMON [C]RUSTACEANS

[T]he open seas are the [m]ain home of copepods [an]d ostracods, although [so]me kinds are found in ponds and lakes. [C]opepods resemble slim woodlice with very long [fe]elers. They are among the most numerous [cr]eatures found in plankton, and many kinds of [se]a creatures depend upon them for food. [O]stracods look like tiny versions of mussels or [cl]ams. They are sometimes called mussel shrimps [or] seed shrimps, and are more at home on the sea [fl]oor, where they filter food from water or mud. The largest kinds are just 0.25 inch (5 mm) across.

◩ The oniscus woodlouse is very common and lives in woods, parks, and gardens.

◪ The pillbug is a woodlouse that can roll up into a ball for protection.

Some ostracods release substances into the water that glow with a greenish-yellow light. This may be a signal that breeding time has arrived. Or it may serve to confuse predators, such as shrimps.

WATER FLEAS AND FISH LICE

Water fleas have large, feathery antennae, which they use to row through the water. As they move, they both feed and breathe using their legs, which work as gills (page 102) to take in oxygen and as sieves to gather food. Fish lice are not true lice, but louse-shaped crustaceans. They are blood-sucking parasites on fish and other water-dwellers.

MORE CRUSTACEANS
(continued from page 91):

Barnacles
• 1,000 species
• live in the sea
• featherlike legs
• some have shells and attach to rocks
• some are parasites

Ostracods
• 5,700 species
• most live in the sea
• very small
• oval body enclosed in hinged shell

Copepods
• 8,400 species
• most live in the sea
• shrimplike body
• long feelers
• largest are coin-sized
• swim jerkily

Water fleas
• 480 species
• mainly freshwater
• oval shell
• long branched feelers for rowing
• bob up and down

Fairy shrimps and brine shrimps
• 175 species
• fairy shrimps live in freshwater pools, brine shrimps in salty water
• long body
• feathery legs for swimming and feeding

Tadpole shrimps
• 15 species
• live in freshwater pools
• shell-like covering at front, long forked tail
• up to thumb-sized

Amphipods
• 3,600 species
• most live in the sea
• small and shrimplike
• narrow body
• includes freshwater shrimps, sandhoppers, and beach fleas

Isopods
• 4,000 species
• most live in the sea
• flattened body
• seven pairs of legs
• includes woodlice

SPIDERS

SPIDERS ARE MEMBERS OF THE ARTHROPOD
GROUP CALLED ARACHNIDS. The main feature
of an arachnid is that it has eight legs, unlike an
insect which has six, and a crustacean which has ten or
more. Other arachnids include
harvestmen, scorpions, ticks, and
mites. With some 80,000 species,
arachnids form the second largest group of
arthropods, after insects. Like insects, they are mostly
land-living, although a few kinds of spiders and mites
inhabit fresh water. Unlike insects, they lack wings.
Most arachnids are predators or hunters, but some mite
and ticks are parasites of other animals. Arachnids live
all over the world, in a wide range of habitats.

🔺 Tarantula

🔺 Some spiders, like the Costa
Rican orb-weaver, build an
extra-visible zigzag area of silk
in the middle of the web. This is
called the stabilimentum.

Spiders have one important ability that sets them
apart from most other arthropods, including
other arachnids. They make a kind of silk
thread using special parts at the rear of the
body, called spinnerets. Spider silk is used
for various purposes—to spin protective
cocoons around the eggs, to make a
parachute for a baby spider so that it can
blow in the wind to a new place, to act as a
safety line in case the spider loses its footing and
falls, to line a burrow or tunnel, to wrap up and
subdue prey before it is eaten, and to weave webs
for catching prey.

🔻 Huntsman spiders live in
tropical forests. They are large
and strong enough to catch
prey by force, and do
not spin webs.

◀ Bird-eating spiders hav
large mouthparts, or cheli
with sharp fangs. The
have long palps (whic
like a front pair of le
touching and ta

Spider silk is one of th
strongest materials
known. It can take more
strain than a steel thread of
the same thickness. Different
sorts of silk are used for different
purposes. Cocoon silk is thick and smooth, while
web silk is like sticky, coiled elastic.

HIDDEN DANGER

Trapdoor spiders live in burrows, using their si
to make a hinged, doorlike covering to the
entrance. The trapdoor spider detects
vibrations in the ground as a suitable small
creature passes by. Or it lays silk threads a
tripwires that the creature touches. The
spider then darts out of its burrow and
bites the victim with its large fangs,
which all spiders possess. It injects
poison and drags its meal down into th
burrow, closing the trapdoor behind.

...KING A WEB

...common type of web is the orb web. It is roughly circular with radial threads like spokes in a ...eel. First, the spider must choose a suitable place with twigs the correct distance apart. The ...der sets out the top frame and makes a couple of radial threads (1). Next comes the rest of ...frame and more radial threads (2), then the last of the spokelike radials (3). These are all ...de from a strong, tight, nonsticky type of silk. The spider then works around in a spiral from ...outside toward the center, spinning a much looser, elastic, sticky silk to snare its prey (4).

1   2   3   4

◻ This yellow agriope orb-web spider has wrapped a moth in silk thread to eat later. If the spider has plenty of food, it may leave the victim tied up but alive, hidden in the fork of a nearby twig.

...BS GALORE

...eb-spinning spiders make all shapes and ...es of webs. Some are woven in amazingly ...ecise geometric patterns. Others are a tangle ...threads in a dark corner. But when a victim ...s the web, the silk threads quickly entangle it. ...the web is badly damaged, ...e spider eats the silk and ...cycles it to spin ...other one.

...ISONOUS SPIDERS

...l spiders have poisonous bites. But only about 30 ...ecies have fangs strong enough, and poison ...werful enough, to harm people. The most deadly ...e the black widows, *Latrodectus*, that live in many ...rm countries, the Australian funnel-web spiders, ...d the Brazilian huntsman.

◻ The net-casting spider spins a small web and holds it out with its three front pairs of legs. The web is a net ready to throw over the prey. This spider's huge eyes watch for victims and see where to cast the net.

◻ Wolf spiders do not make ...s. They run quickly across soil, ...ocks, and tree bark after their ...y, using their extra-long legs. ...ince they have no home base, ...female wolf spider carries her ...whitish silk egg cocoon ...under her body.

ARACHNIDS

• members of the arthropod group
• about 80,000 species
• adult has eight legs

Spiders
• 50,000 species
• worldwide, all habitats
• body has obvious waist
• make webs from silk

SCORPIONS AND OTHER ARACHNIDS

A SCORPION'S LONG BODY AND LARGE PINCERS MAKE IT LOOK LIKE A SMALL LOBSTER. But the scorpion's eight legs show that it is an arachnid, not a crustacean. The sting at the end of its long, arching tail is occasionally used to paralyze prey, but is mainly for self-defense. Several kinds of scorpion can inflict very painful stings on larger animals and people, and a few are even fatal. Although scorpions have from four to eight eyes, like spiders, their sight is poor. But this is not important since most scorpions hide by day, squeezed into a rocky crevice or wedged under a stone or log. At night they come out and detect prey mainly by feeling vibrations in the ground. A scorpion grabs its victim using its large pincers, or pedipalps. It may sting the prey to stop it struggling, before tearing it to pieces using its strong, clawlike mouthparts called chelicerae.

◣ The giant red velvet mite one of the biggest mites, about 0.6 inch (15 mm) long lives in the dry terrain of Afri where it hunts tiny worms a insects, and scavenges on de plants and anima

HEAVIEST... !

The heaviest and largest arachnids are tropical scorpions from India and West Africa. Some species grow up to 10 inches (25 cm) long. They look ferocious, but their stings are rarely more painful than a wasp's sting.

False scorpions or pseudoscorpions, are tiny arachnids—only as long as this letter 'm'. They look like miniature scorpions, but lack the stinging tail and are quite harmless to humans. False scorpions walk backward as well as forward, and often wave their large claws in the air. They live among dead leaves and moss, and under bark.

TICKS AND MITES

There are about 32,000 species of ticks and mites, which are the smallest arachnids. Some mites are less than one hundredth of an inch (0.2 mm). Both mites and ticks look like small, fat spiders.

◣ A false scorpion uses its pincers in the same way as its larger relative, to grab prey.

◢ A female scorpion takes care of her young. She lays from one to 100 eggs, depending on the species. The eggs hatch into tiny babies, which clamber onto their mother's back, protected by her great pincers and poison sting. They leave after a week or two.

All ticks are parasites of larger animals such as mammals, birds, and reptiles. They bite into the skin and suck the host's blood. Some ticks spread diseases, such as Rocky Mountain fever and Lyme disease (spread by deer ticks). Some mites are also parasites. They infest plants and animals, including humans, sucking their fluids. Others feed on food and skin flakes in dust.

The sun spider runs on its six rear legs, using the slimmer front pair and its very long palps to feel vibrations in the ground. It can outpace most prey, even lizards.

Some people are allergic to dust mites, or rather, to their dry, powdery droppings. They may develop breathing problems such as asthma. Mites also infest food stores, especially dry foods such as grains, flour, or bran. The flour mite lives all over the world and causes immense damage in food stores. Yet other kinds of mites catch small insects and other prey.

Some kinds of harvestmen can inflict a painful bite or even spray nasty-smelling liquid at an attacker. These arachnids eat tiny animals, bits of plants and molds.

HARVESTMEN

Harvestmen, sometimes called harvest spiders, are like very long-legged spiders. But they have a small, rounded, one-piece body, without the "waist" that divides the body of a true spider into two parts (the front cephalothorax and the rear abdomen). Harvestmen live in rotting leaves, old logs, damp grass, and similar places.

SUN SPIDERS

These desert-dwelling arachnids, also called wind spiders or solifuges, look very much like spiders. They have extremely strong fanglike pincers, but lack a poisonous bite. They lurk under stones or in burrows and race after their prey of insects, worms, lizards, and even spiders and scorpions.

Parasitic mites have bladelike mouthparts that they drive into their host, to suck sap or blood.

ARACHNIDS
(continued from page 95):

Scorpions
• 1,200 species
• worldwide, but mainly in warm places
• large pincers
• slim curved tail with poisonous sting
• prey on smaller animals

Ticks and mites
• 32,000 species
• most mites are smaller than ticks
• resemble small, fat spiders
• ticks are parasites of mammals, birds, or reptiles
• some mites are parasites, others are free-living
• some mites are brightly colored

False scorpions
• 2,000 species
• tiny
• look like miniature scorpions, but without a stinging tail
• live in soil, decaying leaves, old wood

Harvestmen
• 4,500 species
• worldwide
• live in woodland, grassland, gardens
• resemble a spider but with a one-piece body and long, stiltlike legs

Sun spiders (Solifuges)
• 900 species
• live mainly in deserts
• huge, nonpoisonous pincer jaws
• run extremely fast

CENTIPEDES AND MILLIPEDES

△ Various kinds of pill millipedes roll into a ball when in danger. The curved plates, tergites, covering each body segment are jointed so that they overlap to form a smooth, rounded ball.

CENTIPEDES LIVE AND HUNT UNDER LOGS AND STONES, IN SOIL AND AMONG DEAD LEAVES. The locate prey with their long, sensitive feelers on the head, and bite with the sharp, clawlike fangs on the first body segment, injecting a poison that stops the prey struggling The centipede then tears it apart with its strong jaws. Many centipedes can run very fast on their numerous pairs of legs. The name centipede means "hundred legs," but most species have about 40, although some have more than 340. Millipedes look like centipedes, but have a more rounded, tube-shaped body, shorter feelers, and move more slowly. The name millipede means "thousand legs," but the maximum is about 750. Millipedes eat bits of plants, such as roots, buds, and flowers, and also old, moldy plant parts. Large centipedes can give an extremely painful bite, but millipedes cannot. Instead, they ooze or spray a horrible-tasting fluid from small glands along the sides of the body, to defend themselves against attack.

△ A millipede such as t one, polydesmus, has sh feelers and no tail filamen Its hard body gives go protection against predat such as birds and spide

▽ A giant tropical centipede has two long feelers or antennae on its head, and two long tail filaments. Its poison fangs on the first body segment are held alongside and just under the head.

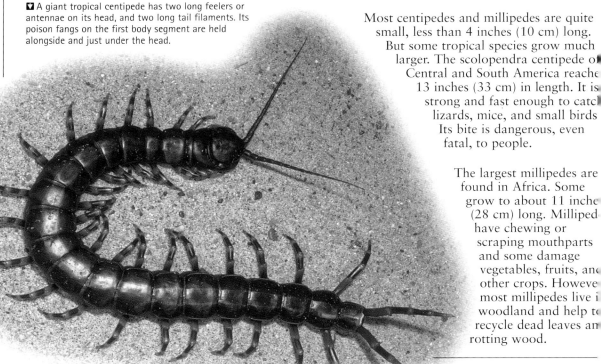

Most centipedes and millipedes are quite small, less than 4 inches (10 cm) long. But some tropical species grow much larger. The scolopendra centipede o Central and South America reache 13 inches (33 cm) in length. It is strong and fast enough to catc lizards, mice, and small birds Its bite is dangerous, even fatal, to people.

The largest millipedes are found in Africa. Some grow to about 11 inche (28 cm) long. Milliped have chewing or scraping mouthparts and some damage vegetables, fruits, an other crops. Howeve most millipedes live i woodland and help t recycle dead leaves an rotting wood.

▲ Velvet worms (onychophorans or peripatuses) seem like a combination of centipede and worm. They feed on small animals such as real worms and insects.

▼ The two-headed centipede has only one head, on the right. Its tail is shaped and colored to look similar and confuse predators.

VELVET WORMS

These caterpillarlike creatures live in warm, damp forests. Their bodies are soft, squishy, and velvety, with stumpy clawed legs for walking. Like all arthropods, they grow by moulting.

BLIND CREEPERS

Two smaller groups of arthropods are related to millipedes and centipedes. These are symphylans and pauropods. They are like miniature centipedes, about the same size as ants. They have no eyes and creep about in leaf litter and moist soil. Symphylans eat tiny bits of plants while pauropods scavenge on anything edible.

SEASHORE HUNTERS

Sea spiders are well named because they look like spiders, with four pairs of long legs, and live in the sea. But they have their own arthropod group. Most are 1–2 inches (3–5 cm) across their outstretched legs. They clamber about on rocks and seaweeds on the lower shore, where they feed on sponges, corals, and anemones by piercing them with their sharp mouthparts. Some deep-sea species grow to 30 inches (75 cm) across.

CENTIPEDE OR MILLIPEDE?

These two types of multilegged arthropods look quite similar, but there are several differences, as shown here (the millipede is on the left). They also live very differently. Centipedes are fast, active carnivores. They do not mind bright light and sometimes hunt during the day. Millipedes are slow herbivores or detritivores (eating old, decaying bits of plants or molds). They hide from bright light and usually come out to feed only at night.

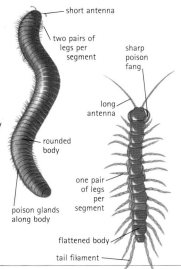

short antenna

two pairs of legs per segment

sharp poison fang

long antenna

rounded body

one pair of legs per segment

poison glands along body

flattened body

tail filament

OTHER GROUPS OF ARTHROPODS INCLUDE:

Centipedes
• 3,000 species
• worldwide, mainly in soil, under rocks and leaves, in old wood
• bendy, flattened body
• two legs per body segment
• long feelers
• sharp fangs and strong jaws
• prey on smaller animals

Millipedes
• 8,000 species
• worldwide, mainly in soil, old leaves, rotting wood
• tubular, rounded body
• four legs per body segment
• short feelers
• feed on plants, molds

Symphylans
• 160 species
• live in soil
• small, ant-sized

• look like small centipedes
• 12 pairs of legs

Pauropods
• 400 species
• live in soil
• tiny
• look like tiny centipedes
• nine pairs of legs

Sea spiders
• 1,000 species
• live in the sea
• resemble true spiders
• four pairs of long walking legs
• prey on other animals

Velvet worms
• 120 species
• live in tropical forests
• resemble large caterpillars
• 17 pairs of stumpy legs

This spotted eagle ray has large eyes and, just behind each one, a flap-covered opening or spiracle. This lets in water which flows over the gills, so that the ray can breathe (take in oxygen from the water). The water then leaves through gill slits on the ray's underside.

SECTION 4
FISH

FISH ARE EASY TO IDENTIFY. They live in water, breathe through their gills, are covered by shiny scales, and swim by swishing their fins and tail. But there are exceptions. Lungfish can live out of water and breathe air. Some eels have no scales. Lampreys and hagfish, and some types of ray, have no fins or tail. But fish, like all other vertebrates, have an inner skeleton with a backbone.

Fish make up a vast and varied group. Their habitats range from the deepest oceans to the clearest mountain streams, from sunlit tropical lagoons to dark, chilly underground lakes. They have a greater size range than almost any other animal group, from dwarf gobies that could fit onto your little fingernail, to massive whale sharks as big as a truck. Fish are almost every shape and color imaginable, from sharp-nosed, super-streamlined swordfish and marlin, to enormously bulky groupers, snakelike eels, and flatfish that are just that.

Fish obtain food in varied and imaginative ways. Some nibble at seaweed. Others filter tiny bits of food from the water. Sharks are the ultimate razor-toothed predators. Anglerfish use a "rod and line" made from their own bodies to catch their meals—of other fish!

WHAT ARE FISH?

FISH ARE VERTEBRATES (ANIMALS WITH BACKBONES) THAT ARE COLD-BLOODED, LIVE IN WATER, BREATHE BY GILLS, SWIM WITH FINS AND A TAIL, AND HAVE A BODY COVERING OF SCALES. At least, this is true of most fish (page 101). Fish make up by far the largest group of vertebrate animals. There are some 24,000 species, which is more than all other vertebrate animals—amphibians, reptiles, birds, and mammals—combined. The first fish to evolve on Earth, some 470 million years ago, were jawless fish. They had sucker-like mouths, rather than biting jaws with teeth. Two small groups, the lampreys and hagfish, survive today. A larger subgroup of fish is the sharks, rays, and chimaeras. These are known as cartilaginous fish because they have a "backbone," or vertebral column, made of tough, gristly cartilage rather than true bone. Easily the largest fish subgroup is the bony fish, with skeletons of true bone—as people know if they get the bones stuck when the eat fish. Fish are extremely important as food in many parts of the world.

World Watch

Human activities are putting ever more fish species at risk. Some, such as cod, are victims of overfishing—we simply catch too many. Others suffer because we pollute their waters, divert or build dams across their rivers, or take too much water for our own use. We also take fish species to new areas, on purpose or by accident. The large, predatory Nile perch (page 122) was introduced into Africa's Lake Victoria in the early 1960s. It has now eaten many of the lake's own cichlid fish and completely upset the natural balance of life there.

△ The monkfish, which is an unusual type of shark, has the flattened body shape typical of bottom-living fish.

◀ The red-spotted hawkfish is an alert and agile fish of shallow tropical waters around coral reefs.

All animals need oxygen to live. We breathe oxygen gas from the air into our ʟungs. A fish takes in oxygen dissolved in the ᴡater through gills on either side of its head. ᴍost fish have four sets of gills, which are red ᴀnd feathery. They are made of rows of lamellae, ᴀat, delicate structures, filled with blood. Water ᴏows into the fish's mouth and over the gills, ᴡhere oxygen passes through the gill coverings ᴉnto the blood, to be carried around the body. In ᴂarks and other cartilaginous fish, the water ᴍen flows to the outside of the body through gill ᴉits. In bony fish, the gills are covered by a bony ᴀap, the operculum or gill cover, with a single slit ᴀlong its rear edge.

INSIDE A FISH

A typical fish like the salmon has a body that is mainly blocks of muscle, arranged in a zigzag pattern along either side of the backbone. These pull the backbone from side to side to swish the tail and make the fish swim.

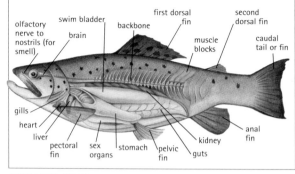

olfactory nerve to nostrils (for smell) — swim bladder — brain — backbone — first dorsal fin — second dorsal fin — muscle blocks — caudal tail or fin — gills — heart — liver — pectoral fin — sex organs — stomach — pelvic fin — guts — kidney — anal fin

JAWLESS FISH

Jawless fish have a skeleton made of cartilage, not bone. They also have no side fins, no scales on the long, thin body, round gill openings, and a sucking, disk- or funnel-shaped mouth. These creatures are survivors from a very early stage in the evolution of fish. They are mostly scavengers or parasites, sucking the blood of other water creatures.

FISH FINS

Fish have two kinds of fins. These are paired fins, usually somewhere along the sides of the body, and unpaired fins, which are generally the dorsal fins on the top or back, and the anal fins on the underside or belly. The unpaired fins help the fish to swim straight or lean to one side. The tail or caudal fin is also unpaired and provides the main thrust for swimming. The paired fins are the pectoral fins just behind the head and the pelvic fins, usually lower and to the rear. They help the fish turn sideways, slow down, and even swim backward.

This scene shows members ᴏm all the main fish ᴀbgroups. In the center is a ᴧrge cartilaginous fish—a ᴏbbegong or carpet ᴀark. It lurks on the sea ᴀd, disguised as a rock. ᴉn the lower right is a ᴂimaera, another type of ᴀrtilaginous fish. The eel-like ᴄeature just above the "wobby" ᴀ lamprey, a jawless fish with a ᴄker mouth. On the far left three ᴀgfish, also jawless, suck rotting ᴇsh from a carcass. The large ᴀvery fish, upper left, is a tarpon, ᴀ type of bony fish.

▲ The common spotted dogfish is one of the smallest sharks.

Fish (Pisces)		• live in the sea and fresh water
• 24,000 species • most have gills, fins, a tail, and a body covered with scales		Sharks and rays (Chondrichthyes) • about 900 species • skeleton of cartilage • no gill flap over gill slits • most live in the sea • includes sharks, dogfish, sawfish, rays, skates
Hagfish (Myxini) • about 50 species • eel-like body • suckerlike mouth (no jaws) • live in the sea		
Lampreys (Cephalaspidomorphi) • about 38 species • eel-like body • suckerlike mouth (no jaws)		Bony fish (Osteichthyes) • over 23,000 species • skeleton of bone • gill slits covered by gill flap • live in the sea and fresh water • includes vast majority of fish

SHARKS AND RAYS

SHARKS AND RAYS, AND THE CREATURES CALLED RATFISH OR CHIMAERAS, MAKE UP THE GROUP CALLED CARTILAGINOUS FISH. Their skeletons are not made of bone, as in other fish, but of cartilage—a gristly substance that is tough, yet light and bendy. The typical shark has a long, streamlined body. It is propelled by a tail with an upper lobe that is usually larger than the lower lobe. The shark's mouth is set back from the snout tip and is full of sharp teeth. The skin is not covered with the usual fish scales, but with tiny pointed structures called dermal denticles. These are much smaller versions of the teeth in the mouth. If you stroke shark skin the wrong way, from tail to head, the dermal denticles make the skin feel so rough that it could cause your hand to bleed.

A "mermaid's purse" washed up on a shore is the empty case in which a baby shark or ray developed. It attaches to rocks or weeds by the long, stringy tendrils

A typical ratfish has a large head, big eyes, fleshy lips, sharp teeth, a long, tapering body, and a "rat's tail" instead of the usual tail fins.

The largest predatory or hunting shark is the great white or white pointer, feared in all warmer oceans of the world. It can grow more than 20 feet (6 m) long.

Most sharks are fast-moving, torpedo-shaped hunters of the open ocean. But others, such as the carpet sharks or wobbegongs, have a flattened body shape. They also have fringes and tassels of skin to camouflage their bodies as seaweed-covered rocks. They spend much of their lives lying on the seabed, waiting to ambush and gulp down any prey that comes near.

This spotted eagle ray has large eyes and, just behind each one, a flap-covered opening or spiracle. This lets in water which flows over the gills, so that the ray can breathe (take in oxygen from the water). The water then leaves through gill slits on the ray's underside.

World Watch

Every year around the world, 30–50 people are reported as killed by sharks. Also every year, about 100 million sharks are killed by people. They are caught for many reasons—for food, for sport by anglers, because their body parts are thought to have healing powers, and because they might menace tourist areas. Several kinds, including the great white, are now very rare. Some are protected by world wildlife laws.

FLYING THROUGH THE WATER

Most rays also have a body flattened from top to bottom. Their wide, flaplike pectoral fins look and work like a bird's wings. The ray flaps or undulates them to "fly" through the water. The majority of rays have wide, flattened, crunching teeth and feed on shellfish and worms that they uncover on the seabed.

▲ The Caribbean reef shark, or black-tip cruises along the edges of coral reefs in its search for sick or injured fish, seals, seabirds, and other likely victims.

POISON FOR DEFENSE

Chimaeras, the fish group also known as ratfish, usually live on or near the seabed. They can live at great depths, more than 6,600 feet (2,000 m). Most chimaeras have long, scaleless bodies. The ratfish (short-nose and long-nose chimeras) have stringy, ratlike tails. Plownose chimaeras have a tail similar to that of a shark. All chimaeras have a long spine at the front of the dorsal (back) fin. This is linked to a venom gland. The poison in the spine can cause a painful wound to an attacker. Most chimaeras eat small sea-bottom creatures such as crabs, clams, and shrimps, as well as other fish.

BIGGEST... !
The largest fish in the world is the whale shark, at more than 40 feet (13 m) long. It is not a fierce hunter. It feeds by filtering the tiny plants and animals of the plankton from sea water.

MAKING BABY SHARKS

Different sharks and rays have different ways of producing young. Some, such as the horned or Port Jackson sharks and the dogfish, lay eggs protected by tough, leathery cases. The mother hides these in seaweed or rocks. The youngster develops inside for several weeks, nourished by its large yolk sac, until it is ready to hatch and fend for itself. Others, such as the tiger sharks, produce eggs with thin shells that are kept inside the mother's body. The young feed from their yolk sacs, hatch from the thin shells and are then born. More extraordinary still are the hammerheads, blues, white-tips, and bull sharks. The young grow inside the mother, but not inside egg shells. When their yolk is used up, they are nourished directly from the mother's blood. Finally they are born as well-formed young.

Sharks
(*Elasmobranchii*)
• about 375 species
• all but a couple live in the sea
• includes hammerhead, dogfish, carpet shark, mako, great white

Rays
(*Rajiformes*)
• about 450 species
• most live in the sea
• includes electric ray, stingray, skate, manta

Chimaeras
(*Chimaeriformes*)
• about 30 species
• live in the sea
• includes ratfish, chimaera

Most rays, like this southern ray, stay near the seabed. Like sharks, they have dozens of tiny electricity-sensing pits on the head. These detect weak pulses of electricity from the muscles of buried prey animals, which the ray then digs out. To hide from predators, the ray buries itself in the sand.

STURGEONS AND GARS

THE GROUPS OF FISH THAT INCLUDE STURGEONS, PADDLEFISH, AND GARS WERE VERY COMMON AND WIDESPREAD MANY MILLIONS OF YEARS AGO WHEN DINOSAURS WALKED THE LAND.

◩ There are about 100 species of elephant-nose fish. They live mainly in rivers and swamps in Africa. The fish uses its long, flexible snout to probe in the mud and gravel for small animals to eat.

Today there are far fewer species. A typical sturgeon has a long, heavy body with five rows of bony plates. Its mouth has fleshy "whiskers," which are known as barbels. These feel and taste for prey on the bottom of a lake, river, or sea. Some types of sturgeon live in rivers and lakes in North America, Europe, and Asia. Others grow up in fresh water, then swim out to sea for several years, returning to their rivers to breed. Paddlefish live only in the Mississippi River in North America and the Chang Jiang (Yangtze River) in China. They grow to 6 feet (1.8 m) long and have a flat, spoon-shaped snout. The paddlefish swims along with its mouth wide open, filtering tiny animals from the plankton. The gars or gar pikes of North America are also long, slim fish, with a covering of especially thick, hard scales to protect against attackers. The very long, slender jaws are studded with small teeth. Gars lurk in water weeds, waiting to grab prey.

Most kinds of sturgeon spend part of their lives in the sea, where they feed on bottom-living creatures such as worms, shrimps, and flatfish. When they are fully grown, they swim into rivers to breed.

ENDANGERED! !

Sturgeons are well known for their shiny black eggs, which are called caviar. These are gathered as an expensive food for people to eat. The female sturgeon may be killed in order to take her eggs. Or the eggs can be "milked" from her while she is alive, and then she is put back in the water. Taking eggs for caviar has made most kinds of sturgeon very rare.

◩ The alligator gar, at 10 feet (3 m) long, is one of the biggest freshwater fish in North America. Like other gars, it is a fierce hunter. It eats smaller fish and shellfish such as crayfish.

the female lays her sticky black eggs among gravel on the riverbed. A large female normally produces more than two million eggs. A female of the largest type of sturgeon, the beluga or white sturgeon, produces up to seven million eggs. After about one week the tiny young hatch out. They stay in the river for up to three years, feeding on small creatures such as water insects, shrimps, and worms, which they detect in the mud with their whiskery barbels. Then they swim out to sea, to continue growing.

The plates along a young sturgeon's body are not scales but bony slabs called scutes. These will enlarge and thicken with age.

This sturgeon has the thick bony slabs or scutes of an older fish.

BONYTONGUES
The bonytongue fish group includes the goldeye, mooneye, pirarucu, aruana, butterflyfish, and knifefish. They all live in fresh water. The name of the group comes from the structure of the tongue, which has large, stiff bones and teeth.

GIANT OF FRESH WATER
The pirarucu or arapaima is a huge bonytongue fish that lives in the Amazon region of South America. It grows to more than 10 feet (3 m) long and weighs 440 pounds (200 kg).

Sturgeons (Acipenseriformes)
• about 25 species
• most live in fresh water and may travel into the sea
• includes sturgeon, beluga, paddlefish

Bonytongues (Osteoglossiformes)
• about 215 species
• live in fresh water
• includes pirarucu, elephant fish

Gars (Lepisosteiformes)
• about 7 species
• live in fresh water
• includes longnose gar, alligator gar

Elephant-nose fish (Mormyriformes)
• about 100 species
• live in fresh water in Africa
• can make and detect electrical pulses
• some types are caught or farmed for food

❏ The beluga of Central Asian lakes and rivers is one of the world's largest fish. The biggest specimens once grew to 26 feet (8 m) long and weighed well over 1.5 tons. However, few belugas today live long enough to reach 15 feet (4.5 m). This is due to overfishing and water pollution, and also dams across rivers that interfere with their migration to the sea.

❏ Gars have very thick, diamond-shaped scales. They seize prey such as small fish in their long, slim jaws. The common gar pike grows to about 3 feet (90 cm) in length.

This makes it one of the biggest freshwater fish in the world. (Some sturgeons grow larger, but they live partly in the sea.) The pirarucu inhabits stagnant, swampy places where the water has little dissolved oxygen. However, it can gulp air into its swim bladder, which works as a simple lung to absorb the oxygen from the air.

Unlike most fish, the female pirarucu takes good care of her young. She lays her eggs in a sheltered part of the river, hidden among plants. She guards the eggs against hungry predators, and she also protects the babies or fry when they hatch.

ELECTRIC FISH
Elephant-nose fish are mostly less than 3 feet (90 cm) long. They use the long, flexible snout to dig in the mud for food. These fish are electric! Special muscles at the rear of the body produce weak pulses of electricity, which pass through the water around the fish. The pulses are detected by tiny sensors over the head. The electricity is too weak to stun prey. But another animal nearby disturbs the pattern of pulses and so the elephant-nose fish can detect it. This helps the elephant-nose to avoid enemies and also to find its prey—even in very muddy, murky water and at night.

OLDEST!..
Fossils show that coelacanths lived more than 300 million years ago. They were thought to have died out with the dinosaurs, 65 million years ago. Then they were discovered still living in the Indian Ocean near Africa in the 1930s. The fins have fleshy lobes at the base. The legs of the early land animals may have evolved from fins like these.

EELS AND HERRINGS

MOST EELS ARE LONG, SLIM, SNAKELIKE FISH WITH TINY SCALES OR NONE AT ALL, AND NO PELVIC (REAR SIDE) FINS. Most herrings are small, silvery ocean fish and swim in huge groups or schools. Both these kinds of fish are extremely numerous and are caught by people for food. The largest type of herring is the huge wolf herring, a fierce hunter that can grow more than 10 feet (3 m) long. But most herrings, including sardines or pilchards, sprats, and anchovies, are less than 3 feet (90 cm) long. They feed on tiny animals in the plankton. Herrings are, in turn, important food for many large creatures, including dolphins, and seabirds. Some types of herring live in fresh water in North and South America parts of Africa, and Australia. Most eels live in the sea, but some kinds spend much of their lives in rivers and lakes, and then travel to the sea to lay their eggs. The eggs hatch into thin, see-through young, or larvae. These drift in ocean currents for years before developing into young eels and swimming into rivers.

◙ The Atlantic herring is a slender fish with large, silvery, easily damaged scales.

◙ A spotted moray peers from its lair, read snap at prey or bite enem There are about different species of mo

◙ The conger, like all eels, has long dorsal and anal fins on the top and underside of the body.

LURKING DANGER
Moray eels live in tropical and subtropical waters, often around coral reefs. Most have scaleless bodies, boldly patterned with bright colors, and strong, sharp teeth. Morays are powerful hunters and tend to hide in crevices in rocks, watching for prey such as fish and squid. The largest morays measure more than 12 feet (3.5 m) long.

◙ The wolf herring has a long body and large, sharp teeth. It lives in the warm, shallow waters of the Indian and West Pacific Oceans.

THE EEL'S JOURNEY

Freshwater eels live in rivers and lakes, but travel to the sea to spawn (lay their eggs and breed). American and European eels migrate to the weed-rich Sargasso Sea, in the western North Atlantic. Here, ocean currents swirl warm water down to great depths. The adult eels dive down many hundreds of feet, breed, and then die. The eggs hatch into leaf-shaped larvae as long as a thumbnail. European eel larvae drift across the Atlantic in the current known as the Gulf Stream for three or four years, altering their shape as they go. Near European coasts they change, or metamorphose, into young eels, called elvers. These swim into rivers, where they live for several years until they are 20–40 inches (50–100 cm) long and ready to breed. American eel larvae drift west and their journey takes only a year or two.

NORTH AMERICA

ATLANTIC OCEAN

EUROPE

SARGASSO SEA

■ one year after hatching

■ two years after hatching

■ three years after hatching

■ four years after hatching

eel eggs laid in deep water in Sargasso Sea

larva about one year old

newly hatched larva (leptocephalus)

larva about two or three years old ("glass eel")

elver ready to swim into fresh water

adult eel in fresh water

DEEP-SEA EELS

Gulper eels live in the darkness of the deep ocean, where prey is hard to find. They swim with their enormous mouths wide open, ready to engulf any creature that will fit through the jaws. These eels have tiny eyes or none at all, since they live in permanent blackness more than 3,000 feet (900 m) below the surface. They grow to about 2 feet (60 cm) long.

A GARDEN OF EELS

Garden eels live in colonies on the seabed, usually in a shallow, sunlit area where water currents bring plenty of plankton. Each eel digs a burrow with its tail and spends much of its time with its rear half anchored inside. Its top half extends upward so it can feed on the plankton. Lots of these eels close together sway in the current like tall flowers in a garden. If danger comes near, such as a predatory fish, the eels quickly whisk themselves into their burrows and the entire "garden" disappears.

BREEDING HERRINGS

Most types of herring, including the Atlantic herring, lay their eggs close to the seabed. The eggs stay there until they hatch into tiny larvae 0.25 inch (5 mm) long. These drift in the plankton until they are able to swim in schools. The herring grows to about 16 inches (40 cm) long, while the sardine is 10 inches (25 cm). The various kinds of anchovies are about 8 inches (20 cm) long.

◘ The gulper eel can swallow prey larger than itself, into its stretchy stomach.

◄ Thousands of sardines shoal in the shallow waters near the Galapagos Islands in the Pacific Ocean.

Eels
(Anguilliformes)
• about 690 species
• mostly live in the sea, a few are freshwater
• includes moray, conger, garden, snipe and gulper eels

Herrings
(Clupeiformes)
• about 360 species
• live in the sea, filtering plankton
• includes sardine or pilchard, anchovy, shad, menhaden

SALMON, PIKE, AND HATCHETFISH

SALMON AND THEIR COUSINS—TROUT, CHARR, WHITEFISH, SMELT, AND GRAYLING—LIVE MAINLY IN RIVERS AND LAKES IN NORTHERN CONTINENTS.

They are mostly sleek fish with slender, tapering bodies and forked tails. Their small, sharp teeth show that they hunt animals for food. The various types of salmon make regular journeys or migrations between salt and fresh water. The young are born in rivers but after a few years' feeding and growing, they swim into the sea, where they spend the next few years. Then they return to the rivers where they grew up, to spawn. Pike and pickerels spend all their lives in fresh water. Hatchetfish and viperfish live in deep oceans. Many have special light-producing parts on their bodies. The eerie glow from these lights helps to lure prey, attract a mate, and confuse an enemy.

⬧ A viperfish dangles glowing bait in front of its mouth. Its "fishing rod" is made from the greatly lengthened first or second ray (spine) of its dorsal (back) fin.

⬧ A close-up of the viperfish's mouth shows its long, needle-shaped teeth, at the front of the lower jaw. Viperfish grow to about 12 inches (30 cm) in length.

⬧ The rainbow trout has pink-tinged sides and spots on its tail. It has escaped from fish farms into rivers around the world.

POP-EYED! ⚠

The baby black dragonfish looks pop-eyed. Its eyes are on long stalks, almost like a garden snail. As the dragonfish grows, the stalks shrink back into the head. The eyes finally settle and slot into the normal sockets in the skull.

How Atlantic and Pacific salmon return from the middle of the ocean to the exact stream where they hatched from eggs is one of the marvels of the animal world. It is known that they can detect the "smell" of their home river, from dissolved minerals and other substances, but how they navigate from far out at sea is not fully understood. The journey upstream is dangerous and tiring. Pacific salmon, in particular, must leap many waterfalls on the way. The males change in color and the lower jaw grows a hooked tip as they reach home.

⬧ Deep-sea hatchetfish are named from their silvery, narrow deep-chested body shape, which resembles an ax or hatchet.

Salmon gather below a waterfall, ready to surge upward and leap the obstacle.

the spawning stream, male and female court riefly. Then she sheds her eggs (spawn) on the ravel bed and he fertilizes them with his sperm nilt). By this time many of the salmon are so xhausted that they are easy prey for eagles, ears, or wolves. Most Pacific salmon die after pawning. Atlantic salmon may survive, return to e sea, and make the journey again two or three mes. Large salmon grow to 4 feet (1.2 m) in ngth and weigh 60 pounds (27 kg).

IE VARIABLE TROUT
here are two forms of the common trout. These re the silvery sea trout, which migrates between ver and sea, and the smaller, darker-spotted rown trout, which stays in fresh water.

Copper sweepers are reddy-gold members of the hatchetfish oup, the bristlemouths. This shoal is sheltering from danger low a deep rock overhang.

Salmon leap up rapids and waterfalls with powerful thrusts of the tail. They can swim 60 miles (100 km) upstream each day.

Most trout eat baby fish, worms and other small prey. Some types are farmed as food for people.

HIDDEN DANGER
The largest member of the pike group is the muskellunge or muskie of North America, up to 5 feet (1.5 m) long and 65 pounds (30 kg) in weight. The northern pike looks similar, but shorter. It lives in rivers and lakes in northern regions around the world. This huge-mouthed predator lies hidden among water plants, watching for prey. When it spots a victim, the pike lunges like lightning from the weed and seizes the prey with its sharp teeth.

SWIMMING HATCHETS
Common hatchetfish are numerous in warm seas, at depths of about 600–2,500 feet (180–750 m). They are only 3 inches (8 cm) long and are preyed on by many larger sea hunters. The common hatchetfish has a deep, flattened body, a large mouth, bulging eyes, and rows of light-producing organs along the belly. The pattern of lights along the body helps each type of hatchetfish to recognize its own species at mating time in the darkness.

Fierce-looking deep-sea viperfish have long, backward-pointing teeth. They grab prey, which are lured by the long fin spine tipped with a light-producing organ.

The female salmon hides her eggs in the gravel on the riverbed. The eggs contain reddish-yellow yolk, which nourishes the baby fish.

almon *(Salmoniformes)*
about 140 species
freshwater and sea-dwelling
includes salmon, trout, smelt,
charr, grayling

ike *(Esociformes)*
about 12 species
freshwater

• includes pike, pickerel,
muskellunge *(muskie)*

Bristlemouths *(Stomiiformes)*
• about 250 species
• live only in the sea
• includes hatchetfish, dragonfish,
viperfish, snaggletooth, loosejaw

CHARACINS, CARP, AND CATFISH

THESE THREE GROUPS INCLUDE NEARLY A THIRD OF ALL FISH—MORE THAN 6,000 SPECIES. They vary widely in appearance, but most live in fresh water. The majority can detect sounds in water, by picking up sound waves in the swim bladder, which other fish cann[ot] do so well. In addition, these fish have special alarm substances in the skin that are released into the water if the skin is damaged. When a fish is seized by a predator the substance passes into the water, alerting other members of the species to escape.

◩ Various kinds of characin tigerfish are named after their tigerlike stripes and the way they stalk and eat other fish.

◩ The many colors and sha[pes] of goldfish have been b[red] over centuries from wild c[arp]

Members of the carp group live across North America, Europe, northern Asia, and Africa. They lack teeth in their jaws. Instead, they have a pair of toothed bones in the lower throat that they use to crush and grind food against a hardened pad at the base of the skull. Most carp eat a wide range of foods, including plants, fish, and shellfish.

◪ The European catfish, or wels, is one of several kinds of catfish that grow to a massive size, more than 6 feet (1.8 m) long.

Some types of carp, including the roach, bream common, and crucian carp, have been introduc[ed] to lakes and slow rivers around the world. The[y] are caught by anglers and are popular as food. These types of carp are bottom feeders. They gr[ub] in the mud, using their sensitive whiskerlike barbels to find worms, snails, and shrimps.

AN UNUSUAL NURSERY

Most members of the carp group simp[ly] scatter their eggs in water and leave the young to hatch and fend for themselves. But the small carp, known as the bitterling, has [a] more unusual method. At [the] start of the breeding season the female develops a long egg-laying tube, the ovipositor.

She uses this to place her eggs inside the shell of a freshwater mussel. The male bitterling releases his sperm near the mussel. As the mussel filter-feeds, the sperm are sucked in to fertilize the eggs.

Blue
iranha

The neon tetra's colors are bright, they seem to glow electric neon lights.

Glassfish, types of small carp, n large schools. Like most , they feed at night.

One piranha cannot do much harm. But a large school of them can strip the flesh from a large animal like a horse in minutes. Piranhas are attracted by blood in the water. So a wounded animal that comes to drink at the river is in real danger.

❑ Bream

CHARACINS
The characins live in rivers and lakes in Central and South America and Africa. They include the piranhas of South America, and the tetras that have been bred in many colors as popular aquarium fish. Some characins eat plants, others eat small creatures such as insects and worms, and still others are hunters of larger animals such as fish and frogs. One group, the toothless characins, survive by sucking up the slime that covers leaves, stones, and other underwater objects.

CAT'S WHISKERS
Catfish are named for the very long, whiskerlike barbels around the mouth. The fleshy barbels taste the water to find food. Most catfish also have stiff spines at the front of the dorsal and pectoral fins. These can be "locked" in position, sticking outward, so the fish is hard to swallow.

SHOCKING FISH
Knifefish are close relatives of catfish. They have special muscles that can produce pulses of electricity in the surrounding water. These pulses help them to find their way in muddy, dark lakes and rivers. The knifefish that produces the most powerful electrical pulses is the electric eel of northern South America. The electricity is so strong, it can stun prey fish.
Another amazing catfish is the walking catfish. It can crawl on land, using its strong pectoral fins, and breathe air while it does so.

❑ The electric eel is shaped like an eel, but it is really a type of knifefish. It grows to 7 feet (2.1 m) long and can give a 550-volt electric shock.

Carp (Cypriniformes)
• about 2,050 species
• almost all live in fresh water
• includes goldfish, loach, minnow, tench, barbel, mahseer

Characins (Charciformes)
• about 1,400 species
• live in fresh water
• includes pike characin, tetra, piranha, pacu, giant tigerfish

Catfish and knifefish (Siluriformes)
• about 2,415 species
• most live in fresh water
• includes wels, walking catfish, knifefish, butterfish, electric eel

T ALL SO FIERCE
e piranhas of South America have a fearsome utation as bloodthirsty hunters. But some types piranha, such as the pacu, feed on plants. The h-eating types include the red piranha. They only about 12 inches (30 cm) long, but y have strong jaws and razor-sharp teeth slicing chunks of flesh out of their victims.

❑ A female bitterling lays her eggs into a mussel, and the male waits to fertilize them. The baby fish emerge about 2–3 weeks later.

he mirror carp has shiny, ra-large scales.

COD, ANGLERFISH, AND TOADFISH

THE VARIOUS TYPES OF COD INCLUDE HAKE, HADDOCK, AND WHITING. They are mostly long, fast-swimming fish with large fins, and live in cool seas around the world, some at great depths. They are extremely valuable as food and in the past millions of tons were caught every year. But overfishing has greatly reduced their numbe in some areas. Anglerfish, batfish, and frogfish live in warmer seas and are much more squat in shape, with a short body, large head, and gaping mouth.

◩ Atlantic cod can be recogni by their three dorsal f

They are not built for speed and prefer to lie wait for prey. The front spine of the anglerfis dorsal (back) fin is separate from the rest of th fin. It forms a long "fishing rod" with its fleshy tip a bait to attract other fish. Once a victim is near enough, the angler opens its huge mouth and the rush water sucks in the prey. Toadfish live in warm coastal waters. They have excellent camouflage with lots of flesh fringes, flaps, and whiskery barbels around the big head and wide mouth, so they look like seaweed.

◩ The football-fish is a type of anglerfish. It is about 2 feet (60 cm) long and has studlike bony plates on its body. Like all anglerfish, it lures its prey.

The Atlantic cod grows to about 4 feet (1.2 m) long and is the best-known fish of the cod group. This group includes many other fish eaten as food, such as ling, pollock, rockling, and pout. Like many of these, the haddock has a fleshy, sensitive barbel on its chin to help it find food such as worms and shellfish on the seabed.

◪ The rosy-lipped batfish crawls well on its strong, leglike fins. It spends more time walking than swimming.

Haddock usually spawn in spring, shedding larg numbers of eggs into the water, where they floa near the surface. When the young fish hatch, th stay in the surface waters until they are about 2 inches (5 cm) long. Then they move closer the ocean floor.

RAT-TAILS

The cod group also includes the grenadier or rat-tails, which live 600–6,000 feet (150–1,800 m) below the surface. With large head, short body, and long, ratlike tail, the grenadier resembles the ratfish (page 104). The male makes loud sound using muscles linked to his swimbladder probably to attract a mate.

Toadfish look like toads, and make toadlik croaks. The male makes a nest hole in weed an mud, and croaks by vibrating his swimbladder encourage a female to lay eggs in the nest.

◀ A toadfish's face, with its broad mouth and big eyes, looks like the face of a toad.

▶ A flagtail rock cod shows off its small, sharp teeth and its gills in the cheek region.

❱ This deep-sea anglerfish has a glowing lure above its head. Its long, frilly chin barbel resembles a frond of seaweed.

e female glues each egg
o the nest by a sticky disc on its
derside. The male guards the nest
il the baby fish hatch. They remain glued
the nest for a few days. Even when they
ak free, he continues to guard them.

GLERS AND FROGFISH

glerfish are so-named because they do what
man anglers do—use a "rod and bait" to catch
er fish. There are coastal and deep-sea kinds.
e lure or bait of the female deep-sea anglerfish
ws in the darkness, to attract curious fish. The
le deep-sea angler is one tenth the size of the
male. He has no lure, and no teeth either, so he
not feed. But he does have an
cellent sense of smell,
find the female.

Once he locates a mate, he attaches himself to her and fertilizes her eggs. He may then merge partly into her body and live as a parasite on her. This saves both partners a long search, since mates are difficult to find in the vast, deep ocean!

The frogfish lies on the seabed, watching for prey. Its lumpy, frilly body gives amazing camouflage among seaweeds, corals, and sponges. It can even change color to match the surroundings. Frogfish grow up to 8 inches (20 cm) long and eat small fish, shellfish, and worms.

❱ Among the sponges and corals of the Caribbean lurks a dark gray, long-lure frogfish (its mouth is to the left of the picture). Behind it, a smaller, pale frogfish looks at the camera.

Cod
(Gadiformes)
• about 500 species
• nearly all live in the sea
• includes cod, grenadier, hake, ling

Anglerfish
(Lophiiformes)
• about 300 species
• all live in the sea, often at great depths
• includes frogfish, batfish, football-fish, sargassumfish

Toadfish
(Batrachoidiformes)
• about 70 species
• most live on the sea bed
• includes midshipman

SCORPIONFISH AND SEAHORSES

SCORPIONFISH RANGE IN SHAPE FROM LONG AND SLENDER TO ALMOST AS ROUND AS BALLOONS. Most have spines, especially on the head and fins. Some, including the lionfish and stonefish, are extremely dangerous because the venom from their spines can kill people. Scorpionfish are all predators, catching

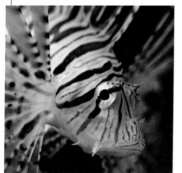

other fish and shellfish. The pipefish and seahorse group is also extremely varied in shape, but most of the members have long, tube-shaped snouts. They live in warm, shallow waters near the coast. This group includes seadragons, shrimpfish, sea moths, and trumpetfish. There is also a fish called the tubesnout, with a tubular snout, but it is in yet another fish group—the sticklebacks. They are found in rivers and lakes in northern continents and the Atlantic and Pacific Oceans. Sticklebacks get their name from the strong, pricklelike spines on their backs.

The lionfish has lacy, fan-shaped fins. These look delicate, but their spines jab deadly poison.

The scorpionfish's lumpy, mottled body is difficult to see as it lies among stones on the seabed, watching for prey. Sharp spines in its dorsal and pelvic fins are linked to venom glands and can cause serious wounds. Its close relative, the lionfish, is far easier to see, with its bright colors, fanlike fins, and lazy swimming. These features warn other creatures that the lionfish has deadly poison in its fin spines.

SUCKERED TO THE ROCKS
The lumpsucker, a relative of the scorpionfish, has a sucking disk on its throat formed from its pelvic fins. With this disk, the fish clings onto rocks in the shallows, to avoid being battered b waves. The small, dark eggs of lumpsuckers are sold as a type of caviar.

FATHER GIVES BIRTH
The seahorse does not lay eggs, but seems to give birth to its baby fish—and it is not the female that does this, but the male! The female seahorse lays her eggs into a special pouch on the male's fron He keeps the eggs safe here while they hatch and grow.

The stonefish lies in shallow wa among weed and rocks, or part-burie sand. People sometimes accidentally step it when wading along a beach. The sn spines on its back contain one of the m powerful venoms in the animal kingd

▶ Seahorses use their curly tails to hang onto coral branches or seaweed fronds. They swim slowly by rapidly flapping the dorsal fin on the back.

The flying gurnard of the Atlantic Ocean has ͏rmous pectoral fins, like wide wings. But this ͏ cannot fly, or even glide like the flyingfish.

͏e male seahorse even nourishes the tiny babies ͏ith a special substance from his own body. ͏hen the young are ready for the outside ͏orld, they shoot out through the opening of ͏e pouch. They quickly attach themselves to ͏ating weed or other objects and, like their ͏rents, feed on tiny animal plankton.

͏PEFISH

͏he pipefish has a pencil-sized body encased in ͏ny armor plates. Like its cousin, the seahorse, it has a ͏ng snout but no teeth, and feeds by sucking in tiny animals from the plankton. Also like the seahorse, the male pipefish keeps or incubates the female's eggs in a pouch on his own body. The largest pipefish grow to about 20 inches (50 cm) long.

◀ Pipefish curve themselves into the shape of seaweed, for better camouflage.

͏ARING PARENT

͏he male three-spined stickleback takes good care of his young. He builds a nest ͏om bits of water plants stuck together with sticky substances from his own body. ͏e then "dances" to attract a female, swimming to show off his brightly colored ͏roat and underside. These have turned bright red for the breeding season. The female comes to the nest and lays her eggs, then the male fertilizes them. He stays at the nest and chases off intruders. When the fry (baby fish) hatch, he guards them for a few weeks, until they can fend for themselves.

male in breeding colors

nest

female

Scorpionfish
(Scorpaeniformes)
• about 1,200 species
• most live in the sea, some in fresh water
• includes stonefish, sea robin, sculpin, lionfish, lumpsucker, tub gurnard, sablefish

Seahorses and pipefish
(Sygnathiformes)
• about 275 species
• live in the sea and fresh water
• thin, tubular snout for sucking in food

Sticklebacks
(Gasterosteiformes)
• about 10 species
• live in the sea and fresh water
• includes three-, four-, nine-, and 15-spined sticklebacks

FLYINGFISH, SILVERSIDES, AND KILLIFISH

THE FLYINGFISH GROUP INCLUDES NEEDLEFISH, LONGTOMS, AND HALFBEAKS. They are mostly very silvery, slim and streamlined, with spearlike pointed snouts, and dorsal and anal fins near the tail. Flyingfish themselves should really be called glidingfish. They swoop above the surface for a few seconds using their winglike pectoral fins. Silversides are small, shoal-dwelling fish of tropical and temperate seas and fresh water. Most have large eyes, extremely shiny and silvery scales, and two dorsal fins. Some, such as the rainbowfish, are popular in aquariums. Killifish are mostly small and hardy, and live in fresh water—even in the stagnant or brackish (slightly salty water of ditches, canals, salt marshes, and estuaries. Most types live near the surface, feeding on insects and bits of plants. One of the most common is the mosquitofish, named because it feeds on mosquit larvae. It has been introduced to most parts of the world. Without it there would be many more mosquitoes!

◩ Mosquitofish have been put into strea around the world, to control mosquito pes

◧ The Atlantic flyingfi is about 16 inch (40 cm) long, and "four-winged." Its lar pelvic fins lie behi and below the ma pectoral fi

flyingfish have
e, winglike pectoral
just behind the
d. Some "four-
ged" types also
e large pelvic fins,
elp them glide. If
ger threatens the
ngfish builds up
ed just under the
ter's surface,
ashing its tail

The four-eyed fish has only two eyes, but each is divided into two by a dark band. The lower part is curved to see clearly in water, while the curvature of the upper part is suited to air. Floating at the surface, this fish can look out for prey and enemies, both above and below the water.

verfully and holding its fins against its body. Then it leaps into the air and tches its fins out sideways to soar along. A long glide may last 20–30 onds and cover 600 feet (180 m) at 3-6 feet (90–180 cm) high. Flyingfish d on plankton and small animals. They, in turn, are eaten by many larger t-swimming fish, such as tuna and marlin.

LF A BEAK

e slender-bodied halfbeak is named for its half-a-beak—its long, sharp
ut is made of its lower jaw only. The upper jaw is much shorter. Many
fbeaks feed on the seaweed called sea grass, which they gather with the
ver jaw. Others feed on smaller fish or floating insects.

UNIONS

e grunion is a
verside about
nches (20 cm)
g that lives along
orth American
cific coasts. Its
eding times are
ked to the cycle of the
on and tides. At a full moon
d spring (extra-high) tide, huge numbers
grunions "surf" ashore on the incoming breakers.
hey mate on the beach, lay their eggs in the sand, and
turn to the sea on receding waves. Two weeks later, at
e new moon and next spring tide, the eggs hatch and
e young grunions are swept out to sea.

JPPIES GALORE

uppies come from tropical South America, but have
ow been introduced to most other parts of the
orld. Like mosquitofish, they eat the water-dwelling
larvae and pupae of
mosquitoes. The babies
develop inside the
female. So she gives birth
to tiny young,
rather than laying
eggs. The babies
are ready to breed
at 10 weeks old.

The silver needlefish is typical of the 25 or so kinds of needlefish and garfish. Some needlefish in the Amazon region grow to only 2 inches (5 cm) long.

Guppies belong to the killifish group. They are bred in many colors for aquariums.

The small, pointed teeth of longtoms grab small, wriggling prey.

Flyingfish (Beloniiformes)
• about 160 species
• live in the sea and fresh water
• includes two- and four-winged flyingfish, halfbeak, garfish, saury, houndfish, ricefish, needlefish

Silversides (Atheriniformes)
• about 250 species
• live in the sea and fresh water

• includes grunion, silversides, rainbowfish, swordtail

Killifish (Cyprinodontiformes)
• about 600 species
• live mainly in fresh water
• includes guppy, mosquito fish, four-eyed fish, mummichog or common killifish, toothcarps

FLATFISH AND TRIGGERFIS

FLATFISH LIVE IN ALL THE WORLD'S OCEANS, EXCE
IN POLAR REGIONS. There are a few species in fresh
water. The body of a flatfish is extremely flattened fror
one side to the other. (Rays look similar, but their bodi
are flattened from top to
bottom.) The flatfish spends
much of its life swimming or
lying on one side on the seabed.

△ Different types of pufferfish have vivid colors and patterns. They "puff" up by swallowing water, so becoming too big to be swallowed.

Both its eyes are on the other side, facing upward, so
it can watch for prey and predators. Some flatfish
have both eyes on the right side; others have them on
the left. Many flatfish are also masters of camouflage.
They change their coloration and pattern to match the
surroundings, making them very hard to see. All
flatfish are predators and feed on shellfish, worms, and
similar seabed animals. The triggerfish group includes
poisonous pufferfish, spiny porcupinefish that can
puff up their bodies like balloons, and the
giant ocean sunfish. In most of these
fish the mouth and a few teeth form a
structure like a bird's beak. Most live
along tropical coasts near the seabed.

△ The peacock flounder has both ey on the left body side. It also has a la spiny dorsal fin that begins just belo its mouth.

△ Ocean sunfish

When a baby flatfish first hatches from its egg, it has a normal fishlike
body shape, with an eye on each side of its head. Over the next few weeks,
one eye moves across the top of its head, so it is close to the other eye. At
the same time the body becomes thin or flat and the mouth twists so that it
lies on the same side as the two eyes. Turbots, some flounders, topknots, brill,
and the windowpane (an exceptionally flat flatfish) usually have both eyes on the
left side, and so lie on the right or blind underside. Halibut, plaice, dab, other
flounders and most soles are right-eyed. A resting flatfish
usually flicks a little sand or gravel over its body, to conceal
its fins and blur its outline
for even better
camouflage.

TASTY?! ⚠

Some pufferfish have
extremely poisonous flesh,
yet they are eaten as a
delicacy, fugu, by people in
some Asian countries. The
fish are prepared by
specially trained chefs, who
know which body parts
contain the poison.

△ The common flound grows to about 20 inch (50 cm) long. It lies on its le side, unlike the summer, star and peacock flounde

BIGGEST FLATFISH

The Atlantic halibut is one of the biggest of all the flatfish, at 8 feet (2.5 m) long and 650 pounds (295 kg) weight. However, due to overfishing, halibut of this size are now rare. They are more active than most flatfish, and chase prey rather than just lying in wait on the sea floor. Halibut feed on other fish, as well as on squid and crustaceans such as shrimps.

◀ The cowfish is a type of triggerfish named for the two spines above its eyes, which look like a cow's horns.

TRIGGERFISH

Most triggerfish are brightly colored and live around coral reefs. They are named for the special tilting spines of the first dorsal fin. The front, larger spine can be "locked" upright by the second spine just behind it, like cocking the trigger of a gun. When in danger, the triggerfish takes shelter in a crevice among the rocks and locks its strong spine in the upright position. It is then very difficult for a predator to attack and remove the triggerfish.

▶ Plaice, like most flatfish, have a pale or white underside. This is because it is rarely seen.

PUFFERS AND PORCUPINE SPINES

The slow-swimming porcupinefish grows to about 3 feet (90 cm) long and lives in warm coastal waters, where it feeds on prey such as sea urchins, starfish, and shellfish. For protection, it is covered with large, sharp spines. Normally these lie flat against the body. But if threatened, the porcupinefish gulps in water to make its body swell in size, until it is almost round. This forces the spines to stand out, making the fish like a huge prickly beach ball.

SUNBATHING FISH

The amazing ocean sunfish is shaped like a huge pancake. It has tall, thin dorsal and anal fins, and a fleshy frill for a tail. This massive fish grows to 13 feet (4 m) long and weighs up to 2 tons. Ocean sunfish are rare and live far out at sea, eating jellyfish, comb-jellies, and other soft-bodied creatures. The name comes from this fish's habit of lying on the sea's surface, as though it is sunbathing.

◀ The porcupinefish can puff itself up and has the added deterrent of sharp spines. Its hard, beaklike mouth crushes shellfish, urchins, and crabs.

Flatfish
(Pleuronectiformes)
• about 540 species
• nearly all live in the sea
• includes sole, plaice, turbot, brill, tonguefish, adalah

Triggerfish
(Tetraodontiformes)
• about 350 species
• mostly sea-dwelling, some freshwater species
• includes boxfish, pufferfish, burrfish, cowfish, filefish

121

PERCH, GROUPERS, AND DRUMS

THE HUGE GROUP OF PERCHLIKE FISH, THE PERCIFORMS, CONTAINS MORE THAN 9,000 SPECIES— ALMOST HALF OF ALL KINDS OF FISH. They range from tiny gobies smaller than the word "goby," to huge, strong, superfast, open-ocean predators such as marlin and barracudas, to ponderous, massive, vast-mouthed, heavy bodied groupers. Perchlike fish live in all aquatic (watery) habitats, from rushing mountain streams to tropical coral reefs, icy polar seas, and the ocean depths. Most have a front dorsal fin with spiny fin rays (the "rods" that hold up the soft fin parts). Some have a second dorsal fin too, but this has soft, bendy fin rays. There is also a spine at the front of each pelvic fin, and the pelvic fins are quite far forward on the body, below the pectoral fins.

◩ Archerfish are small, perchlike fish of tropical rivers, swamps, bays, and estuaries. The archer gulps in a mouthful of water and squirts it hard from just under the surface at a small insect or similar target on a plant above. The victim is knocked into the water and gobbled up.

◩ The Nile perch, 6 feet (1.8 m) long, lives in rivers across Africa.

Groupers and seabass make up one of the biggest sea-dwelling families of perchlike fish. Most have robust, powerful bodies and two or three spines on the gill flap. Some seabasses and groupers, such as the striped bass and Nassau grouper, are important food fish and are caught in large numbers. The giant seabass of the Pacific North American coast grows to 6 feet (1.8 m) long. The jewfish is the largest member of the family. It can grow to more than 7 feet (2.4 m) long and weigh as much as 650 pounds (295 kg). It usually lives in shallow water close to the shore, where it preys on fish, squid, crabs, and shellfish.

and seize anything that comes near in their huge mouths. Dusk is the favorite hunting time. Groupers have been known to follow human divers, but attacks are rare.

AGGRESSIVE GROUPERS
Groupers are fierce hunters and usually ambush their prey. They hide among rocks

▣ A coney grouper, 12 inches (30 cm) long, watches from near its lair, a cave in a coral reef.

NOISY FISH
Another large group of perchlike fish is the drum and croaker family. Most live in shallow tropical seas. As their names suggest, these fish make a variety of sounds using special muscles to vibrate the swim bladder. The black drum of the western Atlantic Ocean grows to 6 feet (1.8 m) long and 140 pounds (65 kg) in weight. The white seabass is also a type of drum, and about the same size.

◗ The Murray cod is a type of seabass, but it lives in lakes and rivers in eastern Australia. It may reach a length of 6 feet (1.8 m).

Jack-knife drum fish

FAST DARTERS
The largest freshwater group of perchlike fish is the perch family itself, with more than 160 species living in North America, Europe, and Asia. The perch, with its spiny dorsal fin and greenish dark-barred body, has been introduced to lakes and slow-flowing rivers in many parts of the world. Some members of this family are small, colorful fish called darters, which live along the beds of fast-moving streams in North America. Most are less than 4 inches (10 cm) long. The males are especially brightly colored during the breeding season, when they swim and dart to attract females.

The male finds a nesting area among gravel on the stream bed, where the female lays her eggs. He fertilizes the eggs and guards them until they hatch.

The walleye is one of the largest in the perch family, at 3 feet (90 cm) long. It lives deep in large rivers and lakes, eating fish, frogs, and insects. Newly hatched fry drift for a few days near the surface, nourished by their yolk sacs. Then they feed on plankton until they are big enough to catch fish.

SOME PERCHLIKE GROUPS:

Perches (Percidae)
• about 160 species
• live in fresh water
• includes darters, ruffe, zander

Groupers and seabass (Serranidae)
• about 400 species
• most live in the sea
• includes jewfish, coney

Drums and croakers (Sciaenidae)
• about 270 species
• most live in the sea
• includes Atlantic croaker, jack-knife fish, red drum, black drum, red mullet, spotted seatrout

The brown marbled grouper is one of several groupers that grows larger than an adult human. It can easily swallow prey up to 3 feet (90 cm) long, into its cavernous mouth.

TUNAS AND MARLINS

FEW FISH ARE SLEEKER
AND FASTER THAN THESE
SUPER-STREAMLINED
MEMBERS OF THE PERCHLIKE
GROUP (PAGE 122). Tunas and their
smaller cousins, bonitos and mackerels, are
known as scombrids and have torpedo-shaped
bodies. The crescent tail gives maximum power as it
thrashes from side to side, to thrust the fish through the
water. These types of fish live around the world, especially
in warm waters, and are caught in huge numbers as food
for people. The marlins and sailfish, called billfish, are also high-speed
swimmers. They cruise long distances across oceans in their hunt for prey.
Barracudas are another type of fierce fish predator. They usually prefer tropical
waters, especially around coral reefs. Smaller barracudas tend to hunt in school
(groups). Larger barracudas travel alone and may threaten human divers.

◣ The swordfish has t
crescent-shaped tail of a ve
fast swimmer. Unlike marli
and sailfish, it has a flatten
snout and lacks pelvic fi▮

◣ Small barracuda, each about 3 feet (90 cm) long, form a hunting group. They may
circle prey fish, to round them into a school that is easier to attack.

Most kinds of tuna,
such as the bluefin
and yellowfin, are
large, powerful fish.
They prey on
smaller fish and
squid, and in
turn are eaten by
large sharks and
toothed whales such as the killer whale. The
skipjack tuna is smaller, only 3 feet (90 cm)
long. It swims in vast shoals of tens of thousands
of fish, and is caught as a food by people.

MACKEREL

Large schools of mackerel are common in the
Atlantic Ocean. In spring, summer, and fall, they
usually stay near the surface and the shore, whe▮
they feed on small fish and crustaceans.

◣ The bluefin tuna
the biggest of the tu
family. It c
grow
to 3
long a
weigh m
than 635

The blue marlin has a long, pointed nose like a bird's beak or bill, hence the name "billfish."

winter, mackerel move into deeper water and ppear to eat little. They usually breed in late pring or early summer, when females shed as any as half a million eggs into the water. The inhead-sized eggs float until they hatch about ve days later, although most are eaten by small ankton-feeders. The tiny young mackerel grow st and reach a length of 14 inches (35 cm) at only two years old. When fully grown they may reach 26 inches (65 cm) long.

◄ The sailfish is named for its dorsal fin, which sticks up like the sail of a boat. It lives in cooler seas in summer, but migrates back to tropical areas for winter.

GER OF THE SEA

here are some 18 species of barracuda living in arm oceans around the world. The largest is the eat barracuda, a slender fish found worldwide, pecially well known in the Caribbean Sea. It ows to 6 feet (1.8 m) long and about 0 pounds (41 kg) in weight. It is an aggressive unter, known as the "tiger of the sea." It charges its prey and bites off mouthfuls of flesh with its arp teeth. Some barracudas are believed to operate in groups, herding their fish prey into shoal before racing in for the attack.

SWORDS AND SPEARS

The mighty swordfish may weigh more than 1,100 pounds (500 kg) and be more than 13 feet (4 m) in length. Almost one third of this is the "sword."

A young swordfish has jaws of equal length. The upper jaw lengthens into the sword as the animal grows. The spearfish is very similar to the swordfish, but slightly smaller. The sailfish is another large, fast predator. It grows to more than 12 feet (3.5 m) long and stays closer to coasts than the swordfish and spearfish. It has a huge sail-like fin on its back and long pelvic fins. The upper jaw comes to a point at the front, but is rounded like a long rod, rather than flattened as in the swordfish.

Tuna and mackerel *(Scombridae)*
• about 160 species
• all live in the sea
• includes bonito, wahoo

Swordfish *(Xiphiidae)*
• 1 species
• lives in the sea
• long, flattened snout

Sailfish and marlin *(Istiophoridae)*
• about 11 species known as billfish
• all live in the sea
• long, rounded snout
• includes sailfish, blue marlin, black marlin, striped marlin, spearfish

Barracuda *(Sphyraenidae)*
• about 20 species
• all live in the sea
• includes sennet

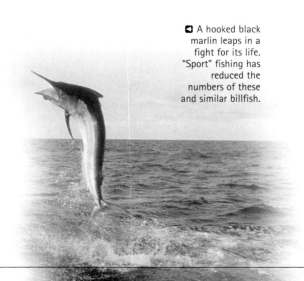

◄ A hooked black marlin leaps in a fight for its life. "Sport" fishing has reduced the numbers of these and similar billfish.

CICHLIDS, DAMSELS, AND PARROTFISH

THE CICHLIDS, DAMSELFISH, AND PARROTFISH ARE YET MORE TYPES OF PERCHLIKE FISH (PAGE 122). Cichlids are one of the largest groups of fish that live entirely in fresh water. Most dwell in tropical and subtropical lakes and rivers, mainly in Africa and also in South America. Most are less than 20 inches (50 cm) long, and they are generally silver in color. They all share the feature of a set of teeth in the throat, called pharyngeal teeth, as well as the normal teeth in the jaws. The throat teeth are used to slice and grind up the food grabbed by the jaw teeth. Their shape varies according to the type of food they eat. Shellfish eaters have large, flat throat teeth, and in fish eaters they are sharp for cutting through flesh. Damselfish are brightly colored and common around coral reefs. Some species eat little coral polyps, some rasp at seaweeds, and others feed on tiny plankton. Parrotfish also live on coral reefs and, like cichlids, have throat teeth as well as jaw teeth. The jaw teeth are fused or joined into a sharp parrotlike beak for scraping and chopping food.

The male garibaldi, a type of damselfish, collects red seaweeds to make his nest. Here, he guards his mate's eggs.

Sea-living angelfish like the emperor angelfish are mostly tall, thin and colorful. They are related to the butterflyfish group and popular as aquarium fish.

A clown fish peeps from its safe home among the stinging, paralyzing tentacles of a sea anemone.

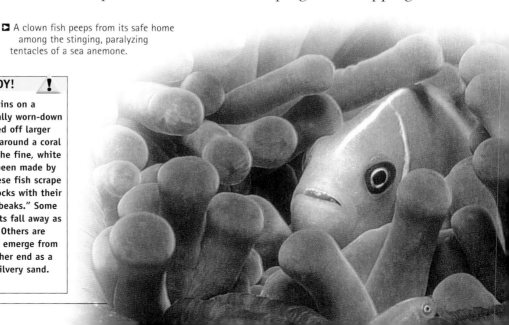

SANDY! !

Sand grains on a beach are usually worn-down chips cracked off larger boulders. But around a coral reef many of the fine, white grains have been made by parrotfish. These fish scrape food off the rocks with their very strong "beaks." Some stony fragments fall away as they feed. Others are swallowed, to emerge from the fish's other end as a shower of silvery sand.

Male cichlids are usually more brightly colored than females. They perform courtship displays, swimming to and fro and waving their fins to show off their patterns and attract a mate. The firemouth cichlid has a red patch on its chin that becomes even brighter and more glowing during the breeding season. Some male cichlids even build a special structure to attract a female and serve as a nest for the eggs. This may be a deep pit in the mud on the bottom of the river or lake, or a mound of sand up to 3 feet (90 cm) high.

⚠ At night, a parrotfish makes a baglike cocoon of mucus (slime) around its body, to protect it from predators while it sleeps. The mucus "sleeping bag" may make it harder for predators to detect its smell.

World Watch

The great lakes of Africa include Victoria, Malawi and Tanganyika. They contain more different species of fish than any other lakes in the world. And most of these fish are cichlids. For the great majority, each species is found in one lake—and nowhere else. Sadly, many of these cichlid species are in grave danger of extinction. This is due to overfishing, pollution, and especially the introduction of predatory fish such as the Nile perch (page 103).

All members of the cichlid group look after their eggs or babies in some way. Some simply guard the eggs in their nest on the river or lake bed, until the baby fish hatch. Others take the eggs into their mouths and carefully hold them until they hatch. Some cichlids even care for the baby fish in the same way. This is called mouthbrooding. It looks as if the adult has sucked them in and swallowed them! But after a few minutes, the babies emerge.

Various types of damselfish have become popular as aquarium fish. However, they can be aggressive to other fish in the tank. This is because, in their natural home, they have to battle for their patch of territory on the crowded coral reef.

SEX CHANGE

Parrotfish, like wrasses (page 128), are able to change sex. Most parrotfish start life as females. As they grow older they become males. Some species also change color when they change sex. For example, female stoplight parrotfish of Caribbean coral reefs are brownish-red. Males are blue and green. Old males of the blue parrotfish even change shape too. They develop a large bump on the upper snout that looks like the beginning of a nose-horn! The feeding activities of parrotfish keep the life of the reef turning over, since they clear areas of rock for new growths of sponges, corals, sea mats, barnacles, and similar animals, as well as seaweeds.

HELPFUL PARTNERS

Damselfish are mostly less than 8 inches (20 cm) long. Several types, known as clown fish, have partnerships with sea anemones. The clown fish lives among the anemone's stinging tentacles, where it is protected from attack by predators. It survives mainly because it has a special coating of slime that resists the anemone's stings or prevents them being fired (pages 34–35). In return, the clown fish cleans any dirt or scraps of food from the anemone. Its presence may even lure predators to the anemone, which can then sting and eat them. Such a relationship, in which both partners gain, is called symbiosis.

⚠ Mouthbrooders are named because they care for, or brood, their eggs and young in the mouth. There are many mouthbrooders in the cichlid group, such as this Nigerian mouthbrooder.

Cichlids *(Cichlidae)*
• at least 1,200 species (may be many more to discover)
• live in fresh water
• includes zebra cichlid, discus fish, freshwater angelfish

Damselfish *(Pomacentridae)*
• about 300 species
• live in warm seas
• includes clown fish *(anemone fish)*, sergeant major, garibaldi, beau-gregory

Parrotfish *(Scaridae)*
• about 70 species
• live in warm seas
• includes blue parrotfish, stoplight parrotfish, rainbow parrotfish

BLENNIES, GOBIES, AND WRASSES

MOSTLY SMALL AND FOUND IN SHALLOW WATER, THE BLENNIES, GOBIES AND WRASSES ARE THREE LARGE FAMILIES OF FISH, EACH WITH HUNDREDS OF SPECIES. They belong to the main perch group (page 122). Most blennies have a tall dorsal fin, and small pelvic fins that are in front of the pectoral fins (rather than behind them as in other fish). They also have a hairlike covering, cirri, on the nostrils or eyes—which are on stalks in some species. Gobies are found all over the world, except in polar waters. Most are less than 4 inches (10 cm) long and have two dorsal fins. The two pelvic fins are joined to make a sucker on the underside. This enables the fish to cling to rocks or seaweed. Wrasses are mostly less than 6 inches (15 cm) long and are very brightly colored. They live singly not in schools, along coral reefs and rocky shores in all warmer seas.

⬛ A cleaner wrasse picks dirt and pests from the huge mouth of a coral hind, which does not try to eat the cleaner.

⬛ The sailfin goby erec its flaglike dorsal fin. rivals of the same speci this means: "Stay off patch of shor

⬇ Mudskippers live among the tangled roots of mangrove, especially on the shores of the Indian and Pacific Oceans. Their pectoral fins are almost like walking legs.

⬛ Snappers, like this school of blue-striped snappers, are yet another group of perch-like fish. There are about 230 species. Most are brightly colored fish of warm seas.

SMALLEST...!
The smallest fish are dwarf gobies in the Philippine Islands. They are 0.3 inch (8 mm) long.

Like most shore fish, the mudskipper has a tough, rubbery body, as protection against crashing waves and ...ing pebbles on the shore.

...he largest blenny is the giant kelpfish, at 2 feet ...0 cm) long. Like all the kelp blennies, it lives ...ong seaweed. Its coloring varies from red to ...llowish-green or brown, to match the type of ...lp or other weed in its surroundings.

...argazer blennies, like many other blennies, have ...es on stalks. The stargazer buries itself in the ...nd or mud of the seabed, but its eyes stick out ...ove the surface, like periscopes, so it can still ...tch for danger or food.

...EFUL SERVICE
...any kinds of wrasse carry out a useful service ...r other creatures on the reef. They are called ...aner fish. A large "customer" fish, such as a ...ouper, swims to a certain place, the cleaning ...tion, and stays still, with mouth and gill covers ...en. The cleaner wrasse approaches. The ...stomer recognizes its bright ...lors and zigzag way of ...imming, and allows the ...aner wrasse to use its sharp ...ont teeth to nip off fish lice ...d other pests and parasites ...m around its head, gills,

mouth, and scales. The wrasse eats the parasites as food and the customer is cleaned of its pests.

A NASTY TRICK
This helpful partnership between different kinds of animals is known as symbiosis. But it is open to trickery. The saber-toothed blenny looks so like a particular cleaner wrasse that it is very hard to tell one from the other. This resemblance is known as mimicry. A customer fish allows the saber-tooth blenny to swim near. But the blenny does not clean—it takes a bite out of the customer with its sharp teeth. If the customer reacts and tries to eat the blenny, the saber-tooth bites the inside of its mouth and is quickly spat out.

FISH OUT OF WATER
Mudskippers are small types of goby that can live out of water for minutes, even hours. They take in oxygen from small pools of water trapped in their large, cheeklike gill chambers.

Every few minutes the mudskipper dips its head into a puddle to refresh this water.

■ Montagu's blenny is typical of its group. It is a hardy fish of rock pools that grows to 3 inches (8 cm) long and eats a wide variety of food.

Mudskippers live in coastal mangrove swamps in tropical areas. At low tide they come out of their burrows to feed on insects and other small animals. They skitter across the mud on their strong pectoral fins, and watch for danger with their "popeyes" on stalks.

Blennies (Blenniidae)
• about 275 species
• nearly all sea-living
• includes shanny, redlip, rock, and boss and butterfly blennies

Gobies (Gobiidae)
• about 2,120 species
• most live in the sea
• a few are cave fish
• includes mudskippers, guavina, bunaka

Wrasses (Labridae)
• about 600 species
• live in the sea
• includes bluehead, ballan, and cuckoo wrasse, corkwing, hogfish, razorfish

⬛ The red salamander of North America.

SECTION 5
AMPHIBIANS & REPTILES

AMPHIBIANS LIVE A STRANGE DOUBLE LIFE. Most begin as tiny black dots in little balls of jelly floating in water. These eggs, or spawn, hatch into tadpoles that breathe by gills and swim with their tails. But as they grow, tadpoles undergo an amazing change called metamorphosis. They lose their gills and tails, and develop lungs for breathing air and legs for hopping on land. They develop into adult frogs, toads, salamanders, and newts.

Most amphibians have soft, moist skin. Reptiles do not. They can be recognized by their tough, scaly skin. The reptile group includes some of the most dangerous animals. There are poisonous snakes with deadly venom, such as cobras, rattlers, and vipers. Constrictor snakes, like pythons and boas, squeeze the life from their victims. Crocodiles and alligators threaten enemies with their large, gaping mouths, equipped with rows of pointed teeth.

Turtles, tortoises, and terrapins live a slow-paced life, safe in their domed protective shells. Much speedier are the lizards, another reptile subgroup. Some dart about so fast that we can hardly follow their movements. Lizards range in size from little geckoes that make a big meal of a fly, to monitors, such as the Komodo dragon, that can swallow a goat in one gulp.

WHAT ARE AMPHIBIANS?

AMPHIBIANS ARE COLD-BLOODED ANIMALS THAT HAVE A
"DOUBLE LIFE." They begin in water, as jelly-covered eggs which hatch into
tadpoles that breathe by gills and swim with their tails. The
tadpoles change shape or metamorphose as they grow, into
adults that breathe by lungs and walk
on land on four legs. The 4,000
or so species live in all regions
except Antarctica and the far north.

◩ The spring peeper frog is
named for its "teep-teep" call.

Like fish and reptiles, amphibians are cold-
blooded. Unlike birds and mammals, they cannot
make body heat to keep themselves at a constant
warm temperature. Their bodies are usually at
about the same temperature as the air or water
around them. When they are warm, they can
move actively. But in cold conditions, they
cannot. They become still and their body
processes slow down. This is called torpor. In
temperate regions, many
amphibians are torpid or
"asleep" in winter.

BIGGEST... !
The largest
amphibians are the
giant salamanders of
Eastern Asia,
especially China and
Japan. They grow up
to 5 feet (1.5 m) in
total length.

AMPHIBIAN EGGS
An amphibian begins
life as a small, dark,
dotlike egg. This
contains yolk for
nourishment and is
surrounded by several layers of jelly. It does not
have a protective outer shell like a reptile egg, so
it must be laid in water or moist surroundings, t
prevent it drying out. Lots of jelly-covered eggs
clustered together are known as spawn.

◩ Some newts have
frilly crests of skin along t
back. At breeding time, t
male's crest becomes larger a
his body develops brighter colo

BREATHING IN WATER
The eggs grow and
become comma-
shaped, then hatc
into larval
amphibians—
tadpoles. These have
feathery gills on the
sides of the head (externa
gills) for absorbing oxygen
from the water. Most
amphibians lose their gills when
they become adults, and take in
oxygen through their lungs and
moist skin. But some, such as the
mudpuppy, keep their gills.

FROZEN! !
The spring peeper frog of North
America can survive for as long
as three days in icy
temperatures, with almost half
of the blood and other fluids in
its body frozen solid. The frog
produces extra glucose sugar,
which concentrates its body
fluids and reduces the amount
of ice that forms, especially
around its heart and brain.

◩ A frog
leaps using its
powerful back
legs. Each section of
the leg is larger than the
one above it. So the thigh
is shortest, then the shin, and
the foot is the longest. The hip,
knee, and ankle joints straighten
to fling the frog into the air.

GROUPS OF AMPHIBIANS
More species of amphibians are
being discovered every year,
especially in their main habitats, tl
tropical rainforests. There are thre
main kinds of amphibians. They a
newts and salamanders, frogs and
toads, and caecilians.

A typical newt or salamander has a
long lizardlike body and a long tai

◧ Many frogs have brightly colored skin, like the tomato frog. Usually, the brighter they are, the more horrible-tasting the frog's flesh. The colors warn predators to leave the frog alone.

◧ Caecilians, also called apodans, have no legs. They live underground, feeding on grubs and worms, although a few dwell in ponds and streams. They are eyeless and find their prey by touch and smell. They also have small scales in their skin, like reptiles.

has four usually small, sprawling legs at its ̣des, and smooth, scaleless skin. Most are active ̣ the evening or at night, when they hunt for ̣̣all creatures such as insects, spiders, and ̣orms. In fact, all amphibians are predators. ̣hey cannot chew so they gulp down their victims whole, often still alive and struggling.

A typical frog or toad is in many ways the opposite of a salamander. It has a short, compact body, ̣ry long back legs for jumping, and no tail. The ̣ird amphibian group is the caecilians. These ̣̣ve no limbs at all and resemble ̣ergrown earthworms. They burrow ̣ the earth and dead leaves of ̣opical forests, searching for and ̣vouring small soil creatures.

◧ The axolotl is a strange ̣lamander that keeps its ̣athery gills even when adult ̣age 134).

spawn (jelly-covered eggs)

tadpole (larva)

legs grow and tail shrinks in young adult

adult frog is tail-less

LIFE OF CHANGE

The lives of most amphibians start in water and move onto land. The drastic change in shape from legless tadpole to four-legged adult is known as metamorphosis. It takes about 3–4 months in the common frog.

◧ Bullfrogs are large, powerful frogs that eat a range of fish, insects, lizards, snakes, small mammals such as mice, and other prey—including smaller frogs. There are bullfrog species in North America, South America, and Africa.

NEWTS AND SALAMANDERS

NEWTS AND SALAMANDERS ARE SHY, RARELY SEEN CREATURES. Most live in the northern half of the world, although there are some species o salamanders in South America. They usually stay hidden in cool, damp places during the day and come out at night to catch small creatures such as insects, snails, and worms. Some are typical amphibians in that they spend time both on land and in water. Others live entirely on land, or wholly in the water. The name "newt" is usually given to the types that are mainly aquatic (water-dwelling). Some salamanders have bright warning colors on their bodies. These signal to predators that their flesh is foul-tasting. Some can also ooze poisonous or horrible-tasting fluids from their skin.

⊡ The fire salamander has distinctive black and yellow markings. These warning colors are shared by other animals, such as wasps, bees, and poisonous beetles.

Salamanders and newts are hunted by many other creatures, including birds and snakes. So apart from their nasty-tasting flesh, they have various ways of defending themselves. If the Chinese spiny newt is seized by a predator, it pushes its sharp-tipped ribs through its skin. The ribs pass through its skin glands on the way and release an extremely unpleasant poison.

⊡ Many newts have long flaps of finlike skin along the upper and lower surfaces of the tail, which they keep from their tadpole stage. The fishlike tail is swished from side to side and helps the newt to swim faster.

HOT! ‼

Legend says that the fire salamander walks through flames. Of course, it does not. But it does tend to hide away during winter ir an old fallen log—which may be collected as firewood. When the log is thrown on the flames, the heat wakes the salamander which quickly tries to escape!

BREEDING TIME

In most salamander species, male and female do not have to link in a mating position. Instead the male leaves a "packet" o sperm on the ground, which the female then takes into her body. The sperm may join with or fertilize her eggs straight away, or they may be stored until she finds a more suitable time or place for her eggs.

FEW EGGS OR MANY?

Some salamanders lay their eggs in damp places on land, such as under stones or old logs, or in moss Others attach them to rocks or logs under the water.

◨ The yellow-eyed salamande is one of many species that li on the damp forest floor. Its large eyes show that it is nocturnal, or active at night.

The red salamander of North America is also called the eastern [n]wt. It has an extra stage in its life known as the eft. This is a [su]badult, a halfway form between the tadpole and the full adult. [Af]ter the tadpole stage, the eft develops and lives on land for up [to] three years before growing into a mature adult.

◘ The olm is a pale, thin, almost blind, cave-dwelling salamander from lands bordering the Adriatic part of the Mediterranean Sea.

The number of eggs a salamander lays varies from only four or five to more than 5,000, depending on the species. If eggs are laid in water, they hatch out into tadpoles (larvae) with feathery gills. These gradually change to the adult form, [de]veloping legs and lungs. However, eggs laid on land usually miss out [th]e tadpole stage and hatch into fully formed miniature salamanders. [So]me species, such as the fire salamander, do not lay eggs at all. The eggs develop inside the female's body and she gives birth to tiny offspring.

Mudpuppies never lose the feather gills that [th]ey have as tadpoles. These salamanders grow to [ab]out 16 inches (40 cm) long and inhabit creeks [an]d rivers in North America. They hunt small fish, water worms, and young crayfish.

WARNING COLORS

The gaudy markings of many amphibians warn enemies that they are very nasty-tasting indeed. The skin glands of the fire salamander ooze a poisonous fluid that causes severe redness and swelling if another animal bites it. The effects are so severe that they can even kill small mammals, including pet dogs, if they pick up a salamander. Potential predators learn to recognize these types of warning colors and avoid the salamanders.

[TH]E SALAMANDERS THAT NEVER GROW UP

[T]he axolotl (page 133) is a kind of mole salamander from Mexico. Some [ax]olotls develop into full adults and live on land, like other salamanders. [B]ut others stay in water throughout their lives and keep their larval [fe]atures, such as feathery gills. They become mature and breed, even [th]ough most of the body is still in [th]e immature larval stage. This [co]ndition is called neotony.

[Lu]ngless salamanders have no lungs. [Th]ey must absorb oxygen through [th]e skin and the lining of the mouth. [Th]is means the skin must always stay moist. If it [dr]ies, oxygen cannot pass through. Most lungless [sa]lamanders are found in North and South America.

SOME GROUPS OF SALAMANDERS (continued from page 133):

Lungless salamanders (*Plethodontidae*)
• about 200 species
• long, slender body and tail
• live in water or caves
• includes red salamander, dusky salamander

Mole salamanders (*Ambystomatidae*)
• 32 species
• broad head, thick body
• adults usually live on land
• includes axolotl, tiger salamander

Newts (*Salamandridae*)
• about 60 species
• slender body and long tail
• strong legs
• includes fire salamander, warty newt, striped newt

Sirens (*Sirenidae*)
• 3 species
• eel-like body and feathery gills
• live in water
• includes dwarf siren, greater siren

Olm and mudpuppies (*Proteidae*)
• 5 species
• feathery gills
• long body and short tail
• live in water

Giant salamanders (*Cryptobranchidae*)
• 3 species
• large, heavy body
• short tail
• live in water
• includes hellbender

◘ Spiny salamanders like the Chinese spiny newt have sharp ribs that almost poke out of the skin. They are too prickly for most predators to eat.

FROGS AND TOADS

FROGS AND TOADS ARE BY FAR THE BIGGEST GROUP OF AMPHIBIANS, WITH MORE THAN 3,400 SPECIES. They live on all continents except Antarctica, and in habitats ranging from deserts to cold mountain streams. But they are mo[st] common in tropical and subtropical swamp[s] and rainforests. The name "frog" was once used for the slender, smooth-skinned types that could leap well, and "toad" for the plum[p] rough-skinned species that prefer to waddle. Now both names are used for similar species and there is n[o] clear difference between a frog and a toad.

⬆ Surinam toad

⬆ Tree frogs have sucker-like disks at the ends of their toes.

All frogs and toads are tail-less and have strong back legs for jumping. Th[e] front legs are smaller and cushion the landing. A frog's body is short, with a strong backbone to cope with the physical stresses of jumping, and there is no narrow neck between the head and body. The large eyes are usually on the top of the very wide-mouthed head, so the frog can still see when it is almost submerged in water.

A FROG'S LIFE CYCLE

A typical frog or toad lays its eggs in water. These hatch into tiny tadpoles with tails for swimming and fluffy gills for breathing in water. The young tadpole feeds on plants. As it grows, it loses its external gills and develops lungs in its chest for breathing air. It gradually loses its tail too, and develops legs. The head broadens, the body become short and thick, and the tadpole has metamorphosed into a froglet, ready to venture onto land.

SMALLEST... !
One of the smallest frogs in the world was discovered in Cuba in 1997. Its scientific name is _Eleutherodactylus iberia_. It measures only 0.4 inch (1 cm) long.

⬇ A frog pushes off with its toes, launching its small, streamlined body into a leap at least 10 times its own length.

⬆ The water-holding frog of Australia lives in the desert. During a drought, it stays in a burrow underground. Its outer layer of slime detaches to form a cocoon that fills with the frog's urine and other body fluids, like a water-filled sleeping bag.

▷ In Central American rainforests, it is so damp that the strawberry poison-arrow frog can carry her tadpole on her back, without it drying out.

The cane toad is also called the marine or ~~g~~iant toad. It was taken from South America to ~~A~~ustralia, to eat beetle pests in sugarcane ~~fi~~elds. But it prefers small creatures that are ~~n~~atural inhabitants in the area, making some of ~~th~~em very rare animals.

~~F~~ROG CALLS

~~M~~ale frogs and toads make loud calls to ~~a~~ttract females. Each species has its own ~~p~~articular call, and the green frog can be ~~h~~eard hundreds of yards away. The calls of frogs are made louder in a ~~v~~ocal sac below the chin, as air from the lungs is forced over the vocal ~~co~~rds in the neck. Females do not usually make any sounds.

~~C~~ARING FOR YOUNG

~~S~~ome frogs do not leave their eggs in water to hatch, but carry them ~~a~~round to make sure they do not get eaten. As the female marsupial frog ~~la~~ys her eggs, the male fertilizes them and helps her pack them into a ~~ba~~ckpack-like skin pouch on her back, where they hatch and start to ~~de~~velop. After a few weeks the young hop into the water to complete their ~~g~~rowth. The female Surinam toad carries her young in separate skin ~~p~~ouches on her back, until they are fully formed mini-toads.

~~Many frogs and toads make ~~th~~eir calls louder by blowing ~~up~~ the chin skin like a balloon. ~~Th~~e stretched skin vibrates or ~~re~~sonates to increase the ~~vo~~lume of the sound.

~~⚠~~ USEFUL! ⚠

~~The~~ poison fluid or secretion ~~i~~n poison-arrow frog skin ~~ma~~y have medical uses. The ~~secr~~etions of the phantasmal ~~po~~ison-arrow frog are far ~~mo~~re effective at stopping ~~~~pain than the usual ~~pai~~nkilling drugs. Those of ~~the~~ golden poison-arrow frog ~~may~~ help patients who have ~~~~had heart attacks.

POISONOUS FROGS

The bright colors of the poison-arrow (or arrow-poison) frogs warn other animals to stay away. Glands in the body release a strong venom into the frog's skin. Even a few drops of this can be lethal to a predator. Traditionally, local people in Central and South America tip their hunting arrows with this substance.

The flying frog of Southeast Asia does not really fly, but spreads its huge webbed feet to glide 40 feet (12 m) from tree to tree.

SOME GROUPS OF FROGS AND TOADS (continued from page 133):

Ranid or "true" frogs *(Ranidae)*
• about 650 species
• slim, smooth-skinned body
• pointed head
• mostly live in water but some dwell in trees
• includes common frog, bullfrog

Bufid or "true" toads *(Bufonidae)*
• about 400 species
• stout body
• often rough, warty skin
• most live mainly on land
• includes cane toad, natterjack

Tree frogs *(Hylidae)*
• more than 770 species
• slender body
• long legs
• most live in trees
• webbed feet with sticky pads on disklike toetips

Leptodactylid frogs *(Leptodactylidae)*
• more than 900 species
• varied body form
• land-living and water-living species
• includes horned frog, chirping frog

Narrow-mouthed frogs *(Microhylidae)*
• more than 320 species
• stout body
• small mouth
• live in burrows or trees
• includes rain frog

Poison-arrow (arrow-poison) frogs *(Dendrobatidae)*
• over 170 species
• mainly tropical rain forests
• slim, small body
• sticky disks on toes
• brightly colored
• live on ground or in trees

◁ Green tree frogs are camouflaged among the leaves as they wait for their small insect prey. They can cling to twigs, wet glossy leaves, and even window glass using the sucker-like disks on their toes.

137

WHAT ARE REPTILES?

REPTILES ARE ANIMALS WITH BACKBONES (VERTEBRATES) THAT ARE COLD-BLOODED, HAVE SCALES ON THEIR SKIN, AND LAY EGG (PAGE 131). Most reptiles have four legs with five toes on ea foot, but snakes have no limbs at all. Most reptiles live on land, but marine turtles and sea snakes stay in th sea, except to come ashore briefly and lay their eggs. Most reptile eggs have shells that are tough yet leathery and flexible, unlike the hard, brittle shells of birds' eggs. However, some snakes do not lay eggs, but give birth to babies.

🔼 The pond slider is a common turtle in North, Central, and South America. It rarely leaves the water.

The main groups of reptiles are the turtles and tortoises, the crocodiles and alligators, the lizards, and the snakes. Most live on land, but many turtles and terrapins, also most crocodiles and alligators, and even some snakes, spend time in ponds, swamps, and rivers. A few, including the saltwater crocodile, venture into the sea.

Reptiles may not seem to be social animals, in the way that birds form flocks or monkeys live in troops. Yet they have many ways of communicating, especially with others of their own species at mating time. Lizards bob their heads and show off their skin crests and brightly colored patterns. Snakes leave chemical messages for their partners, which consist of scentlike substances called pheromones, produced in their bodies. Some reptiles, including crocodiles and geckoes, make hisses, grunts, and calls to attract mates.

THE REPTILE'S EGG

The leathery shell of a repti egg gives protection and prevents it from drying ou even in the desert heat. Inside are layers of fluid t protect the developing embryo (unhatched baby) and yolk to provide it wit nourishment.

🔽 Worm lizards are not worms, or lizards, but reptiles that resemble large earthworms. They burrow in the soil of tropical forests.

🔼 Hingeback tortoises can tilt down the rear of the shell to give extra protection to the back legs and tail.

SCALY! !

The skin of a reptile is covered with hard scales. These are made of keratin the same substance that forms our nails and hair. I some reptiles, such as crocodiles, the scales are strengthened by plates of bones, making a tough armor.

🔽 The shell of a softshell turtle does not ha horny, strengthening plates, as in other turt tortoises. So it feels slightly soft and rubber

When breeding, most female reptiles lay eggs and then leave these to develop and hatch on their own. But a few species, such as some skinks, pythons, and crocodiles, guard their eggs and even the babies too, protecting them from enemies. Some snakes and lizards keep their developing eggs inside their bodies, where they hatch and the mother gives birth to the young.

Marine iguanas are some [of] the few reptiles that [spe]nd time in the sea. These [se]a lizards dive to munch [on] seaweeds.

[CO]LD BODIES

[Re]ptiles are cold-blooded creatures. This means [th]ey cannot control their body temperatures [th]emselves. They depend on the heat of the sun to [be]come warm, so that they can be active and [m]ove about. In cold conditions, reptiles move

REPTILES	
• about 6,560 species • cold-blooded vertebrates • scaly skin • lay eggs • most have four legs • worldwide except polar regions	Tuatara *(Rhynchocephalia)* • 1 species • lizardlike, with head and back crest • only in New Zealand
Lizards *(Sauria)* • about 3,750 species • long, slim body, long tail • includes skinks, geckos, chameleons, iguanas, monitors	Worm lizards *(Amphisbaenia)* • about 140 species • long slender body, no limbs • includes worm lizards, shield snouts
Crocodiles *(Crocodilia)* • 22 species • long body armored with thick scales, long tail • includes crocodiles, caimans, alligators, gharial	Snakes *(Serpentes)* • about 2,400 species • long wormlike body, no limbs • includes pythons, boas, vipers
	Turtles and tortoises *(Chelonia)* • about 250 species • body protected by a hard, domed shell • includes tortoises, terrapins, turtles

slowly or not at all. This cold, immobile condition is known as torpor. One advantage of being cold-blooded is that reptiles do not need to use so much energy as warm-blooded animals, who must "burn" energy from their food to produce body heat. So reptiles need to eat far less food than warm-blooded birds and mammals of the same body size—perhaps only one-tenth of the amount.

Water dragons (below) are mostly large tropical lizards that swim [ ] by lashing their tails from side to side. Caimans (right) are smaller [me]mbers of the crocodile group from Central and South America. [The]y grow to about 6 feet (1.8 m) long.

▶ The spotted water snake lives in swamps and creeks in northern parts of Australia. Its nostrils are set high on its head, so it can take a breath without poking its whole head out of the water.

◀ Most terrapins have wide feet with partly webbed toes, for efficient swimming.

139

TORTOISES, TURTLES, AND TERRAPINS

THERE ARE ABOUT 250 SPECIES OF TURTLES, TORTOISES, AND TERRAPINS, FOUND IN MOST WARM PARTS OF THE WORLD. They are easily recognized by the hard, rounded shell that protects the main part of the body. The mostly land-dwelling tortoises thrive in all kinds of habitats, including desert, woodland, and mountains. Turtles and terrapins live chiefly in rivers and ponds. They are slow and ungainly on land, but swift in the water. (Marine turtles are a separate group, page 142.)

◭ The matamata is an extraordinary-looking turtle about 16 inches (40 cm) long from the Amazon region of South America. It has an arrow-shaped head and a very wide mouth, to gulp in fish and other water animals. Its tiny eyes are about halfway along the sides of the "arrow."

◮ Snapping turtles lurk in ponds and lakes from Canada, south through North to Central America. They grab any small animal as prey.

OLD! ❗

Turtles are among the longest-lived of all animals. Box turtles of North America and spur-thighed tortoises in Europe survive to over 100 years old. A Marion's tortoise, taken from the Seychelles to Mauritius in 1766, lived until 1918. It died due to an accident—at least 152 years old.

Turtles, terrapins, and tortoises are known as chelonians. They do not have teeth. Instead, a turtle or tortoise has a strong, beaklike mouth with hard ridges along the jaw edges, for biting food. Many chelonians are predators, catching other animals to eat. Others, including many tortoises, are plant-eaters. They swallow each piece they bite since they cannot chew.

Turtles reproduce by laying eggs, usually in a hole in the ground. The female lays her eggs in a warm place and leaves them to incubate and hatch alone. The young receive no parental care.

THE TURTLE'S SHELL
The shell of a turtle or tortoise has two parts—the upper carapace and the lower plastron. Each part has two layers of plates like jigsaw puzzle pieces. These are made of bone on the inside, and horn on the outside like normal reptile scales. The outer plates are called scutes. The two parts meet at the sides, with openings for the turtle's head, legs, and tail. The ribs and backbone are fixed to the upper inside of the carapace.

scute of carapace

bony plate of carapace

scute of plastron   backbone   rib   bony plate of plastron

◀ Wood turtles catch worms, insects, and grubs, and can climb into bushes. They were once caught and kept as pets, but this has made them rare.

CAMOUFLAGED MATAMATA

Many turtles and tortoises are brownish or green, to blend with their surroundings of mud, leaves and waterweeds. This helps them to hide as they wait for prey to come near or stay unnoticed by predators. The matamata is a member of the snake-necked turtle family, and has most unusual camouflage. With its ridged shell and flattened head, fringed with flaps of skin, it looks like a lump of bark and leaves in the water. When a victim passes by, the matamata simply opens its large mouth. Water—and the prey—rush in. The turtle then closes its mouth, squeezes the water out at the sides, and swallows its meal.

GALAPAGOS GIANT TORTOISE

The largest tortoises are found on the Galapagos Islands, off the coast of Ecuador in the Pacific Ocean. These lumbering giants are strong enough to carry a person. Each island in the Galapagos group has a variety or subspecies of giant tortoise that is recognizable by the shape of its shell or the size and length of its legs. These slight variations were noticed by English naturalist Charles Darwin when he visited the islands in the 1830s. The tortoises, finches, and other animals of the Galapagos set Darwin thinking about the idea of evolution by natural selection. He described this idea in his book *On the Origin of Species* (1859), which is now central to the study of the natural world.

Several kinds of giant tortoises live on Pacific and Indian Ocean islands, such as the Galapagos.

CIRCULAR SHELL

The spiny softshell turtle has an almost circular shell, covered with leathery skin and small, spiny projections on the front. This turtle is a good swimmer and spends most of its life in water, catching insects, crustaceans, and fish.

The largest freshwater turtle in North America is the alligator snapping turtle. It has a large head and a rough, lumpy shell. Inside its gaping mouth is a small, pink, fleshy flap that resembles a worm. When a fish comes to eat the "worm," it is quickly snapped up in the turtle's jaws.

◪ The leopard tortoise of Africa has a high-domed shell with bold markings. It lives in woods and grassland.

MAIN GROUPS OF TURTLES (continued from page 139):

Snake-necked turtles *(Chelidae)*
• about 30 species
• live mainly in water
• most have long necks
• includes giant snake-neck turtle, matamata

Helmeted side-necked turtles *(Pelomedusidae)*
• about 20 species
• live mainly in water
• includes Arrau river turtle, West African mud turtle

Alligator turtles *(Chelydridae)*
• 3 species
• large head and long tail
• live in water
• includes snapping turtle, big-headed turtle

Softshell turtles *(Trionychidae)*
• about 22 species
• shell covered with leathery skin
• live mainly in water
• includes spiny softshell, Indian flapshell

American mud and musk turtles *(Kinosternidae)*
• about 20 species
• musk glands below carapace give off strong-smelling scent
• live mainly in water
• includes striped mud turtle, common musk turtle

Pond turtles *(Emydidae)*
• about 85 species
• well-developed shell, strong limbs and webbed feet
• live mainly in water, some stay on land
• includes box turtle, river terrapin, wood turtle

Tortoises *(Testudinae)*
• about 41 species
• domed shell, strong back legs
• land-living
• includes gopher tortoise, pancake tortoise, spur-thighed tortoise, Galapagos giant tortoise

SEA TURTLES

SEA OR MARINE TURTLES ARE THE LARGEST MEMBERS OF THE CHELONIAN GROUP. There are only seven species, found mostly in tropical and subtropical seas and oceans. Apart from a few sea snakes, they are the only reptiles that spend virtually their whole lives at sea. Only females come ashore, and then for only a few hours each year, to la their eggs. Sea turtles have flatter or less domed shells than freshwater turtles, and swim with their front limbs which are larger than the back limbs. Awkward on land they flap their flipperlike front legs to "fly" through th sea with amazing grace. When on the move, they must surface every few minutes to breathe air. But when resting or sleeping, they may remain underwater for several hours. They have good senses of sight and smell, to find food, detect danger, and locate a mate.

�« The hawksbill is the most tropical of sea turtles, usua found in shallow coastal waters around reefs and bays. is one of the few large animals to feed mainly on spong

�« Turtle front flippers, like this loggerhead's, are wide and flattened. The turtle does not so much row with them, but rather flaps them up and down, like a bird flapping its wings.

SMALLEST... !
The Pacific ridley is the smallest sea turtle. It measures about 28 inches (70 cm) long and weighs less than 90 pounds (41 kg).

Like freshwater turtles and land tortoises, sea turtles do not have teeth. They bite and crush their food with the strong, hard edges to their beaklike jaws. Young turtles feed on plankton, and later, slightly larger creatures. Adult green sea turtles feed mostly on sea grass. But the other species eat creatures such as jellyfish, squid, shrimps, and fish.

�« Loggerhead turtle

She then covers the ne with sand and rakes over the site with her flippers. Final she returns to the sea, leavin her eggs to incubate in the sun-baked sand. She does this several times, laying clutches in differe places at intervals of about ten days.

THE BREEDING BEACH
After mating at sea, female turtles tend to return to the same place year after year, to lay their eggs. At the nesting beach, the female drags herself slowly up the sand to beyond the high tide mark. She digs a pit with her flippers, then begins to lay her eggs, 2–3 at a time. She may lay from 50 to more than 150 eggs in the clutch.

A DANGEROUS JOURNEY
Sea turtle eggs take about eight weeks to hatch. depending on the temperature of the sand. The babies break out of their shells and then have t struggle out of their sandpit nest by themselves.

Turtles have long suffered from human activities. People hunted them and dug up their eggs. "Turtleshell," obtained mainly from hawksbills, was prized for making decorative items such as combs. Now turtles are losing their breeding grounds. Tourist centers are built on the beaches where they nest. Conservationists help by rearing baby turtles in protected hatchery areas and releasing them in the sea, hopefully to return and breed in safety.

It is a group effort and it may take several days to reach the surface. Once out on the beach, the tiny turtles make a dash for the sea. Many fall victim to predators such as seabirds, crabs, otters, foxes, and lizards, who soon gather for the feast. Those that reach the sea begin to swim at once into deeper water. But here they face new hazards such as predatory fish.

LEATHERY BACK
The huge leatherback sea turtle is named for its unusual shell, which is made of a thick, leathery substance strengthened by tiny bones. Leatherbacks feed mostly on jellyfish, which they catch and cut up with their scissor-like jaws. They are known to dive to depths of more than 3,000 feet (900 m) in their search for food.

A female leatherback digs a hole on a sandy beach, where she will lay 50–150 eggs. The leatherback is the largest of all turtles and tortoises. It can weigh more than 1,100 pounds (500 kg), although most of this great bulk is buoyed up by the water.

The loggerhead sea turtle has a large head in proportion to the rest of its body. The sides of the head house powerful jaw muscles that enable this turtle species to crush hard-shelled prey such as clams, scallops, sea snails, crabs, and lobsters.

MIGRATION
Some sea turtles spend their lives within a small area. Others make long journeys between the areas where they usually feed, and the beaches where they breed. Most green turtles are in the second group. Some feed off the Atlantic coast of South America, then migrate to tiny Ascension Island some 900 miles (1,500 km) away.

◩ The green turtle was hunted in great numbers for its meat, shell, eggs, and skin. It has become very rare and, like other sea turtles, it is now on the official list of threatened animals. Trade in its products is strictly controlled.

TURTLES (continued from page 141):

Sea turtles (*Chelonidae*)
• 6 species
• flat, bony shell covered with horny plates
• flipperlike limbs
• includes green turtle, ridley sea turtles, hawksbill, loggerhead

Leatherback sea turtle (*Dermochelyidae*)
• 1 species
• shell covered with leathery skin

CROCODILES AND ALLIGATORS

CROCODILES HAVE CHANGED LITTLE SINCE THEY SHARED THE PREHISTORIC WORLD WITH THEIR CLOSE REPTILE RELATIVES, THE DINOSAURS, MORE THAN 100 MILLION YEARS AGO. There are three subgroups in the crocodile group, known as crocodilians. These are the crocodiles themselves, the alligators and caimans, and the single species of gharial (gavial) from northern India. Crocodilians are found in all tropical and subtropical regions of the world. They are powerful predators, equally at home on land and in water.

◪ The Nile crocodile has become very rare. Its natural river and swamp habitats have been drained and changed to farmland, industrial sites, and tourist areas.

◪ The massive saltwater or estuarine crocodile is regularly seen swimming offshore.

A typical crocodile or alligator has a long body covered with thick scales. Bony plates that are embedded in the skin along the back give further protection. The snout is long too, with nostrils and eyes set high on the head. The tail is also long and tall, and very muscular, for swimming. The two pairs of legs are short but strong, with five toes on the front feet and four on the back feet. All of these toes are partly webbed.

LAZY DAYS, BUSY NIGHTS
Crocodiles spend much of the day basking in the sun on sandy riverbanks and mudflats. They become active in the evening and usually hunt for prey at night. They are among the most patient, silent, and stealthy of all large predators. Often the croc lurks in water near the shore, almost totally submerged like an old floating log.

It waits for an animal to come and drink. When the prey is almost within reach, the crocodile makes a sudden dash from the water, drags the victim below the surface, and holds it there, usually with the croc's jaws clamped onto its throat, until it dies.

◪ A crocodile is almost entirely covered in thick, horny scales, with extra plates of bone along the back.

CROC OR ALLIGATOR?
The main difference between a crocodile and an alligator is that, in an alligator, the fourth tooth on each side of the lower jaw fits into a pit in the upper jaw.

...e gharial's very long, narrow jaws, armed with about 100 ..., can be swished sideways through the water at speed to ... prey. The lump or "pot" at the upper end of the snout is a ...re of old males.

The tooth cannot be seen when the mouth is closed. In a crocodile, these fourth lower teeth are visible when the mouth is shut, on the outsides of the upper jaw. Crocodiles live in tropical and subtropical areas of Central and South America, Africa, Asia, and Australia. Most alligators and caimans live in North, Central, and South America, with one species, the Chinese alligator, in East Asia. The gharial lives in northern India and neighboring countries, and is recognized by its very long, narrow snout.

CROCODILE DIET

The food of a crocodile or alligator tends to change as the animal grows. A young Nile ...codile less than 20 inches (50 cm) long feeds ...stly on small creatures such as frogs, insects, ... spiders. As it nears 40 inches (100 cm) in ...gth, it starts to catch larger prey such as birds, ...rds, small mammals, and fish. The full-grown ...e crocodile preys mainly on larger mammals up to the size of zebras.

NEW TEETH

A crocodile has teeth which are strong and pointed, but not especially large. Each tooth is set in its own deep socket in the jawbone. As teeth become worn, they are replaced by new teeth which grow at the bases of the old ones.

ON THE MOVE

On land, crocodiles walk slowly with the legs splayed out to the sides, swinging the body with a snakelike wriggling motion. But a crocodile in a hurry holds its legs straighter, stiffer, and more upright under its body. This "high walk" allows a speed of about 3 mph (5 km/h). A few species, such as Johnston's crocodile, can even break into a gallop and sprint almost as fast as a person, at a speed of about 12 mph (20 km/h).

In water, the crocodile is an excellent swimmer. It pushes itself along with side-to-side sweeps of its powerful tail. It can also use its tail to drive itself suddenly and powerfully out of the water, in a sudden upward lunge to snatch prey. The legs are held close against the body to reduce resistance as the reptile swishes along.

LARGEST... !

The biggest reptile is the saltwater or estuarine crocodile of the Indian and Pacific Oceans. It grows to 23 feet (7 m) long and weighs about a ton.

◨ The black caiman is not always black. It may be brown and have creamy patches on its chin and underside.

◪ All crocodilians have their nostrils, eyes, and ears on the top of the head. They can breathe, see, and hear while almost submerged.

MAIN GROUPS OF CROCODILIANS
(continued from page 139):

Alligators and caimans (Alligatorinae)
• 7 species
• teeth not visible when mouth is closed

Crocodiles (Crocodylinae)
• 14 species
• fourth tooth in lower jaw visible when mouth is closed
• includes mugger, false gharial

Gharial (Gavialinae)
• 1 species
• long, slender jaws

145

HOW CROCODILES BREED

◣ Young crocodilians have longer legs, larger eyes, and shorter snouts relative to their body size, compared to the adults. But they are still fearsome hunters.

CROCODILES MAY SEEM LIKE ROBOTIC, UNTHINKING KILLERS. We notice few facial expressions or sound signals to show their moods and intentions. But among themselves, crocodiles have surprisingly complicated behavior, social lives, and breeding methods. They communicate using a wide variety of sounds, smells, and movements. And, unlike nearly all other reptile the female guards her nest and takes care of her young.

◣ In the backwater swamps of the Everglades National Park, in Florida, a female American alligator lurks half submerged. Her back provides a safe resting place for her babies.

◂ A female crocodile deposits her eggs in the nest hole. Breeding time is usually in the warmest, dampest part of the year. It may be delayed if the rains do not come to soften the soil.

Crocodiles are polygamous animals. This means member of one sex, in this case the male, mates with several partners. But the male crocodile mu first establish a territory, by pushing out rival males. Then he must attract the attention of possible mates. He swims high in the water with his body exposed, occasionally slapping the surface with his chin to make loud sounds. His antics may also attract rival males, who try to take over by having head-butt contests. Females watch the males and, before mating, rub the male's head or blow bubbles underwater.

HE CROCODILE'S NEST

oon after mating, the
male prepares to dig
er nest. The details
ry slightly among the
ecies, but the Nile
rocodile is fairly
pical. She finds a
uitable site, in sunny
oft ground up to
50 feet (50 m) from
ater. She may have to
reaten rival females,
nce the best sites are
short supply and
sed year after year.

e digs her nest with
er strong back feet and
ositions herself over
e hole, to start laying
ggs. Young females
ay lay only about 20
ggs, but older ones can
end up to an hour
ying about 80 eggs.
She then covers the
eggs, and watches over the nest. She does not
feed during this time, and only moves away
from the nest to drink. Even so, rapid
predators such as mongooses, foxes, or
monitor lizards may dart in and steal an
egg or two.

CALLS FOR HELP

Crocodile eggs usually incubate for
60–100 days, depending on temperature.
When the babies are ready and hear
footsteps above, they call from inside their
eggs with loud squeals. The mother digs
down to the eggs, and the hatchlings start to
reak out of their shells. As they emerge, the
other reaches down and gently picks them up,
e at a time, in her sharp-toothed jaws.

INSIDE A REPTILE

A crocodile has most of the main body parts of other
vertebrates, including birds (page 185) and mammals (page
192). However, its digestive wastes (feces), liquid wastes
(urine), and reproductive system all open into a common
chamber, the cloaca, which leads to the outside. This is similar
to birds, but different from mammals.

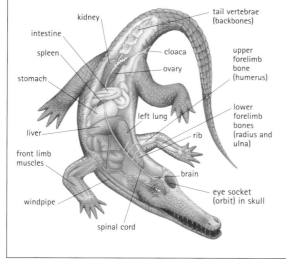

kidney
intestine
spleen
stomach
liver
front limb muscles
windpipe
spinal cord
tail vertebrae (backbones)
cloaca
ovary
upper forelimb bone (humerus)
lower forelimb bones (radius and ulna)
left lung
rib
brain
eye socket (orbit) in skull

When she has collected
several, she carries them
in her mouth to a safe,
quiet "nursery pool,"
where she releases them
into the water. She then
quickly returns to the nest
to collect the next batch.
Finally all the young and
the mother are safe in
their nursery pool.

CLOSE TO MOTHER

For the first few weeks,
baby crocodiles stay close
to their mother. At any
sign of danger, the mother
vibrates her body muscles.
The vibrations pass
through the ground and
water, and are a signal for
her young to dive beneath
the surface. In some
species, the male may help
to defend the offspring.
But if food is very scarce,
he may eat one of them!

ALLIGATOR NESTS

Alligators and caimans lay their eggs in mounds,
which they scrape together from plants, soil, and
dead leaves. The mounds are usually up to 6 feet
(1.8 m) across and 3 feet (90 cm) high, and the
mother guards the eggs and the babies.

The sex of a crocodile is determined by the
temperature of the egg during incubation. American
alligator eggs at 90–94°F (32–34°C) produce males,
while below 86°F (30°C) the babies are females.
Both males and females result at 86–90°F (30–
32°C). In crocodiles, high and low temperatures
produce females, while in-between temperatures
result in males.

◧ A mother
crocodile
scoops up
one of her newly
hatched young to
carry it to the
nursery pool.

IGUANAS, AGAMIDS, AND CHAMELEONS

Galapagos marine iguanas grow to 5 feet (1.5 m) in lengt (including the tail). They vary i color from green-brown to pin

LIZARDS ARE THE LARGEST GROUP OF REPTILES. There are more than 3,700 species. They are most common in tropical areas, but there are species in nearly all regions except the far north and Antarctica. The iguanas are one of the largest lizard subgroups. Most live in North and South America, but there are some in Madagascar and Fiji. The agamids, or chisel-teeth lizards, are similar in appearance and habits to the iguanas, but live in the Old World—Africa (except Madagascar), Asia, and Australia, with one species in Europe. Most chameleons come from tropical Africa and India, and are well adapted for life in the trees.

A frilled lizard in defensive posture.

Some iguanas and agamids are quite large for lizards, growing to more than 20 inches (50 cm) in length (including the tail). Many are adorned with crests and frills, and the males especially are brightly colored. They live on land and in trees, and are active during the day. Most

prey on insects and other small creatures, but a few species, such as the chuckwalla and desert iguana of North America, feed on plant material.

RUNNING AT SPEED
The basilisk lizard is a type of iguana from South America. It has very muscular back legs and long, thin toes. It is one of the fastest runners of all lizards, reaching more than 6 mph (10 km/h).

Stri aga

LITTLE AND LARGE... !
Chameleons range in size from the tiny brown brookesia, about as long as a little finger, to the huge oustaleti chameleon at 22 inches (55 cm).

Chameleons change color to blend in with their surroundings.

The basilisk lizard runs so fast that it can even move for short distances over water, its long toes supported by the film-like film on the surface.

It runs with its long tail held out behind for balance. Male basilisks have a large, bony "helmet" on the head and crests of skin along the back and tail. In females the helmets are smaller.

DIVING BELOW

Unlike other iguanas, the marine iguana (page 139) spends much of its life in the seas around the Galapagos Islands. An expert swimmer and diver, it uses its strong tail to propel itself through water, diving to eat seaweeds. Although the iguana must come to the surface to breathe, it can eat while submerged. Its heart rate slows as it dives, to reduce its need for oxygen, so it can stay under water for longer.

FRILLED LIZARD

The frilled lizard is an agamid from Australia and New Guinea. It has a very long tail and an unusual, brightly colored collar of skin, like a ruff, around its neck. Normally this neck frill lies folded flat against the shoulders. If the lizard is alarmed, it opens its mouth wide and spreads out the frill around its head. This makes it appear much larger, to deter possible enemies.

FLYING LIZARDS

The flying dragon is another type of agamid lizard, found in Southeast Asia. It lives in thick rainforest and has also taken to rubber tree plantations. It does not really fly, but can glide long distances between trees without having to come down to the ground. It has winglike flaps of skin at each side of its body, which viewed from above, make a circular shape. The flaps are held against the body, and extended as the lizard launches itself into the air.

LIFE IN THE TREES

The chameleon is adapted for hunting insects in trees. Its feet are specially arranged to provide a strong grip on branches, with three toes wrapped around one side and two on the other. The chameleon also has a strong prehensile tail, which can be curled around the branch and used like an extra leg. With these gripping aids, the chameleon can remain still for long periods. It also changes its color to match the background. When prey comes near, the chameleon takes aim with the help of its excellent eyesight, and shoots out its long, sticky-tipped tongue at the victim.

Collared lizard

The chameleon's tongue darts out so fast that it can reach its prey in less than one-hundredth of a second.

SOME GROUPS OF LIZARDS:

Iguanas (Iguanidae)
• more than 850 species
• limbs usually well developed
• includes marine iguana, basilisk lizard, anole

Agamid lizards (Agamidae)
• about 350 species

• large head and long tail
• includes frilled lizard, flying dragon

Chameleons (Chamaeleontidae)
• 135 species
• flattened body, prehensile tail
• large eyes can move separately
• changes color to match scenery

GECKOS, LACERTIDS, AND TEIID LIZARDS

GECKOS ARE AMONG THE MOST SUCCESSFUL LIZARDS. They live in all warmer areas of the world, and are particularly common and varied in the tropics. Typically, a gecko is active at night. It has large eyes to help it see in dim light. Most geckos do not have eyelids. A special transparent version of the normal reptile scale permanently cover each eye. Most wall and sand lizards, or lacertids, live in warm parts of Europe, Africa, and Asia. But one species, the viviparous lizard, survives in Scandinavia, inside the Arctic Circle—farther north than any other lizard. Most teiid lizards live in South America. In many ways they are New World versions of Old World lacertids.

◪ Leaf-tailed gecko

◪ The viviparous lizard gro to about 7 inches (18 cm total length. It is usually g brown, or yellow, but like m lizards, the color varie different parts of its ran

Geckos are known for their ability to climb smooth surfaces, even glass, with ease. The underside of each toe is covered with many tiny bristles, like a miniature brush. Each bristle ends in a disklike sucker. These disks help the gecko cling to smooth surfaces. The night lizards of the southern USA and Central America look similar to geckos, and are also active at night.

◪ Day geckos are only about 6 inches (15 cm) long, active by day, and live mainly in forests. Their green color is good daytime camouflage.

LEAFY TAIL
The leaf-tailed gecko has a spotted body and flattened tail, which gives amazing camouflage a the lizard lies flattened against bark or lichen o a tree trunk. Like other geckos, it often licks its eyes with its long tongue, to keep them clear of dust and dirt.

The tokay gecko, like several other geckos, is a welcome visitor in homes across Asia. It feeds on troublesome insects, from mosquitoes to cockroaches. Like most geckos, the female tokay gecko lays only a couple of eggs at a time. They are slightly sticky and the female attaches them to a rock or tree. Several females may lay eggs in the same place.

◩ The caiman lizard, a type of teiid, spends much of its life in water, being an excellent swimmer and diver. It feeds mainly by crushing water-living snails with its strong jaws and flattened teeth. Caiman lizards grow to 3 feet (90 cm) long and have large, rough scales along the back, similar to those of a crocodile.

LACERTIDS

Lacertid lizards include the green and wall lizards, sandracer, and racerunner. A typical lacertid has a long, slim body and tail. Males usually have larger heads than females and are often brightly colored, particularly in the breeding season. Like most lizards, lacertids ~~lay~~ eggs hidden under stones or in holes. The ~~exception~~ is the viviparous lizard. It gives birth to ~~babies~~ rather than laying eggs, as described below. ~~This~~ species lives over much of Europe, including ~~the~~ far north, and Central Asia. In the summer ~~months~~ it is lively and active, feeding on insects, ~~worms~~, and other small creatures. When the ~~weather~~ gets cold in the north of its range, it becomes inactive or torpid, and stays in its burrow for up to six months.

THE TUATARA

The tuatara (or sphenodon) may look like a lizard. In fact, it is a rhynchocephalian—a type of reptile common many millions of years ago, at the time of the dinosaurs. There is only one species alive today, and it is found only on a few offshore islands of New Zealand, in sanctuaries. They are extinct on the New Zealand mainland, largely due to human-introduced predators such as cats and rats, which eat their eggs. Tuataras shelter in burrows during the day and come out at night to hunt insects, snails, and spiders. These "living fossils" are 18–24 inches (45–60 cm) long. Their eggs take 15 months to hatch—longer than any other reptile.

LIZARD EATER

Like lacertids, teiid lizards have long bodies and tails, are active by day, and hunt ~~insects~~ and other small creatures. The jungle ~~runner~~ is a teiid from Central and South America. ~~It~~ is an extremely busy predator, catching small ~~birds~~ and mammals, and even smaller lizards.

◩ The tokay ~~gecko~~ is named ~~for~~ its barking ~~"to-keh!"~~ call.

EGGS OR BABIES?

Most lizards, like most reptiles, reproduce by laying leathery-shelled eggs. But geckos produce hard-shelled eggs, like those of birds. In most cases, the eggs are left to incubate and hatch by ~~themselves~~. In a few species, the ~~male~~ may curl around her eggs ~~to~~ protect them, but this is rare ~~among~~ lizards. However, some ~~lizards~~, including types of geckos, night ~~lizards~~, anguids, lacertids, and skinks, do not lay eggs. The female keeps the developing babies inside her body, in their thin-walled shells. The young are nourished by their egg yolks, and also by substances from the female's body, in a similar way to a mammal mother. The babies hatch from their eggs inside the mother, and then she gives birth. The viviparous lizard produces about 6–8 young in this way. But after the mother has given birth to her babies, she takes no interest in them. They must manage for themselves straight away.

◩ Whiptail lizards are among the few reptiles ~~whose~~ females lay eggs without first mating ~~with~~ a male. This is called parthenogenesis.

SKINKS, MONITORS, AND SLOW WORMS

SKINKS ARE THE LARGEST GROUP OF LIZARDS, WITH MORE THAN 1,300 SPECIES. They live in tropical and temperate areas all over the world, particularly in Southeast Asia and Australia. Skinks are very varied in body shape and are found in almost every habitat, from rainforest and stream bank to desert and mountaintop. They have tiny legs, or none at all. Slow worms are limbless lizards. Monitors are large, powerful lizards with strong legs, a long neck and tail, and a snakelike forked tongue.

▲ Gila monsters feed mainly other lizards and snakes, small mammals, birds, and the eggs reptiles and birds.

▲ The slow worm eats worms, slugs, grubs, and spiders. It is about 20 inches (50 cm) long and lives in Europe, Asia, and North Africa.

The monitor lizard family includes the largest of all lizards, the Komodo dragon of Southeast Asia. It lives on Komodo and neighboring Indonesian islands, where it hunts wild pigs, deer, and monkeys. It also scavenges on carrion. Young komodo dragons catch insects and small mammals. These mighty creatures, once very rare, now benefit from being a tourist attraction. People pay to throw them dead animals to eat, while taking photographs and videos.

RACY MONITORS

Monitor lizards live in Africa and Southeast Asia, and also in Australia, where most species are found. Some are known as goannas. The sand monitor is also called the racehorse goanna because it runs so fast. The shy Australian perentie of desert and rocky scrub is the world's second-biggest lizard, at 8 feet (2.5 m) long.

LEGLESS SKINK

Many skinks are slim and fast-moving. They wriggle on their bellies, rather than walking on their legs.

◄ The gila monster is one of only two kinds of lizard with a poisonous bite. The other is the Mexican beaded lizard.

WORM LIZARDS

The snakelike worm lizards are neither worms, nor lizards, nor snakes. They make up a separate reptile group, amphisbaenids. typical worm lizard has a scaly, loose-skinned body from 4–28 inches (10–70 cm) long, and no legs (although a few have tiny front limbs). It lives in burrows, which it digs by forcing its blunt head through the soil. Most live in Africa, South America, and the West Indies.

Indeed, some skinks have no limbs. The legless skink has a snakelike body and lives in burrows in South Africa and Madagascar. It moves surprisingly quickly with curving body movements.

◄ The blue-tongued skink of Australia grows to about 18 inches (45 cm) long. It lives in dry scrub and eats small animals, fruits, and berries.

LEG FLAPS

Scaly-foot lizards, also known as snake lizards, have long snakelike bodies. They have no front legs. The tiny back legs are little more than flaps held close against the body.

POISONOUS LIZARDS

The gila monster and the beaded lizard are in a group of their own, related to monitors. They live in southwestern North America and parts of Central America, and are the only venomous lizards. They feed mainly on small animals and eggs, so their poison is probably more for defense than for killing prey. Both of these lizards have thick tails, used to store body fat in times of food shortage.

WEDGED IN A CRACK

Plated lizards live in Africa, usually in rocky, dry areas. The imperial flat lizard, as its name suggests, has a flattened head and body so it can slide into narrow crevices among the rocks. Once in the crack, the lizard puffs itself up with air, wedging its body and making it almost impossible to remove.

▲ Plated lizards include the armadillo lizard from Southern Africa. It is named for its defence of rolling into a ball like an armadillo, its spiny scales sticking out. It is fairly small, only 20 cm long including its tail, and hunts by day for a wide range of small creatures, including spiders.

▲ The Komodo dragon of Indonesia grows up to 10 feet (3 m) long and weighs more than 330 pounds (150 kg).

SLOW LIZARDS

The anguid lizards include some legless types, such as the slow worms, and also species with large and strong legs, such as the alligator lizard. The galliwasp is an anguid lizard from Central and South America with an orange head, a red underside, and a dark blue back with black crossways stripes. It has smooth, shiny skin and looks more like a brightly colored salamander than a lizard.

MORE GROUPS OF LIZARDS:

Skinks (Scincidae)
• more than 1,300 species
• body typically long with a small head and short legs
• some limbless species
• includes Great Plains skink, sandfish, blue-tongued skink

Monitor lizards (Varanidae)
• 48 species
• large body, long neck, strong legs and tail
• includes Komodo dragon, Gould's monitor, Nile monitor

Anguid Lizards (Anguidae)
• about 100 species
• long, smooth body and tail
• some limbless species
• includes slow-worm, alligator lizard, legless lizard, glass snake, galliwasp

Scaly-foot lizards (Pygopodidae)
• about 35 species
• very long slim body, tiny back legs, no front legs
• includes western scaly-foot, Burton's snake-lizard

Girdle-tailed lizards (Cordylidae)
• 50 species
• heavily armoured body covered with bony plates
• includes imperial flat lizard, plated lizard, armadillo lizard

Blind lizards (Dibamidae)
• 11 species
• small, long-bodied with tiny limbs
• includes Asian blind lizard

Beaded lizards (Helodermatidae)
• 2 species
• bulky body, large head, short thick tail
• venomous
• includes gila monster, beaded lizard

PYTHONS, BOAS, AND THREAD SNAKES

SNAKES HAVE NO LEGS. Yet they can wriggle at speed alon the ground, climb trees easily, swim well—and a few can ever "fly"! Snakes are a hugely successful group of reptiles with almost 2,400 species. They live on all continents except Antarctica. They are also absent from Ireland, Iceland, and New Zealand. They are all predators. Most can open their mouths wide to swallow prey whole. Some have suffocating coils and others strike with deadly poison fangs.

Snakes evolved millions of years ago, from reptiles similar to lizards which had four limbs. Gradually the limbs became smaller, and in most snakes today, they have completely disappeared. But some snakes have tiny, useless remnants of limbs, such as hip and rear leg bones. These include thread snakes, blind snakes, and pipe snakes. They are called primitive snakes because they most resemble their distant ancestors. Like the first snakes, most of them burrow into soil and spend much of their lives undergroun

A The sunbeam snake of Southeast Asia burrows and s well, and eats fish, frogs, mic and small birds. Its body has a mixture of primitive (ancient) advanced (modern) features.

Blind and thread snakes have tiny eyes hidden beneath scales. Most thread snakes are blunt-headed, while blind snakes have narrow heads. Both designs help them to tunnel through soil. They eat small worms, grubs, ants, termites, and similar soil creatures.

PIPE SNAKES

Pipe snakes also spend much time burrowing underground. Unlike most other snakes, a pipe snake cannot open its mouth very wide. So it feeds mainly on slender-bodied animals such as worm lizards and other snakes, which it sucks in like spaghetti.

◄ The green python coils around itself to rest, almost as it would squeeze or constrict its prey.

▶ Boas often rest in trees. Like pythons, they can tilt forward the large scales on the underside of the body. This raises the rear edges of the scales for extra grip as the snake moves forward.

Pythons are mainly large snakes of the tropics in Africa, Asia, and Australia. They like to stay near water and climb trees well. Boas are similar snakes of the Americas, although they stay more on the ground. Both pythons and boas are primitive snakes, with tiny hip and back leg bones embedded in their bodies. They all have two lungs as well. Most other snakes have lost one lung during evolution, to help achieve their narrow, streamlined shape.

⬛ The false coral snake is a type of pipe snake. It grows to about 32 inches (80 cm) long.

Both pythons and boas are fierce predators. They kill their prey by coiling their bodies around it and crushing it until the victim suffocates. They prey mainly on mammals and birds. The reticulated python is the longest snake, reaching 33 feet (10 m). Boas have slightly different bones in the head and the teeth compared to pythons. They include the second-longest but heaviest snake, the anaconda. It spends much of its life in swamps and slow-moving streams, in its rainforest habitat. Half-hidden in the shallows, it lies in wait for animals to come and drink. When a victim is near enough, the anaconda bites and envelops it in crushing coils.

HEAVIEST... !
The bulkiest snake is an anaconda. It weighs up to 550 pounds (250 kg), more than three adult humans.

⬛ The western blind snake is a type of thread snake. It has very small, simple eyes hidden beneath its skin. It can slide into ants' nests to eat the larvae.

This erald e boa is t beginning swallow a oly opossum. may take an hour or re, and the boa may not eat ain for a month. The snake's bright en body gives excellent camouflage among the ves of its forest home in northern South America.

World Watch

Large snakes such as pythons and boas were once hunted for their leathery, beautifully patterned skin. This was used to make shoes, bags, belts, trousers, and similar hard-wearing items. However, the hunting made some species extremely rare. It is more difficult to farm snakes for the skin trade compared to, for example, crocodiles. Most snakes will only eat a victim if it has only just died and is still warm.

🐍 The anaconda is a massive-bodied swamp snake from South America. It grows to 30 feet (9 m) in length and can eat animals the size of goats, tapirs, and peccaries. Females give birth to about 30 babies, each 2 feet (60 cm) long.

CARING MOTHER
Most snakes lay their eggs in holes and leave them to hatch. The Indian python is one of the few snake species that incubate their eggs with their own bodies. The female lays up to 100 eggs and curls around them to keep them warm and protected. She also adjusts her body to cover them more or less, according to the weather.

SOME GROUPS OF SNAKES (continued from page 139):

Thread snakes
(Leptotyphlopidae)
• about 64 species
• small, slender body, blunt head and tail

Blind snakes (Typhlopidae)
• about 150 species
• smooth, cylindrical body
• teeth only in upper jaw

Pipe snakes (Aniliidae)
• 11 species
• blunt head
• body often boldly marked
• includes coral pipe snake, false coral snake

Pythons and boas (Boidae)
• about 60 species
• flexible jaws
• tiny remnants of rear limbs
• squeeze or constrict prey

155

COLUBRID SNAKES

THE COLUBRIDS ARE THE LARGEST GROUP OF SNAKES. Found on all continents except Antarctica, they are the most common snakes everywhere except Australia, where they are outnumbered by the various types of cobras. Most colubrids are medium-sized snakes, about 20–60 inches (50–150 cm) long. Unlike pythons, they have no remnants of any limbs, and the left lung is either very small or absent, in order to streamline the body. Colubrids live on land, in burrows under the ground, in trees, and even in water. They eat a wide range of foods, from eggs to mice and small birds. Most species are harmless to humans. But a few, such as the boomslang, have poisonous bites. They are called back-fanged venomous snakes because their poison fangs are near the rear of the jaws, not at the front.

◪ The brown water snake lurks in muddy creeks and ponds, ready to strike. There are about 30 kinds of water snakes. They all have their nostrils on top of the snout for breathing while almost submerged.

◪ The grass snake is extremely varied in color and pattern. Its bite is poisonous, but only to small animals such as frogs, fish, and voles. It grows to about 4 feet (1.2 m) in length.
◪ This egg-eating snake is ready to crack an egg with its spiny neck bones.

…e poisonous types of colubrid snakes are few in …mber, and they do not have hollow fangs at the …ont of the mouth like other venomous species. …stead they have grooved teeth at the back of the …per jaw, which are linked to a poison gland. As …e snake bites, the poison flows down the groove …o the prey. This means the snake must get its …uth well over the victim, to deliver its venom.

…UMB-THIN SNAKE

…e venom of the African boomslang is strong …ough to kill a human. But this dark or olive …een snake usually prefers to slide away if …eatened, rather than strike. It needs to conserve …poison to kill its prey, which is mostly birds …d lizards such as chameleons. The boomslang is …to 6 feet (1.8 m) long, but its body is very …nder, hardly thicker than a thumb. This means …s also very light and a good climber, spending …ch of its life among the branches.

…he vine snake may be more than 6 feet (1.8 m) long. Yet its …y is as thin as a little finger. This amazing camouflage hides it …ong the creepers and vines in trees. If the wind increases, the …ke sways with the stems around it. Vine snakes eat small tree-…lling lizards and baby birds.

…GS AND SNAILS

…any snakes eat eggs as part of a varied diet. But …e egg-eating snake of Africa eats only …hard-shelled eggs of birds. It can …en its jaws very wide to take the …into its mouth. As the egg passes …o its throat, spiky projections on …snake's neck bones jab and saw …shell open, allowing the contents …ooze out and be swallowed. The …ke then brings up or regurgitates the …s of shell and settles to digest its meal.

…e snail-eating snake is another specialist. …lower jaw is equipped with strong, …ved teeth. The snake hooks these teeth …o the fleshy body of a snail, drags the …il out of its shell, and swallows its meal.

BABIES! ⚠

Garter snakes are among the most numerous and widespread snakes in North America. During the fall, in the north of their range, they gather in holes and caves to spend the winter. However, they may mate first, each large female being almost completely buried under a writhing mass of smaller males. She does not lay eggs. Instead, up to 80 babies develop inside her body. The babies are born as the warmth returns in late spring.

WATER SNAKE

Although water snakes bask on land, they spend most of their time in swamps, streams, and rivers. They are excellent swimmers and pursue fish and other water-living creatures, such as frogs and crayfish.

FLYING SNAKE?

The tree-living paradise snake from Southeast Asia is sometimes known as the flying snake, because it can glide through the air between trees. As it hurls itself from a high branch, it spreads its ribs out sideways and draws its belly up and in, to make a long, ribbonlike shape with a curved underside. This works almost like a bird's wing to provide an upward force. As the paradise snake "flies," it wriggles its body as it would on the ground, gliding perhaps 60 feet (18 m) to the ground or to a lower branch. It is not a very well controlled glide, however, and a gust of wind can blow the snake into the trunk of a tree. The flying snake is about 50 inches (1.3 m) long and feeds on small birds and lizards.

THE LARGEST SNAKE GROUP
(continued from page 155):

Colubrid snakes
(Colubridae)
• about 1,600 species
• no remnants of limbs
• flexible lower jaw to allow mouth to open very wide, for biting and swallowing
• most lack venom, or the venom is not strong enough to harm humans
• includes grass snake, garter snake, rat snake, cat-eyed snake, milk snake, mud snake, slug snake, spotted water snake, gopher snake

✔ Mangrove snakes hunt crabs, fish, and frogs among the mangrove swamps of Southeast Asia and Australia.

COBRAS, VIPERS, AND RATTLERS

THERE ARE TWO MAIN GROUPS OF VENOMOUS SNAKES. These are the cobras and the vipers. The cobras have short fangs, fixed in position at the front of the upper jaw. When the snake bites, venom passes from the poison glands through the fangs and into the victim. The fangs must be relatively short or the snake would not b[e] able to close its mouth. Vipers have longer fangs that fol[low] up and back when not in use, to keep them safe and sharp[.]

◪ An Indian cobra spreads [its] "eyed" hood when ready [to] action, to look more menaci[ng.]

◪ The Gaboon viper has a very noticeable neck for its size. It is one of the largest vipers, at up to 6 feet (1.8 m) long. Its brown pattern makes it blend in among old leaves on the rainforest floor.

The cobra group includes many kinds of poisonous snakes besides the hooded species named cobras, which live in Africa, the Middle East, and Asia. Other group members are the brightly colored coral snakes of North and South America, the highly venomous mambas of Africa, and the fish-eating sea snakes which live all their lives in the oceans. The cobra group is very common in Australia, with far more members there than any other type of snake. They include the eastern brown snake of forests and swamps.

▷ The bandy-bandy is a distinctive black and white snake from Australia. It eats mainly smaller snakes, especially blind snakes, and lives in a wide variety of habitats.

THE COBRA'S HOOD
To warn off enemies, hooded cobras raise the front of the body off the ground, spread the ribs and loose skin at the sides of the head to make the cloaklike hood, and sway gently. This makes the snake look bigger than it really is, and warns the enemy that it may strike. In the Indian cobra, the hood has eyelike markings to further alarm the attacker.

birth to the young, so does not need to go onto land to lay eggs. Sea snakes have other adaptations to a watery life, including a flatten[ed] tail that works as a paddle, and nostrils on top [of] the head so the snake can breathe even when most of its body is under water. Flaps close the nostrils when the snake dives. Sea snakes feed mostly on fish and have extremely powerful venom. On land, without the water to buoy the[m] up, they are floppy and can hardly move.

SNAKES AT SEA
About 50 species of sea snakes, such as the banded sea snake, spend all their lives at sea. The female carries the developing babies inside her body and gives

▷ The sidewinder, a type of viper, pushes up and forward mainly with its head and tail, leaving J-shaped indents in the desert sand.

agler's viper

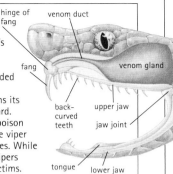

VIPER FANGS

Vipers have the most complicated killing equipment of any snake. A viper's large, thin teeth, or fangs, are much longer than the fangs of a cobra. Also they are hinged so that they can be folded back against the upper jaw when not needed. When the viper attacks, it opens its mouth wide and the fangs swing forward. Venom is pumped into them from the poison glands behind the eyes. Members of the viper family include pit vipers and rattlesnakes. While cobras tend to chase after their prey, vipers usually lie in wait and ambush their victims.

hinge of fang
venom duct
fang
venom gland
back-curved teeth
upper jaw
jaw joint
tongue
lower jaw

MBAS

e African mambas are feared for their prising speed, their readiness to strike, and ir venom. Mamba bites are fatal more often n the bites of almost any other snake. mbas chase birds and small mammals to eat. ey can crawl with a large part of the nt body held upright, so the head is re than 3 feet (1 m) off the ground.

◄ The black mamba, from Africa, is 14 feet (4.2 m) long. It is one of the deadliest snakes. It can slither along at more than 7 mph (11 km/h).

VIPERS

e types of vipers called pit vipers can hunt even the darkest night. They are named for the all, sensory holes or pits on each side of the d. These detect heat (infrared rays) coming m warm-blooded prey. Like infrared "night oculars," the two pit organs provide a "heat ture" of the surroundings. By moving its head m side to side, the snake can pinpoint the ct position of a mouse or small bird.

aving made its warning e, this rattlesnake is in mid- e, mouth wide open and s about to stab poison. largest rattlers grow e than 7 feet (2.1 m) and are the most erous snakes in h America.

THE WARNING BUZZ

North American rattlesnakes belong to the pit viper group. At the end of the tail is a rattle made of hard rings of skin. When the snake shakes this, the rings make a buzzing, rattling sound to warn enemies. New rings are added to the rattle as the snake grows.

LARGEST... !
The largest venomous snake in the world is the king cobra, which grows to more than 16 feet (5 m) in length

MAIN GROUPS OF POISONOUS SNAKES:

Cobras (Elapidae)
• about 250 species
• fixed fangs at front of upper jaw
• usually slender bodied
• includes black mamba, king cobra, banded sea snake

Vipers (Viperidae)
• about 200 species
• tilting hollow fangs in upper jaw
• heavy bodied
• includes common viper, puff adder, rattlesnakes

159

The white pelican is one of the biggest waterbirds, with a wingspan of 8 feet (2.7 m). It is known for its big beak with a stretchy pouch.

SECTION 6
BIRDS

BIRDS ARE PROBABLY THE MOST EASILY
RECOGNIZED OF ALL ANIMALS. Any creature
with wings, feathers, and a beak must be a bird.
But not all birds use their wings for flying.
The ostrich uses its wings as a sunshade to keep its eggs
cool in the desert heat. Puffins, razorbills, and guillemots
flap their wings to swim underwater, with the help of
their webbed feet.

Feathers and beaks vary enormously, too. The kiwi is flightless, like the
ostrich, and its feathers look like hairs. The peacock's colorful tail feathers are
longer than your arm. The shape of a bird's beak usually shows the type of
food it eats. An eagle's beak is sharp and hooked, for tearing flesh. A parrot's
beak is thick and massive, for cracking nuts. A pelican's beak has a stretchy
throat pouch which it uses as a fishing bag. A curlew's beak is like long, slim
tweezers for probing into mud.

Birds are one of only two groups of animals that are warm-blooded. (The
other group is mammals.) Being warm-blooded means being able to stay active
even in cold conditions. Penguins survive some of the lowest temperatures on
Earth, in the bitter cold and driving snow of Antarctica. Other birds
experience intense cold at great heights, on mountains and during long-
distance journeys. Some migrating geese fly as high as jet planes.

FLIGHTLESS BIRDS

ALL BIRDS HAVE WINGS, BUT NOT ALL OF THEM CAN FLY. Penguins are so well adapted to life in the sea that they use their short, stubby wings for swimming, not flying. The rare kakapo parrot of New Zealand has lost the power of flight because it has no natural predators where it lives, and so does not need to escape flying. The most distinctive flightless birds are the ratite These are mostly big—ostriches, emus, cassowaries, rhea and kiwis. They are part of a group of birds that, like penguins, never evolved the ability to fly. Ratites have always walked or run everywhere.

◢ The dodo was a huge-beaked, turkey-sized flightless bird from the Indian Ocean island of Mauritius. In this remote place it had no natural predators and so no need to fly. But when European people came to the island in the 1500s, they brought rats, pigs, and monkeys, which ate the dodos' eggs. By 1680, they were extinct—"dead as a dodo."

◢ The emu of Australia grows up to 68 inches (170 cm) tall and weighs almost 100 pounds (45 kg). In some areas they ha become pests because they ea crops and break sheep fences.

OUCH!

The kiwi's huge white eggs are the biggest eggs of any bird, compared to the size of the adult. Each weighs about 1 pound (454 g), which is almost one fourth of the mother's normal body weight—and she may lay two!

FLYING IN WATER

Penguins are so well adapted to life in the water that their wings are more like flippers. Their coats are so thick and well waterproofed with oil that they can survive even in the icy waters of the Antarctic. They are superb swimmers, and dash through the water by flapping their wings with the same motion that other birds use to fly through the air. On snow and ice, penguins often slide head-first down slopes, as if tobogganing. In the water they are swift and agile, pursuing their prey with ease. They eat mainly krill, squid, and fish. Emperor penguins are the largest species. They can dive as deep as 800 feet (250 m) in search of food.

BIGGEST BIRDS

Millions of years ago there were many species of ratites all over the world. Now there are just te species left, scattered as far apart as Africa and New Zealand. They are different to other birds in various ways, besides being flightless. For example, their feathers lack the smooth, flat, airproof surfaces which other birds have for flying. Instead, ratites have downy, "hairy" feathers. The leg bones of ratites are sturdy, more like a mammal's legs than a bird's. This is why some ratites can grow so large. The ostrich is the biggest living bird, towering up to 9 feet (2.75 m) tall.

◢ Penguins dive into the water in a large group to hunt for their food. The mass dive helps to confuse any predators such as leopard seals and killer whales that may be lurking nearby.

◢ The wo biggest bird ostrich, is also only bird with two toes on foot. The toes sharp claws a kick from an os can be de

en bigger than an
trich was the giant
oa of New Zealand.
me moas were 10 feet
m) tall and weighed
much as a pony.
ey became extinct
er people arrived.

◪ The cassowary uses its helmetlike head crest for pushing through thick scrub.

TRICHES AND RHEAS
ith their soft, downy
umage and bare
cks, ostriches look
her comical and
lnerable as they strut
oss the grasslands of Africa. But they can
int at up to 35 mph (60 km/h), and can kick
e a mule—which is why they rarely fall prey to
ns. The idea that they bury their heads in the
d when afraid is a myth. It comes from the
y the bird moves its eggs in the nest so that
ey stay evenly warm.

e rhea lives on the plains of southern Brazil and
gentina. It looks like a small ostrich, but has
ore feathers on its neck, and larger wings. On
e occasions it can struggle a few feet through
e air. Unusually for birds, male rheas and
riches do most of the work at breeding time.
e male scoops out a hole in the ground for a
st. Then, when several females have laid
ir eggs in it, he keeps them safe and at the
rrect temperature until they hatch, and
cares for the young chicks too.

he flightless kakapo of New Zealand is the world's
est parrot. It was once thought to have been
ed out by cats, rats, and dogs. But recently,
w survivors were found and taken to a
tected area on Little Barrier Island near
kland, where there are no such
dators. There the kakapos can breed
the species might be saved.

AUSTRALIAN RATITES
In the thick forests of
tropical Australia and nearby
islands, such as New Guinea,
live three species of shy
ratites called cassowaries.
They are the same size as
rheas, about 5 feet (1.5 m)
tall. But they look more like
long-legged turkeys, with a
brightly colored neck and a
bony crest. They eat fruits,
seeds, and other plant parts. Another Australian ratite
is the emu. It is second only to the ostrich in size, and
can run almost as fast. It eats an extremely varied diet
in grasslands and woodlands.

New Zealand's ratites are chicken-sized kiwis. Their
wings are tiny, hidden beneath furlike feathers. Kiwis
are secretive birds, active only at night in bushy scrub
or forests. They are rarely seen as they search
for grubs, insects, berries, and fruit.

◪ Kiwis are tubby birds, covered in shaggy feathers like a furball. They have the best sense of smell of almost any bird, using the nostrils on the end of the beak to sniff out food in the leaves and soil.

RDS (AVES)
bout 8,800 species
varm-blooded
eathers
eak or bill

me flightless birds:

trich
l species
Africa
avanna
nale black and
white; female brown

eas
species
South America
crub, grassland
rown or gray

Emu
• 1 species
• Australia
• woodland, scrub, and grassland
• dark brown

Cassowaries
• 3 species
• Australia, New Guinea
• rain forest
• mainly black

Penguins
• 16 species
• Antarctic region and southern parts of main oceans

• rocky islands and icebergs
• mainly black and white
• expert swimmers

Kiwis
• 3 species
• New Zealand
• forest and scrub
• brown or gray

Tinamous
• 49 species
• Central and South America
• resemble guinea fowl or pheasants
• some can fly but do so rarely

SEABIRDS

HUGE NUMBERS OF BIRDS LIVE BY, OR ON, THE SEA. Some feed mainly along the shore or dive for fish in coastal waters, such as various gulls, cormorants, and gannets. Others, like auks, terns, skuas, and frigate birds, live for weeks far out in the ocean. They come to the surface occasionally in calm weather, to float and rest. Still others, such as albatrosses, shearwaters, and petrels, spend weeks at a time in the air. They land only rarely, usually to breed. They are superb fliers, soari: across the oceans for thousands of miles.

There are about 90 species of gulls, skuas, and terns. They usually wheel and call along the coast, but gulls especially have adapted to new sources of food far inland. They hunt for worms and grubs in freshly plowed fields, and squabble over leftovers on garbage tips, especially in winter. The herring gull, in particular, is aggressive and threatens other birds. Gulls eat almost anything, including fish, crabs, insects, rotten meat, and the eggs of other birds.

Most gulls have white and gray plumage, matching the reflections of sunlight on the sea. Some species have black markings on the back, wings, and head. The larger gulls, like the great black-backed gull, have heavy, hooked beaks. They can easily kill smaller birds, baby rabbits, and similar prey.

PIRATES AMONG BIRDS

Skuas resemble the larger gulls and have fearsome hooked beaks. In North America they are known by the German name of jaeger, meaning 'hunter,' due to their habit of chasing other birds who are carrying food. They harass the other bird, force it to drop its meal, then swoop to steal it. Big skuas like the great skua may catch and kill birds even larger than themselves.

Terns are like slim, graceful gulls. Many have forked tails, earning them the nickname of 'sea-swallows.' Many terns catch their fish prey by plunge-diving straight down into the water.

△ Shearw:

◩ Albatrosses may be at sea for 2–3 weeks at a time. The wandering albatross has the longest wingspan of any bird, up to 11.5 feet (3.5 m). The waved albatross shown here is slightly smaller.

◪ The male frigatebird has a bright red, balloonlike skin pouch on his throat. He blows this up to attract a female.

◩ Boobies were named from the Spanish word *bobo*, meaning 'stupid,' because the birds were easily caught by sailors for food.

◪ Guillemot

164

◄ Royal terns

◘ Common gulls use the wind to stay aloft without flapping.

LIGHT! ⚠

Arctic terns fly 25,000 miles (40,000 km) each year! They spend the northern summer in the Arctic where they breed. At the end of the summer, they migrate all the way to Antarctica, in time for the southern summer. So they live in almost endless daylight.

...hey are mainly summer visitors to temperate ...gions, migrating to warmer areas to avoid the ...ld winter months.

...KIMMING ALONG

...kimmers are ternlike birds, but with an unusual ...ature. The lower mandible (part of the beak) is ...nger than the upper part. The skimmer flies low ...d dips this lower mandible in the water, to ...atch any fish.

...ASTERS OF THE OCEAN WINDS

...batrosses and petrels are master fliers, feeding ...r out at sea. Albatrosses are so big and heavy ...at they usually need a cliff to leap from, or a ...adwind to launch themselves into the air. Once ...oft, they glide for hours in winds and air ...rrents, without flapping. Shearwaters are smaller ...t have similar bodies, with long, narrow wings. ...orm petrels are smaller and darker.

...UMP DIVERS

...ks are plump seabirds resembling penguins. ...eir tight feathering keeps body warmth in and ...ter out. They spend much time diving for food. ...illemots and razorbills breed in colonies on ...cky ledges and cliffs, where most predators cannot reach.

Cormorants are related to pelicans and have a similar but smaller throat pouch. Their feet are webbed across all four toes. They are

◘ The puffin is a strange-looking seabird that nests in clifftop burrows. Its brightly patterned beak is large enough to hold a dozen small fish such as sand-eels.

black or dark birds, expert at diving and swimming after fish. They prefer rocky coasts and, unusually for seabirds, the oily waterproofing on their feathers is not very effective. So they spend long periods sitting with their wings spread out to dry in the sun.

FRIGATEBIRDS

Frigatebirds live along tropical coasts and are among the most graceful seabirds. The magnificent frigatebird has long wings and a long tail, which it uses as an aerial rudder and air-brake. It can swoop to catch fish leaping above the surface or snatch baby turtles hatching from their eggs on the beach.

SOME GROUPS OF SEABIRDS:

Gulls and terns
• 95 species
• mostly white or gray
• narrow wings

Skuas (jaegers)
• 6 species
• brown and white
• hooked beak

Skimmers
• 3 species
• black or dark brown and white
• long lower bill

Albatrosses, shearwaters, and petrels
• 93 species
• oceanic
• long, narrow wings

Auks
• 22 species
• compact and dumpy
• dive well

• black and white plumage

Cormorants
• 29 species
• black or dark plumage
• swim low in water

Gannets and boobies
• 9 species
• white, with black or dark markings

Frigatebirds
• 5 species
• large and long-winged
• black or dark and white

Tropicbirds
• 3 species
• white with black markings
• graceful fliers
• tail streamers

SHOREBIRDS AND WATERBIRDS

THE WATER'S EDGE IS ONE OF THE RICHEST OF ALL BIRD HABITATS. The shallows of marshes, and the shores of lakes, estuaries, and seas, are home to hundreds of small wading birds, such as oystercatchers, plovers, avocets, stilts, sandpipers, and curlews. They stride through the water on spindly legs, dipping their long beaks into the water to grab worms and other food in the mud. There are bigger wading birds, too, such as flamingoes (page 168), herons, and storks which feed mainly on fish. Many other birds live in these water-edge and shallow-water habitats, but they dive or swim after food rather than wading. The largest diving birds are pelicans. Expert underwater swimmers include grebes, darters, an (despite their name) divers.

◪ Many wading birds have clear, sad-sounding cries, like lonely wails. The curlew's "koor-lee" call can be heard far across the marshes, moors, and mudfl of northern Europe.

> ### ZOOM! ⚠
> Courting western grebes rear up and run at amazing speed across the surface. They zoom along like powerboats, driven by their splashing feet. This shows that they are fit and healthy, and so suitable as breeding partners.

▾ The white pelican is one of the biggest waterbirds, with a wingspan of 8 feet (2.7 m). It is known for its big beak with a stretchy pouch.

The water's edge is home to many of the 300 bird species in the huge group called the Charadriiformes. They include most types of waders, as well as seabirds which fly rather than wade, such as skuas, gulls, and auks.

Waders have long, spindly legs for walking through water, and widely spread toes for standing on soft mud. The black-winged stilt has the longest legs of any bird compared to its body size—they are over half the stilt's total height of 16 inches (40 cm).

◪ Jacanas, or lily-trotters, are waders that spend much time walking across water lily leav They have the longest toes, fo their body size, of any bird.

Waders' beaks are mostly also long and thin, for probing in water and m The precise shape of the beak varies according to how the bird feeds, anc on what. Most waders poke about in mud and sand for small insects, worms, and shellfish. Sandpipers have long beaks for digging softer sand and mud. Curlews have longer bills and gouge farther dow for deeper-dwelling worms. The oystercatcher uses its stron; chisel-like bill to prise apart shellfish such as mussels.

THE PELICAN'S FISHING BAG

Pelicans are among the largest and heaviest waterbirds. They live on shallow coasta lagoons and inland lakes throughou the warmer parts of the world. They waddle awkwardly on land, but they swim and dive well, and soar gracefully.

◨ The stilt sandpiper has long,
thin legs, as its name implies,
to wade in deeper water. The
sandpiper family
includes about 80
species of waders,
found across
the world.

...licans are fish eaters. They feed by dipping their
...ads under the surface and scooping up a huge
...outhful of water and fish, in their big beaks.
...e chin and throat have loose skin that stretches
...e a balloon. The pelican tips out the water and
...allows the fish. The Australian pelican has the
...ngest bill of any bird, measuring up to
...inches (47 cm).

...e pelican's chin-
...d-throat bag,
...gular pouch,
...pands to
...ld more than
...ice as much as
...e stomach. But not
...pelicans scoop for
...h. The American
...own pelican dives from
...ights of 30 feet (9 m)
...o the sea, to dive-
...mb and catch fish.

...EBES

...ebes, unlike pelicans
...d divers, have lobed
...ther than webbed feet.
...ey are found in most

...A red-necked grebe sits on its
...ating nest. Most grebes build
...sts of water-plant stems
...d leaves, piled up so
...t they float.

▲ The avocet is a graceful
wader that sifts tiny worms,
shrimps, and similar animals
from the water with its
slender, distinctive, upcurved
beak. It skims its beak from
side to side across the surface
to gather food.

parts of the world, mainly in freshwater lakes,
rivers, and marshes. In the winter, many grebes
move toward the coasts, to feed along estuaries,
mudflats, and saltmarshes. Grebes are known for
their elaborate courtship "dances." At breeding
time, the female and male often swim and
dive together. They surface holding weeds in
their beaks, which they exchange as though
swapping presents. Then they circle round,
approach front-to-front, touch breasts, and stretch
upward, with beaks
pointing up in the air.

◀ African
darter

SUPREME SWIMMERS

Divers or loons are streamlined
waterbirds of northern regions. In
the breeding season they make
ghostly, wailing cries to attract a
mate. They spend most of their time
on lakes or out at sea, swimming with
ease because their legs are set far back
on their bodies. But this makes them
unbalanced and clumsy when walking
on land. When a diver swims, it
almost lies on the water, so that it can
slip easily beneath the surface. It may
stay submerged for
many minutes.

DARTERS

The darter is one of the
most streamlined of
swimming birds. It has a
slender body, snakelike
neck, and dagger-shaped
beak. It is very agile on
and under the water, but
swims slowly, creeping
up on its prey to deliver
a stabbing peck. Darters
are found mainly in the
tropics and prefer large,
quiet lakes with plenty
of insect and fish life.

SOME WATERBIRD GROUPS:

Waders
• 200 species
• most are wetland birds
• long legs, many have long bills
• medium-sized or small

Pelicans
• 7 species
• gliding and soaring flight
• feet completely webbed (all
  four toes)
• balloonlike throat pouch

Divers or loons
• 4 species
• waterbirds, excellent swimmers
  and divers

Grebes
• 20 species
• waterbirds, very good
  swimmers and divers
• 3 species are flightless

Darters
• 4 species
• thin, snakelike, darting neck

HERONS, DUCKS, AND GEESE

THE FRESH WATERS OF LAKES, RIVERS, AND MARSHES ARE HOME TO A WEALTH OF BIRDS.

There are long-legged waders like herons, storks, and flamingoes, smaller cranes and rails, and hundreds of species of waterfowl—ducks, geese, and swans. Many are excellent swimmers a can cope with fast-flowing rivers, but they prefer the calm waters of lakes and swamps, where there is no energy-sapping current. Some species nest on the water, among reeds and other vegetation, but most nest on the shore an feed in the water. The taller waders are mostly predators, using their long, sharp beaks to spear fish, frogs, shellfish and other water creatures. Waterfowl are mainly vegetari feeding on grass, waterweeds, and other plants, although some ducks take insects and shellfish.

At more than 10 feet (3 m), the marabou stork of Africa has the larges wingspan of any land bird.

⬆ The mute swan weighs 40 pounds (18 kg). It needs a long stretch of water for takeoff and landing.

◀ Flamingoes live and nest in huge colonies in the tropics. To feed, a flamingo bends its neck and tips its head over, to hold its strange, kinked beak upside down and sweep it from side to side. Inside the beak, the tongue works like a piston to suck water in and squirt it out. Hairlike fringes on the beak filter out small shrimps and similar food.

Most wading birds have long, featherless legs for striding through the water, a long neck to reach down and feed, and a long beak to grab or stab prey. The biggest group of large freshwater waders includes herons, egrets, and bitterns, with 60 species throughout temperate and tropical regions. Most are gray or brown. When hunting fish and frogs, a heron stands motionless on one leg in the shallows, apparently asleep,

until it suddenly spears down into th water with its long beak. The prey is caught and then flipped around so t bird can swallow it head-first.

Herons fly slowly with extravagant, steady wingbeats. They keep their lo necks tucked into their shoulders—unlike cranes, storks, and ibises, wh fly with the head and neck extended Herons usually nest in colonies calle heronries, building their untidy pile-sticks nests high in trees.

ROARING STORKS

Storks are even bigger than herons, some standing 4 feet (1.2 m) tall. They fly through the air with slow, strong wingbeats, neck stretched out in front and legs trailing behind. On their long annual journeys, or migrations, they find an upcurrent of warm air to gain height, then flap on their way.

In Europe and Asia, white storks often build their great twig nests on the roofs of houses. Many people see the return of the same pair, year after year from Africa, to build their nest in the same place, as a sign of continuing good luck. Storks raise their young with great care.

SPOON-FED

Spoonbills are medium-sized waders named for their flattened, spoon-shaped beaks. The spoonbill swishes its beak from side to side through the water, to catch prey such as fish and small crabs.

Spoonbills are close relatives of ibises. An ibis has a long, thin, down-curved beak. Like spoonbills, ibises have webbed toes to help them swim and walk on soft mud. Both ibises

The heron is a patient hunter, standing still and intent on one leg for hours. Then it makes a lightning dart with its long beak, to spear a fish which mistook the heron's single leg for a reed stem.

BOOM BOOM! !

The male bittern has one of the loudest bird calls. It is an extraordinary boom, made to warn others off its territory. The bittern makes this deep booming in its throat, and it can sound almost like a bull roaring as it echoes across the marsh at night. The bittern's scientific name is <u>Botaurus</u>, which comes from an ancient Latin term meaning "bellow of the bull."

and spoonbills feed in muddy water, detecting prey with their sensitive beaks. The brilliant pink plumage of the scarlet ibis makes it one of the most striking of all tropical birds.

WATERFOWL

The body of a duck or goose is so buoyant, it can float for hours, paddling with its big webbed feet. But on land, waterfowl—especially ducks—waddle awkwardly. The pochard and tufted duck are diving ducks, descending to the bottom to find roots, shoots, shellfish, and insects. Dabbling ducks such as the mallard lap at the water's surface, or up-end to sift waterweeds and snails from the muddy bed.

Swans are the largest waterfowl. A swan uses its long, elegant neck to reach down and grab plant bits and small creatures. Most swans have pure white plumage, apart from the black swan of Australia and the black-neck swan of South America. Geese are slightly smaller, and come onto land to graze on grass. Geese and ducks are powerful long-distance fliers. Bar-headed geese have been seen from planes at altitudes of 36,000 feet (9,000 m), crossing the Himalayas. Many geese breed in the Arctic, and migrate south in the fall.

▲ Scarlet ibis

▶ The roseate spoonbill is one of the most colorful of waders. It dwells in the warmer areas of the Americas.

HERONS, EGRETS, AND BITTERNS		
• 60 species • long legs, long neck, long bill • most species are quite large • neck curved or hunched back in flight	• neck outstretched in flight	• most species are long-necked • bill usually flattened, quite short and wide (spatulate)
Storks • 17 species • long legs, long neck, long bill • most species are quite large • neck outstretched in flight	**Flamingoes** • 4 species • long legs, long neck, stubby bill • large, with pink plumage • neck outstretched in flight	Some groups of ducks, geese, and swans: Swans and geese • 21 species Dabbling ducks • 40 species Sea ducks • 20 species Diving ducks • 16 species Shelducks • 16 species Perching ducks • 13 species Whistling ducks • 9 species Stifftails • 8 species
Spoonbills and ibises • 31 species • long legs, long neck, bill curved or flattened	**Cranes** • 15 species • tall, with long legs and neck • white or gray • neck outstretched in flight	
	Ducks, geese, swans • 150 species • webbed feet, good swimmers	

169

BIRDS OF PREY

A SHARP, HOOKED BEAK AND CURVED CLAWS CALLED TALONS MARK OUT THE RAPTORS—BIRDS OF PREY—AS THE DEADLY HUNTERS OF THE BIRD WORLD. Most are masterful fliers, able to stay aloft for hours while searching for prey with their incredibly keen eyes. Then they dive l a bullet onto the chosen victim. Smaller raptors like the sharp-shinned hawk are no bigger than a robin. They eat mainly insect frogs, and similar small creatures. Hawks and eagles take rats rabbits, snakes and lizards, and other birds. The huge harpy eagle of the Amazon jungle snatches monkeys and sloths fr the treetops. The osprey and fish eagles grab fish. Vulture and condors feed mostly on carrion (dead animals).

◪ Despite wildlife protection laws, golden eagles are still shot and poisoned by farmers and gamekeepers.

◪ The hobby is one of the most brightly colored of hawks. It is so speedy and agile that it can catch dragonflies, swallows, and swifts.

There are some 295 species of raptors. They hunt across a huge range of habitats, from mountains to rainforests. The condors are among the largest flying birds, with wingspans of 10 feet (3 m). Falcons such as the peregrine are the greatest winged acrobats, able to catch other birds in midflight with amazing power and agility.

All kinds of large predators, such as sharks and tigers, are scarce because of the balance of natur This also applies to large birds of prey, especially eagles. Sadly, people try to kill them in case they attack farm animals or gamebirds. And they are shot as trophies, or their eggs are stolen for collectors.

◩ The gyrfalcon is a powerful flie It plunges, or stoops, from above a tremendous speed, to grip its victim i its sharp-taloned feet. Hawks do th too, but they kill their prey with the claws, whereas a falcon's fatal blow a sharp bite to the nec

DIVE! ⚠

The peregrine falcon is the fastest-moving of all animals. It can streak down onto prey, or charge at an intruder in its territory, in a powered dive called a stoop. Some stoops have been timed at more than 210 mph (350 km/h).

A buzzard glides
a warm air
rrent, waiting to
t its prey.

They soar high and scan the scene below, ready to swoop. The kestrel is often known as the windhover, because it hovers in midair, wings and tail moving but head held still, focusing on the ground. When it sees a victim, it drops suddenly and pounces on its prey.

The bald eagle is not bald, but its white head looks featherless from a distance. It is a fish-eater, like the osprey.

any large raptors survive today only in remote, ten mountainous terrain. However others, like rtain kestrels and kites, have adapted to living ar people. They wheel over high-rise city ildings and by highways, just as they ould soar along cliffs or shores.

MBOL OF POWER
gles, with their graceful
aring that can turn into a
adly swoop, have
ng been symbols
power. The bald
gle is the national
rd of the USA. The
lden eagle was the
gurehead of the
mies of Ancient Rome.
e golden eagle is often
lled the "king of birds." It
nts rabbits, marmots,
ound squirrels, and birds. Its
st, or "eyrie," is a bed of
igs perched high on a cliff, to
hich pairs return year after year.

e American bald eagle has
en the victim of hunting,
ater pollution, and loss of
tural habitat. By the mid-
970s there were just 2,000 left
the USA. Conservation laws were introduced
and now there are more than 20,000.

The osprey has rough-skinned toes which help the sharp, curved claws to grip slippery fish.

WINGED SCAVENGERS
The biggest birds of prey are not predators, but carrion feeders. Vultures and condors have weak bills and the flesh they eat must be soft and rotten before they can rip off mouthfuls. The bearded vulture or lammergeier takes bones from the carcass and flies high to drop them onto rocks. The bones smash to reveal the soft, juicy marrow inside. All of the vultures have vast wings and spend hours soaring high, peering across the landscape for corpses. Condors have such keen smell that they can even locate dead meat under a canopy of trees by scent alone.

Condors are among the biggest flying birds. The wingspan of the Andean condor of South America can exceed 10 feet (3 m). Sadly, as a result of human persecution, the Californian condor is now one of the world's rarest birds. It also tends to crash into power cables. Conservationists in the 1980s captured the few remaining wild birds in a desperate bid to breed them in captivity. Some of the young have been released into the wild, but this species remains on the very edge of extinction.

SMALLER RAPTORS
Hawks, sparrowhawks, goshawks, falcons, kestrels, and hobbies are smaller than eagles. They often take other birds as well as ground-living animals.

There are two main kinds of hawks: accipiters and buteos. ccipiters, such as the goshawk, tend to wait on a anch and then dash out to ambush smaller rds under the cover of the foliage. They have ort, rounded wings and a long, narrow tail, for eat maneuverability. Buteos, such as the kestrel, ve longer wings and fan-shaped tails.

The rare Everglade kite feeds only on one type of water snail, the apple snail.

MAIN BIRDS OF PREY:	
Eagles, hawks, buzzards, and vultures • 224 species • worldwide • medium to large • sharp hooked beak • sharp curved talons	Osprey *(fish eagle)* • 1 species • worldwide • hunts fish • brown and white
American vultures • 7 species • large • naked head and neck • soaring flight	Falcons, falconets, and caracaras • 62 species • worldwide • small to medium • long tail
	Secretary bird • 1 species • African grassland • long legs and feathered head crest • eats reptiles

GAMEBIRDS AND RAILS

⬆ A peacock is a male peafowl. He is the most spectacular pheasant, with a metallic turquoise neck, shimmering indigo breast feathers, and a long train of brilliant green tail feathers. A courting peacock throws up his tail feathers into a gigantic fan, revealing dozens of beautiful eyelike spots.

MANY LARGE BIRDS THAT LIVE MAINLY ON THE GROUND HAVE SUCH TASTY FLESH THAT THEY HAVE LONG BEEN HUNTED FO MEAT, AND SO ARE CALLED GAMEBIRDS. They include pheasants, grouse, partridges, capercaillies, quails, wild turkeys, guinea fowl, curassows, and the guans of South America. Most of the females have dull, mottled brown plumage that blends in well with their woodland, scrub or moor home. Their chicks also have this camouflage pluma; Yet some of the males, especially pheasants and their relatives the tragopans, have extremely striking coloration. Their huge and brilliantly patterned feathers shimmer in all the hues of the rainbow.

The gamebird group, Galliformes, includes more than 240 species. The world's most numerous bird, the domestic chicken, is among them. Gamebirds are mostly quite large, stout-bodied, heavily built birds that spend their time on the ground, pecking for seeds, buds, shoots, and fruits. They can fly, but prefer to run, and only take to the air in emergencies.

PHEASANTS

Many of the 165 species of pheasants lived originally in China and central Asia. But they have been taken to many other parts of the world, mainly to be hunted. They range in size from the sparrow-sized painted quail to the turkey-sized argus pheasant. The smaller species, including quails and some partridges, are usually drab browns and grays. So too are the females or hens of the larger species, to escape the notice of predators while sitting on their eggs. But in the breeding season the larger male or cock pheasants are extremely noticeable, with flowing tails and beautiful blue, red, and gold feathers.

⬅ Cock common pheasant

The peacock's amazing "eyed" tail is well known. The Himalayan monal pheasant also has brilliant iridescent plumage in shiny shades of blue, green, purple, and orange. The male argus pheasant has long wing feathers with eye spots.

WHY ARE THESE BIRDS SO COLORFUL?

To attract a mate. The cocks strut and fluff out their plumage to show how fit and fine they are, using cackles, whistles, and screams to increase the effect. The Reeves cock pheasant shakes its feathers and jumps up high in the air, again and again, to make sure the females notice.

⬆ The word "grouse" co a wide range of birds, incluc quails and partridges. A grouse are often ca partridges! The spruce gro (above) of conifer forests is known as the swamp partri and spruce partric

⬅ A male mo pheasant displ his breed pluma

ival cocks may
reaten or even battle
ith each other to
in a mate.

ATTLE AT THE LEK

rouse, partridges, and
armigan are hunted
many birds of prey
d by mammals such
foxes and cats. So
ey are usually well

The habitat of the ptarmigan (pronounced "tar-mig-un") is the cold mountains and treeless tundra of the north. This bird changes with the seasons. In summer (far left) it has dull brown feathers, like most other grouse. In winter (near left) its plumage turns mostly white, to blend in with the snow and ice. Its diet changes too, from buds and insects in summer to seeds and shoots in winter.

mouflaged, to blend in with the undergrowth. They may be dull in color,
t grouse mating displays are just as dramatic as those of pheasants. Male
percaillies, the largest of the grouse, gather at a traditional breeding place
lled a lek. They strut aggressively to and fro and make extraordinary
ssing, popping, and gurgling sounds, while the females watch from nearby.
ch male tries to gain a site near the center of the lek area, which will
arantee a mate.

ustards are strong, turkey-sized birds of open habitats. Most species live in
frica, with a few in Asia and one in Australia. They are heavily built and
ride along on their powerful legs, reluctant to fly. When they do take to
the air, it is a struggle since they are the heaviest of all
flying birds. A bustard's varied diet includes seeds,
fruits, insects, and other small animals. Like most
gamebirds, the female nests on the ground or on
a low branch, usually in dense undergrowth.

SKULKING RAILS

Rails are related to cranes. They are found mainly in
wetland habitats. All rails swim well, and walk in a slow,
deliberate fashion. They are shy birds and skulk in the
undergrowth, camouflaged by their drab plumage.
The rail group includes moorhens, coots, and the
endangered flightless takahe of
New Zealand.

World Watch

Several types of flightless rails are at risk from dogs, rats, and other animals brought to their region by people (page 162). The takahe of New Zealand is a flightless rail that looks more like a parrot. It was thought to be extinct until its rediscovery in 1948. Only a few hundred takahes survive in the Murchison Mountains of New Zealand's South Island. Introduced deer compete for their food.

Sandgrouse are pigeonlike birds of dry, desert habitats. The males fly tens of miles to a water hole, soak their breast feathers, and then fly back to the nest so the chicks can sip the water.

The great bustard (left) and the kori bustard are the world's heaviest flying birds, weighing some 44 pounds (20 kg).

GAMEBIRDS
• about 250 species
• mainly ground-living
• includes pheasants and grouse
• males often have elaborate plumage at breeding time

Rails
• 124 species
• mostly small, drab gray or brown
• a few are brightly colored
• make calls that sound like engines or machines

• some are flightless
• rivers, lakes, and marshes

Bustards
• 21 species
• large, heavy
• open plains and grassland

Sandgrouse
• 16 species
• resemble pigeons
• deserts and other dry habitats

PIGEONS, DOVES, AND PARROTS

🔺 Parrots have strong hooked beaks to crack open nuts and scoop out soft fruits.

🔺 Crowned pigeon

CITY PIGEONS MAY NOT BE THE MOST APPEALING BIRDS, DRAB AND GRAY, LEAVING A MESS AS THEY FLOCK AROUND LITTER.

Parrots, on the other hand, are among the most attractive of birds, with their vivid colors of scarlet, emerald, and turquoise, their beady eyes, and the ability to mimic our voices and "talk." But pigeons and par have several features in common. Both eat mainly seeds and fruits. Both are bold and curious, but also placid and easy-going. And both have long associations with people. Parrots a doves live near or even in our villages, towns, and cities. Many kinds, including the small members of the parrot group called parakeets, are kept as cage birds and pets. Pigeons and doves are entered for shows and competitions such as racing, and they are even used for carrying messages because of their amazing homing instincts.

Besides familiar town pigeons, there are nearly 300 other pigeon species around the world, ranging from the large and spectacular crowned pigeons of New Guinea to tiny ground doves. In general, the larger and plumper types are called pigeons and the smaller, slimmer species are known as doves. All are

🔺 The budgerigar is a small species of parrot from Australia. It is mainly green for camouflage. Flocks of budgies swoop and chatter around waterholes at dusk

mainly seed-eaters, and most build untidy stick nests in trees. Pigeons are also among the stronges flying birds, and many migrate long distances. Mo pigeons and doves have soothing, rather sad-sounding, cooing songs. These can often be heard in woods, parks, and gardens, especially in early morni and evening.

◀ The pigeons in our cities are not truly wild, but part-wild or fe This means they are descended from domestic pigeons, which w kept widely in the past, both to carry messages and to eat! Th domestic pigeons, in turn, were descended from wild rock do whose natural habitats are sea cliffs and rocky cr

Lorikeets like the Australian varied lorikeet, have long beaks to reach nectar in flowers.

Pigeons and doves are the only birds that feed their young on "milk," like mammals. The parent produces a milky substance from the lining of its throat, to feed to the chicks.

PARROTS

Parrots are tropical birds with strong hooked beaks and bright plumage. They ...o have clinging feet, with two toes pointing ...ward and two backward. This design allows a ...rot to clamber in trees, using its beak as a ...ird foot." The real foot can also hold fruits ...d nuts, to eat.

There are more than 300 species in the parrot group, including macaws, lories, lorikeets, cockatoos, lovebirds, and parakeets. Many are inquisitive and investigate objects with great care, holding and pecking them to see if they are good to eat. Many of the larger species are also long-lived, surviving for 30, 40, or more years in captivity. These are further reasons why they are so popular as cage birds and even as pet "companions." Sadly, this popularity means thousands of parrots are illegally captured from the wild each year. And perhaps half suffer and die before they reach the pet shops. Several kinds of parrot are now endangered in ... wild as a result of this cruel and unlawful trade.

...USH-TIPPED TONGUES

...ries and lorikeets are colorful parrots from Southeast ...ia and Australia. Unlike most other parrots they feed ... on seeds and fruits, but on pollen and nectar from ...wers. They have brushlike tips on their tongues to ... up these foods.

...ESTED COCKATOOS

...e cockatoos have ...thered crests on their ...ads, which they fan ... when excited, such ...when a predator or ...al approaches.

Some species are white or pinkish. Largest is the palm cockatoo of New Guinea and northeast Australia.

THE REAL MACAW

Macaws are big, long-tailed parrots that live in the forests of Central and South America. They rest and nest in tree trunk holes. They are colorful even by parrot standards, in shades of brilliant blue, red, yellow, and green.

The crested cockatoo only erects its crest when aroused in some way.

Most parrots have few natural enemies, apart from hawks and eagles, and monkeys who may steal eggs and chicks. But continuing threats from the pet trade mean many are still endangered.

The gold-and-blue macaw has a beak so strong that it can easily crack open Brazil nuts.

Parrots, cockatoos, and lories	Pigeons and doves
• 330 species	• 300 species
• strong hooked beak	• dumpy bodies
• two toes facing forward, two backward	• tree-dwelling
• bright greens or reds	• mournful calls
• mainly tropical or southern hemisphere	

175

CUCKOOS AND TURACOS

IN EUROPE, A SOFT "CUCK-OO" CALL HERALDS SPRING, AS THESE BIRDS ARRIVE FROM SOUTHERN AFRICA OR ASIA TO BREED. The cuckoo is also known from its habit of laying eggs in the nests of smaller birds. The large cuckoo egg develops rapidly for its size, so that it hatches at the same time as the smaller eggs of the unknowing foster parents. The baby cuckoo is looked after by its foster parents—even thoug it grows far bigger than them. There are about 130 kinds of cuckoos, roadrunners, and coucals all over the world. Many of the tropical species are large and colorful. The heavy-bodied turacos or plantain-eaters from the tropica forests of Africa are also colorful. They include the go-away bird, named for its persistent "g'way! g'way!" call.

Coucals are among the ma colorful cuckoos living in the forests of the tropics. Unlike European and American cucko they stay mostly on the groun

Many birds have feathers in sha of green. But turacos are the o birds that actually mak green pigment, or color substance, in their feath In other birds, the gre color is due to tiny rid on the feathers. Th split up the white li of sunlight into rainbow colors of spectrum, and refl only the green ra

BASH!

roadrunner kills its prey very simple way. When it ches a snake or lizard, it ply bashes the reptile to th by pecking, pounding, banging it with its beak. the roadrunner swallows its meal head-first.

About one third of all cuckoo species, including the common or European cuckoo, are brood parasites. Instead of hatching their own eggs, the male and female mate, and then the female lays her eggs in the nests of another bird

ies, such as a reed warbler, meadow pipit, nock, or redstart. She chooses the foster nts carefully. Usually, they are the same ies as her own foster parents when she was a k. She must also choose her moment with , otherwise the foster parents may abandon nest and eggs. She must put her own egg into nest as soon as the foster mother has laid her eggs, and while she has left for a short while ed, but before she has started to incubate (sit her eggs.

male cuckoo may lay more than 20 eggs, in a different nest. When the cuckoo k hatches, it tips out the other eggs hicks. The foster parents feed it it were their own, erately trying to keep with the appetite of r giant baby. After six ks the young cuckoo fly and leaves its , tired foster nts.

me Eurasian or Old World cuckoos, like the common cuckoo, ther birds to rear their young. Most American or New World os, such as the black-billed and yellow-billed cuckoos, do not.

The roadrunner of southwestern North America can fly, but prefers to run. It can do so at more than 20 mph (30 km/h), outpacing most predators. Its diet includes insects, snakes, and fruit.

RUNNING THE ROADS

The roadrunner of desert scrub in Mexico and the southwestern USA is a type of ground cuckoo. It is about 24 inches (60 cm) long, but most of this is tail. It gets its name from its habit of racing along roads in front of cars, then quickly darting off into the bushes on the roadside. Roadrunners do not deliberately dice with death by dodging vehicles. They simply choose the road as an easy place to walk, and also as a source of injured animals which might be good to eat.

TROPICAL CUCKOOS

Coucals are mostly large, ground-dwelling members of the cuckoo group that live in the tropics. The pheasant coucal of New Guinea and Australia stalks through dense undergrowth for small insects and other prey. The buff-headed coucal of the Solomon Islands is one of the largest cuckoos, with a beak-to-tail length of 28 inches (70 cm). It eats a wide variety of prey, including lizards, snakes, and frogs.

The hoatzin of the Amazon region is one of the world's oddest birds. The chick clambers about in trees using its legs, beak, and two claws, one halfway along the front of each wing. The adult hoatzin loses the claws, but is the most vegetarian of all birds, browsing only on certain types of leaves, such as arum and mangrove. This unique bird may be related to the cuckoo group.

FEEDING ON FRUITS

The turacos of Africa are forest birds with colorful, silky plumage. Many have bright flashes of yellow, red, green, and blue on their wings and bodies. Some have bare areas of brilliantly colored skin around the eyes or on the face. A few turacos eat a mixed diet of plants and small animals, but most are specialist fruit-eaters, feeding their chicks mainly on fruit pulp. The drabbest member of the group is the go-away-bird, which is gray all over apart from dark wingtip feathers.

racos such as the red-ed turaco are weak fliers. prefer to climb and run tree branches, almost quirrels, hunting for fruit nsects.

Cuckoos and coucals
• 130 species
• most continents
• slim body, long tail
• most are gray or brown
• about one third of species are brood parasites
• mixed diet

Turacos
• 22 species
• Central and southern Africa
• mostly brightly colored
• fruit-eaters

Hoatzin
• 1 species
• Amazon region of South America
• chickenlike with head crest
• leaf-eater

OWLS AND NIGHTJARS

MOST HUNTING BIRDS FLY BY DAY, BUT OWLS, NIGHTJARS, AND FROGMOUTHS HUNT AT NIGHT. They rely on their amazing twilight vision and even more astonishing hearing to locate their prey in the dark. Owls have enormous eyes that take up over half of the skull. They can see in almost pitch darkness. Also their ears are four times more sensitive than a cat's ears. On a quiet night an owl can hear a mouse move 150 feet (45 m) away. It can also pinpoint the direction of sounds with incredible accuracy. Nightjars, too, have large eyes that see especially well at twilight. They feed mainly on moths and other night-flying insects. Frogmouths are also dusk-flying birds, but they tend to swoop from a perch onto prey on the ground.

Owls live in most parts of the world, from the tropics almost to the Arctic regions. There are some 135 species. They vary in size, but all are similar in appearance with a big, broad head, no obvious neck, and a saucer-shaped ruff of feathers, called the facial disk, around the huge eyes. Both eyes face directly forward, unlike those of most birds, which look partly to the side.

THE WISE OLD OWL
The owl's intense forward stare has made it a symbol of wisdom since ancient times (although owls are no more intelligent than other birds). In fact the eyes fit so tightly in the skull bone that they cannot swivel in their sockets. To look to the side, an owl twists its neck and turns its whole head. It can do this to look directly behind!

The tiny elf owl from the southern USA and Mexico is one of the smallest owls. It measures only about 5 inches (12 cm) from beak tip to tail tip. Largest is the European eagle owl, which can be 28 inches (70 cm) long, with a wingspan of 5 feet (1.5 m).

◄ Th (F relativ nightjar. I comes ooo-ing frogmouth hunts on th floor for beetles and other small a It has even been k take whole mice ar birds into its mouth, surrou s bris t

◄ Most owls are mottled gray or brown. But the male snowy owl is almost pure white, the perfect disguise in its snowy Arctic habitat.

The great horned owl does not have horns. Its earlike tufts are simply extra-long feathers. It is one of North America's largest owls, standing almost 2 feet (60 cm) tall.

Owls are wonderfully adapted for night hunting. They have sharp sight and keen hearing, and their wing feathers have soft, almost furry, edges. This muffles the sound of the wings' beating and swooping, so the owl's prey is not disturbed. Smaller owls eat mostly insects. Medium-sized owls, like the barn owl and boobook (morepork), eat mice, rats, lizards, and similar creatures. The biggest owls catch rabbits and squirrels. Eagle owls prey on other birds, including owls and hawks, and even carry away young deer. The fishing owls of Africa and Asia swoop on fish, frogs, and crayfish, dipping just under the surface to grab prey with their sharp claws.

BIG-MOUTHED BIRDS

Nightjars glide gracefully after flying insects, which they snap up in their wide, gaping mouth. Like bats and the oilbird, they may use a type of sonar or echolocation to find their way and avoid obstacles in the dark. After the hunt, nightjars roost by day—but not hidden away in holes, caves, or buildings, like owls. The nightjar rests in the open. It nestles against a tree branch or among leaves on the forest floor. This may sound risky, but its mottled plumage is such perfect camouflage that the bird is almost impossible to spot.

Frogmouths are named for their wide, gaping mouths. They are not very agile in flight. Instead, they catch their prey by dropping onto the ground from a twig or rock. Like nightjars, frogmouths rest by day in the open, relying on their camouflaged plumage for protection.

The nightjar's song is a mechanical "churring" that resembles the sound of a distant motorcycle.

The short-eared owl is one of several owls that hunt by day as well as by night.

ne oilbird of South erica is a relative of the tjars. It is unusual ng the owl-like birds, in y ways. It spends all deep in its breeding e, then comes out at t to feed—not on cts, but on oily fruits. rds find their way in total darkness of cave in the way that do, by making loud ng sounds and yzing the echoes.

The little owl has the dished face typical of all owls. The dish shape acts as a sound trap to funnel the faintest noises toward the owl's super-sensitive ears, under the feathers on the sides of its head.

Owls	Nightjars and frogmouths
• 135 species	• 100 species
• most are nocturnal	• nocturnal
• soft feathers	• sleek and graceful
• large, flat face	• large eyes
• huge eyes	• gaping mouth
• hooked beak	• camouflaged plumage
• sharp claws	
• camouflaged plumage	

SWIFTS AND WOODPECKERS

A WALK THROUGH A TROPICAL RAINFOREST REVEALS A HOST OF SMALL BIRDS, CHATTERING IN THE TREETOP AND DARTING BETWEEN THE BRANCHES. They include hummingbirds, jacamars, toucans, barbets, bee-eaters, and many more. Most have such startling brilliant colors that they seem to have little in common with the drabber birds of temperate woodlands. Yet many of them are closely related. Hummingbirds belong to the same group of birds as swifts. Toucans and jacamars are cousins to the woodpecker. Kookaburras and hornbills are related t the kingfishers, bee-eaters, rollers, and hoopoes. Most of these birds have large beaks compared to their body size.

⯈ Hummingbirds like this violet crowned hummingbird, beat their wings up to 80 times every second. This produces the beelike humming sound of their name.

⬀ Few birds have a beak which is as distinctive as the toco toucan's. The beak is as big as the bird itself, and strong and stiff. But it is made of a very light, spongy, horny substance, so the toucan has no problem flying, balancing, and moving its beak to peck at fruits.

⬎ Woodpeckers like the Downy woodpec hammer at trees to find wood-boring grubs a also to make nest ho

⯈ The kingfisher sits on its perch above a stream, watching for food. When it sees a fish or frog, it dives like a flash into the water, swims below with its wings, and bobs up with its catch. Back on its perch, it swallows the meal whole.

The white-fronted bee-eater is a tropical bird related to hornbills and kingfishers. It catches bees and wasps in mid-air, and bashes them on a branch to kill them and so reduce the risk of being stung.

Most birds spend some time in the air. But swifts are [so] well adapted for flight that they [rarely] settle on a perch. They are on [the] wing nearly all the time, [s]wooping, hovering, soaring, diving, [sp]urting and resting, and, of course, [fe]eding. As a result, their legs and [fe]et have become quite weak. Swifts [an]d hummingbirds belong to the [sa]me bird group, the Apodiformes, [wh]ich means "footless ones." They [ar]e not actually footless, but the legs [an]d feet are certainly tiny.

[T]he kookaburra [of] Australia is a [typ]e of kingfisher, [bu]t it is quite at [hom]e in dry scrub [far] from water. It [eat]s mainly [ins]ects and [rep]tiles. Its [cac]kling call has [ear]ned it the [nic]kname of the [lau]ghing jackass.

[S]WIFT BY NAME AND NATURE
[Sw]ifts really live up to their [na]me. They are among the [fa]stest flying birds. The [sp]ine-tailed swifts of eastern [As]ia have been timed at [ove]r 120 mph (200 km/h) [in] level flight. Swifts [cat]ch insects on the [wi]ng, swooping [th]rough swarms of [gn]ats with their

[T]he male crested [tre]e swift has a red[bro]wn eye patch; [the] female's eye [pat]ch is green.

gaping mouths wide open. They often fly through the night without landing. When they do touch down, they cling clumsily to upright surfaces such as cave walls, tree trunks, and brickwork.

SIPPING NECTAR
Hummingbirds are the helicopters of the bird world. They are brightly colored and sip nectar as they hover close to flowers. They are incredibly agile, flap their wings faster than we can see, and hover in midair, fly sideways, go straight up or down, or even fly backward. The long, thin, curved beak probes deep into flowers for the sugary nectar that fuels their high-energy life. There are more than 300 species of hummingbirds, mostly in tropical America. In the 19th century, millions were killed and made into feathered jewelry such as brooches. Luckily the fashion died out before the birds did.

UNUSUAL FEET
Woodpeckers, toucans, barbets, jacamars, and honeyguides all have the same type of feet. Each foot has two toes pointing forward and two backward (rather than three forward and one backward as in most other birds). A woodpecker uses its feet to cling to the tree while hammering at the wood with its large, powerful beak, to search for insects below the bark. The toucans of tropical South and Central America have massive, brightly colored bills, which they use to feed on berries, fruit, and soft-bodied insects.

The alpine swift wheels over mountains, uplands, and cliffs across southern Europe, Africa, the Middle East, and Asia. It flies even faster than the common swift.

The hornbill is mainly black and white. It uses its enormous beak for picking fruits.

SMALLEST... !
The world's smallest bird is the bee hummingbird of Cuba. Its body is hardly larger than a bumblebee's, with a total length of 2 inches (5 cm)— including its beak and tail!

The honeyguide of Africa eats mainly beeswax—but it cannot obtain the wax for itself. Instead, it perches near a wild bees' nest, and calls out. The sound draws honey-eating mammals, such as the honey badger, which break open the nest to get at the honey. The honeyguide then feasts on the wax.

Woodpeckers		Rollers	
• 200 species		• 16 species	
Hornbills		Barbets	
• 45 species		• 78 species	
Toucans		Honeyguides	
• 38 species		• 15 species	
Kingfishers		Swifts	
• 86 species		• 74 species	
Bee-eaters		Hummingbirds	
• 24 species		• 315 species	

CROWS, SHRIKES, AND BOWERBIRDS

MORE THAN TWO THIRDS OF BIRDS—MORE THAN
5,000 DIFFERENT SPECIES—BELONG TO THE GROUP
KNOWN AS PERCHING BIRDS OR PASSERINES. Of

▲ A male blue bird of parad
shows off his pluma

course, many kinds of bird perch. But passerines have a special design, a
four-toed foot, with three toes pointing forward and one facing
backward. This allows them to cling securely to a twig, branch, or other
perch, but not to swim easily or run fast on the ground. So passerines ten
to live in or near trees and bushes, where they can hop among the branches
and find places to build nests. Most passerines are small. Crows, shrikes,
bowerbirds, and the lyrebird are among the biggest species.

▲ White-cheeked bulbul

LARGEST... !
Ravens are the largest perching
birds. These powerful members of
the crow family can reach
26 inches (65 cm) beak-to-tail
length. They can kill prey as large
as a rabbit, but they usually
scavenge on dead animals.

◼ A male lyrebird courts the
female from the top of an
earthen mound about 3 feet
(90 cm) across, which he
builds himself.

There are more than 100 species in the crow
group, including rooks, jackdaws, jays, magpies,
and the largest type, ravens. Most are noisy,
bold, aggressive birds, which bully other bird
species and are not especially afraid of other
animals or even people. Jays screech and squawk
all year except during the breeding season, when
they go quiet so as not to give away their nests.
Most crows collect and hoard bits of food and
other items. European jays even "steal" shiny
objects such as bottletops and rings. Most crows
have black or drab plumage, except for jays such
as the blue jay, and also some
magpies, which are
quite colorful.

◼ A black cuckoo shrike
feeds its chicks.

THE BUTCHER BIRDS
Shrikes are like birds of prey, but
smaller. They lack sharp talons, but
they do have a fierce-looking hooked
beak, used to catch large insects, mice,
lizards, and frogs. A shrike usually sit
in a bush or similar lookout,
watching for prey. It may store
surplus food by impaling the
carcasses on long
thorns, to eat later.
This gruesome
"larder" has earned
the shrike the name
of butcher bird.

◼ The male satin bowerbird
waits in his decorated bower.

STARLINGS

Starlings are active, noisy birds that often gather together in huge flocks, to feed or roost. In winter a starling roost may number thousands of birds. As dusk falls they gather somewhere such as a clump of evergreen trees or the ledges of a building. Mynahs, bulbuls, and mockingbirds, which live in the Americas, are related to starlings. Mockingbirds mimic human laughter, hence their name. Their songs are loud, clear, and musical.

COME INTO MY BOWER

Bowerbirds take courtship to an amazing extreme. These medium-sized birds from the forests of New Guinea and Australia build elaborate bowers. These are places where the male bird displays to his mate.

▷ The male Baltimore oriole sings his courtship song to a female.

▷ The male spotted bowerbird builds an elaborate courting area, or bower, of twigs and grass decorated with fruits, seeds, and pebbles. The bower helps to attract a female.

SOME PERCHING BIRD GROUPS:

Bulbuls
• 118 species
Crows
• 116 species
Starlings and mynahs
• 106 species
Birds of paradise
• 43 species
Shrikes

• 70 species
Mockingbirds
• 30 species
Orioles
• 28 species
Bowerbirds
• 18 species
Lyrebirds
• 2 species

Each male decorates his bower with flowers, shells, pebbles, berries, leaves, and moss. He may even use natural colored plant juices to "paint" some of the bower's decorations.

⬧ Blue jays frequent parks and gardens in eastern North America.

PARADISE

Perhaps the most spectacular of the larger passerines are the birds of paradise. They inhabit tropical forests, mainly in Southeast Asia. The males are adorned with amazing colored plumes and perform elaborate dances to attract females during the breeding season. The male lyrebird of southeast Australia also sings and displays to attract a female. He fans out and tips forward his lyre-shaped tail streamers, while producing a rich, melodious song that includes sounds like car engines and burglar sirens!

◁ The hill mynah, from India, is sometimes kept as a cage bird for its skill in imitating noises, especially the human voice.

SPARROWS, FINCHES, AND WEAVERS

SPARROWS, FINCHES, AND WEAVER BIRDS ARE FAMILIAR IN GARDENS AND COUNTRYSIDE AROUND THE WORLD. Many species migrate from Europe to Africa in winter. Most of these birds have short, strong, stubby, pointed beaks designed for feeding on seeds. They are sometimes called seed-eating passerines (page 182). There are some 315 species in the New World (the Americas), including cardinals and buntings, and 375 in the Old World, including goldfinches, waxbills, and weavers. They tend to be sociable, feeding and roosting in flocks so as to gain safety in numbers. Some kinds, especially weavers, even breed in groups or colonies. Weaver birds get their name from their nests, woven like baskets from plant stems, twigs, grass, and strips of leaves.

◄ The male paradise whydah's tail feathers are four times as long as his body. He flies with them angled almost straight up when courting the female.

◄ Ma... villa... weav...

LOTS! ⚠

The red-billed quelea of Africa is one of the world's most abundant birds. It is a kind of weaver and gathers in gigantic flocks numbering a million or more birds. They wheel and turn together, darkening the sky. They also ruin crops.

Most sparrows are stocky, active birds with drab brownish plumage. Few birds are more familiar in towns and cities, and their chirruping song is a common garden sound. House sparrows nest under the eaves of buildings even in the center of a busy city. Other sparrows occupy a huge range of habitats—swamp sparrows in swamps, fox sparrows in forests, sage sparrows in deserts, and song sparrows in scrubland. Some sparrows are called buntings and these tend to be more brightly colored, especially the male indigo bunting, painted bunting, and lazuli bunting.

NUTCRACKER BEAKS
Finches of various kinds, with their powerful seed-cracking beaks, are found throughout the world. They often visit bird tables for extra food, especially in winter. The chaffinch is one of Europe's most common birds, nesting in a wide range of wooded habitats. Goldfinches, with their attractive red, gold, and black plumage, often feed in small flocks on the seed heads of thistles or teasels. The powerful bill of the hawfinch can even crush cherry stones with ease. The tips of the crossbill's beak actually cross over at the tip. This allows the bird to extract seeds from pine cones.

▼ The snow bunting nests farther north than any other land bird. It also breeds on high mountains, where its black and white plumage gives good camouflage among the rocks and ice.

▲ The snow bunting ranges in the Arctic Circle, and also up near the summits of the world's highest mountains. A species of bunting is found almost everywhere in the world, from the Equator nearly to the Pole.

INSIDE A BIRD

No birds have teeth, so they cannot chew their food. This means the inner parts must grind and mash the food into a pulp. This happens in a muscular, strong-walled section of the digestive system called the gizzard. First, the swallowed food enters a stretchy storage bag in the chest region, called the crop. A bird can feed very fast, fill its crop, and then digest its food more slowly later. It can also carry food back to its nest in the crop, and bring it up (regurgitate it) for its young.

windpipe
gullet
wing covert feathers
primary wing feathers
lung
crop
gizzard
secondary wing feathers
liver
kidney
main flight muscles (pectorals)
intestine
vent

Hawfinches are big, orange-brown finches that live in broadleaved trees, such as beech or hornbeam, across most of Europe and Asia. The thick, strong beak can crack open nuts and even the seed stones of fruits such as cherries. The hawfinch is very [shy]. It is often only glimpsed in the treetops when it is feeding or when it makes its loud "tik" call.

EXPERT WEAVERS

Weaver birds are related to sparrows and are similar in body shape. But most are larger and more colorful than sparrows, with yellow, black, and red plumage—especially in the males. Weavers make the most complex nests of any bird. Even the simplest designs have long funnels or tubes at the nest entrance to keep out predators (and cuckoos).

The song of the corn bunting sounds like a bunch of jangling keys. This bird is found in farmland and similar open areas.

The sociable weavers of Africa work together to build the most elaborate constructions in the bird world. Their huge colonial nest looks like the thatched roof of a cottage, transported to the branches of a tree. Each pair of weavers has its own entrance on the underside. The whole multinest may measure more than 23 feet (7 m) across. Village weavers also build a colonial nest from intertwined grass stems, with up to 100 compartments inside.

MORE PERCHING BIRDS:

Buntings
• 552 species
Finches
• 155 species
Weavers
• 95 species
Sparrows
• 35 species

185

WARBLERS, THRUSHES, AND FLYCATCHERS

MOST BIRDS MAKE THEIR OWN DISTINCTIVE NOISES OR CALLS. But perching birds or passerines (page 182) do not simply call, they sing. Perching birds admired for their beautiful songs include thrushes, warblers, and nightingales. Indeed, these species are sometimes known as songbirds. Songs have a different purpose to the simpler, shorter calls. A call is designed to communicate a brief message. Chicks call to tell their parents they are hungry. A bird makes alarm call to warn of possible danger. But the songs of songbird are usually made only by the males, and only in the mating season. The male flits from twig to twig around his own patch of land, or territory, and sings loudly at each stop. He is warning off rival males of the same or competing species. He may also be trying to attract a breeding partner of his own specie

◪ The cock-of-the-rock, from Colombia is one of 90 species of tropical perching birds called cotingas.

◪ Antbirds are forest-dwell from South America. No feed on ants. Some eat bee and other animals escap from marching army a

Many warblers have drab plumage in shades of yellow, green, and brown. This makes them hard to see as they dart among the leaves and twigs. But they make up for this with their loud, melodic songs, which are such a feature of temperate regions in late spring and summer. Most warbler species are visitors to these temperate regions.

They time their breeding to fit in with the huge increase in caterpillars, flies, and other insects each summer. They snap up the food in their narrow beaks as they flit about, rarely coming into the open. Most then fly south to warmer climates in the fall, to avoid the cold of winter.

◪ The male Asian paradise flycatcher shares the task of sitting o the eggs to keep them warm. This species has two distinct types phases, of males. Both have blue heads. But a white phase male a white body and tail, while the rufous male (shown here) is red

THRUSHES

The thrush group includes redstarts, wheatears, chats, and the European blackbird.

Most thrushes have loud songs that carry well through trees and bushes, and even better across gardens and parks. The nightingale often sings at night. Its loud, rich voice echoes through the darkened woods in spring. This shy bird usually stays on or near the ground, where there is plenty of undergrowth.

◪ In spring, the male redwing blackbird sings a rich, short, warbling song that sounds like a flute, with short pauses between phrases.

◪ European robin

The American redstart is a
[sma]ll perching bird with a
[loud], reedy song. Its warning
[alar]m call sounds like a rattly
[alarm]ing clock.

Thrushes feed on a mixed diet of worms,
insects, fruits, and berries. Some adults
have bright plumage, but most are dull
and mottled for camouflage. Exceptions
are the red-breasted European robin and
the similar but slightly larger American
robin. Robins are also unusual because
they sing in the fall and winter, as well
as in spring. One of the world's rarest
birds is the Seychelles magpie-robin.
Only about 50–100 survive on a
couple of Seychelles islands.

CATCHING FLIES

Flycatchers like to sing from tree
stumps. Most catch insects in
midair. But the pied flycatcher of
Europe and Asia uses its singing
perch to watch for food.
It waits patiently, then darts
out to snap up a fly.

[M]onarch flycatchers are found in Africa, Asia, and
[Au]stralia. They have bold, bright plumage, especially
[the] paradise flycatcher. The male's long tail
[str]eamers measure 6 inches (15 cm), about twice
[as] long as the bird's head and body. The African
[pa]radise flycatcher is rich chestnut brown with a
[bla]ck head. The Seychelles paradise flycatcher
[is s]imilar in shape, but the male is glossy black
[wit]h a deep blue sheen. Fantail flycatchers
[inc]lude the willy wagtail of Australia. This
[bol]d little bird is not afraid of larger
[ani]mals, and often hitches a ride on the
[bac]k of a sheep!

[◘] This is an Australian pied monarch flycatcher at
[its] nest. Most perching birds build small, neat, cup-
[sha]ped nests in the branches of trees and bushes.
[The] inside is lined with moss and grass, or perhaps
[wit]h soft mud, to protect the eggs from drafts. The
[cu]p shape reduces the risk of the eggs falling out
even if the nest rocks in a high wind.

[T]he song thrush lives up to its name, producing a
[loud] and beautiful song that lasts for five minutes or
[more]. This thrush is seen hopping across the
[law]n, head cocked on one side,
[liste]ning for worms. It also eats snails,
[whi]ch it smashes on a stone
["anv]il" to break the shell
[and] expose the
[juicy] flesh.

MORE PERCHING BIRDS:	
Flycatchers • 156 species • Europe, Africa, Australasia	Old World warblers • 340 species • mainly Europe, Africa, and Asia
Monarch flycatchers • 133 species • Africa, southern Asia, Australasia	New World warblers • 120 species • Americas only
Fantail flycatchers • 38 species • India, Southeast Asia, Australasia, New Zealand	Australian warblers • 60 species • Southeast Asia, Australasia
	Thrushes • 304 species • worldwide

187

LARKS, SWALLOWS, AND TREECREEPERS

SOME OF THE SMALLEST PERCHING BIRDS, OR PASSERINES (PAGE 182), ARE SOME OF THE MOST FAMILIAR BIRDS IN TOWNS AND VILLAGES. The

◭ White-eyes live mainly in southern Asia, with some spe[cies] in Africa and others on Pacific islands. They eat nectar, fruits, and insects.

wren is one of the tiniest birds, but it makes its presence known with its loud, shrill warble. Blue tits are only slightly larger. They display lively, acrobatic behavior, ofte[n] coming to bird tables for food. Swallows and house marti[ns] build their nests under the eaves of houses. The American purple martin often uses a nest box. Treecreepers hop slow[ly] up the trunks of trees in gardens and parks. The small, dr[ab] brown skylark makes a loud, trilling song as it flies, a well-known sound of European fields, meadows, and moors.

◭ The pied wagtail often lives near stables and farms, where there are plentiful flies and other insects to eat. It nests in any suitable hole.

◭ Barn swallo[w]

◭ The wallcreeper searches for insects in crevices in cliffs and walls.

▽ Some swallows nest in holes pecked a[nd] dug out of cliffs and riverbanks. Others b[uild] nests of mud under a cliff—or its mod[ern] equivalent, a bridge or buildi[ng].

◭ Barn swallows are summer visitors to temperate regions, and in the fall can often be seen gathering in large numbers on wires ready for their winter migration.

◀ Dippers are highly unusual perching birds. They feed underwater in fast-flowing rivers and streams. The dipper walks upstream along the gravel riverbed, pressed onto the bottom by the current flowing over its sloping head and tail.

[M]any smaller perching birds have loud songs [wh]ich they make in flight, rather than from a [pe]rch. The skylark is a brownish, well [ca]mouflaged lark that spends much time in the [un]dergrowth, looking for insects. But when the [ma]le skylark soars upward on a clear morning, he [po]urs out a cascade of song as he hangs in the air [fo]r minutes at a time. At last he descends, first [ge]ntly, then quickly as he dives into vegetation.

The nuthatch or "nut-hack" [is n]amed from its habit of [we]dging nuts into a crevice, to [pec]k open with its beak.

Pipits, too, have a distinctive song flight that echoes through the air as they drop to the ground. Pipits are a kind of wagtail, named because they bob their tails up and down as they walk. But they have shorter tails than other wagtails. They are mostly dull, streaked browns, or grays, which makes them hard to see at rest in meadows or dry grassland.

[M]ost wagtails have long tails and slender bodies. [Th]ey feed on insects near marshes and ponds. [Th]eir striking plumage is either black and white, [or] combinations of green, [ye]llow, and blue. They have [sh]arp, metallic calls, and [qu]ieter songs.

◘ The meadowlark of [A]merican grasslands is not a true lark but a [co]usin of the blackbird.

◘ Sunbirds are the African and Asian versions of the American hummingbirds. A sunbird sips nectar from flowers with its long, probing beak and tongue. It also eats some insects and other foods.

DRINKING IN FLIGHT

Swallows and martins are graceful in flight, and swoop over fields and water after flying insects. They can even drink on the wing, dipping the beak into a stream as they zoom over the surface. These birds look like swifts (page 180), but fly lower and more jerkily. Each year, swallows migrate from temperate lands to the tropics, for winter. They return in spring to build cup-shaped nests, often on rafters in a roof. Sand martins scratch nest burrows in sandy banks.

A BEAK FOR INSECTS

Birds that pick up insects from the ground or from crevices in trees, like the treecreeper, need especially long, thin, tweezerlike beaks. The curve helps to lever off flakes of bark.

Nostril

Upper mandible (top part of beak)

Characteristic white eyebrow stripe

Lower mandible (bottom part of beak)

UNDERGROWTH AND UNDERWATER

Wrens and dippers are both tiny, dumpy birds with short tails, but they live in very different habitats. Wrens skulk in thick undergrowth, camouflaged by their brown plumage—but identified by their loud, musical songs. Dippers live around mountain streams and walk underwater as they search the stones and gravel on the bed for insects, worms, and water snails. They even dive into rapids.

TITS AND TREECREEPERS

Tits are common garden birds in many regions. They nest in tree holes and feed largely on insects. Nuthatches and treecreepers both live around trees. The treecreeper climbs up from the base of the tree in a spiral, searching cracks for insects. The nuthatch can climb about the tree trunk moving upward, sideways, or even downward.

MORE PERCHING BIRDS:

Larks, wagtails, and pipits • 130 species	Tits • 62 species
Swallows and martins • 74 species	Nuthatches • 21 species
Dippers and wrens • 64 species	Treecreepers • 14 species
	Sunbirds • 116 species
	White-eyes • 85 species

Blue whales emit ear-splitting,
low-pitched grunts that are the
loudest noises made by any animal.

SECTION 7
MAMMALS

FOR MANY PEOPLE, THE MOST FAMILIAR GROUP OF ANIMALS IS THE MAMMALS. This is partly because we keep many kinds of mammals as pets and on farms, including dogs, cats, rabbits, horses, cows, sheep, and pigs. Also, the best-known animal in the world, and one of the most numerous, is a mammal—the human being.

A mammal is warm-blooded and has a body covering of fur or hair. Most mammal babies grow in their mother's womb, and are born quite well developed. But in marsupial mammals, such as kangaroos, the babies are born tiny and hardly developed at all. They continue their growth in the safety of the mother's pouch. Monotreme mammals do not give birth to babies at all. They lay eggs, like birds, and the eggs hatch into babies. But all female mammals make milk to feed their babies. This is produced by special glands called mammary glands—which is how the group got its name.

There are some 4,000 kinds, or species, of mammal. They include the largest creature ever to live on Earth, the blue whale. Most mammals walk and run on land. However, the whales, dolphins, porpoises, and sea cows spend all their lives in water. Another group of mammals, the bats, have taken to the air. Others, such as moles and mole rats, tunnel underground and rarely see the light of day.

EGG-LAYING MAMMALS

PERHAPS THE ODDEST OF ALL MAMMALS ARE THE MONOTREMES OR EGG-LAYING MAMMALS. There are only three kinds—the platypus and two species of echidnas or spiny anteaters, the short-beaked and long-beaked echidnas. They all live in Australia or nearby New Guinea. The platypus is also called the duck-billed platypus because its mouth is shaped like a duck's beak. These highly unusual mammals do not give birth to babies, like the other 4,000-plus mammal species. The females lay eggs, like a bird or reptile.

◨ The short-beaked echidna grows about 14 inches (35 cm) in length. Both long- and short-beaked echidnas have strong claws for digging up their prey and excavating nest burrows.

STICKY TONGUE

The echidnas look similar to porcupines, being covered with long, sharp, protective spines. They use their powerful front claws to dig into soil, or ant or termite nests. Then they lick up the prey using their long, sticky tongue.

◨ The long-beaked echidna grows to about 28 inches (70 cm) in length.

The female echidna keeps her single egg in a temporary brood pouch which develops on her belly. The egg hatches after about ten days. Then she feeds the tiny, helpless baby on her milk, as other mammals do.

The short-beaked echidna is quite common in Australia and New Guinea. It is found in a wide range of habitats, from dry deserts to cold uplands, scrubland and forest. The long-beaked echidna is found only in the highlands of New Guinea. It is larger than its short-beaked cousin, with fur longer than the spines, and a longer, down-curved snout. Despite its name of spiny anteater, this echidna feeds mostly on earthworms, which it catches using the tough spines on its tongue.

THE PLATYPUS

The platypus lives in eastern Australia, including Tasmania. It is one of the strangest of all mammals. When a preserved platypus body was first studied by scientists in 1798, they thought was a fake made of several animals sewn together. The platypus has a wide beak like a duck, a flattened tail like a beaver and webbed feet like an otter.

◨ The female platypus digs a very long breeding burrow, 60 feet (18 m) or more into the riverbank. At the end of the burrow she makes a nest of dry leaves and grass.

INSIDE A MAMMAL

All mammals have the same basic parts inside. The body has an internal skeleton made of bones, which give strength and support. In the chest are the heart and lungs. The abdomen contains the digestive, waste-disposal, and reproductive parts.

vertebrae (backbones)
brain
jaws and teeth
kidney
intestines
stomach
neck muscles
shoulder blade
lungs
penis
heart
testes (male organs)
humerus bone
leg muscles
toe bones
ulna and radius bones

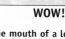

WOW! ⚠

The mouth of a long-beaked echidna is just a small slit at the end of the snout. The tongue can poke out 7 inches (18 cm) beyond the snout tip. The echidna has no teeth. It squashes its tiny prey between its tongue and the roof of its mouth.

...e male platypus has a poison spur hidden in the fur on each hind leg. ...reatened, he kicks out and causes the attacker great pain.

...ese body features make it ideally suited to swimming, ...d a platypus spends up to half its time nosing and ...bbing in the water for food. It uses its tail as a ...der and to store a reserve of fat for the ...ter, when food is often scarce.

...CTRIC BILL

...typuses are not often seen since ...y live along creeks, rivers, and ...es, and are usually active at ...ht. They have an extraordinary ...thod of feeding. They hunt at ...ht along the stream or lake bed, ...ecting prey hidden in the mud by ...tiny electrical impulses given out ...the muscles in the prey's body. The ...typus does this using its wide, ...hery bill. This is very sensitive to ...ch and movements, and also has tiny ...which can detect electricity, like some ...(page 107). As it hunts, the platypus ...ps its eyes and nostrils tightly closed.

...e platypus catches mainly insect grubs, ...rms, little shrimps, and similar small ...hwater creatures. It stores them in ...cheek pouches and eats them later, ...en it returns to its burrow in the ...k. Then the platypus grinds up ...food using horny ridges in its ...s, since like the echidnas, it ...no teeth.

...e platypus catches small ...ures including frogs and fish, and ...water plants. Each dive lasts about ...minute. The head and body are about ...ches (45 cm) long, and the tail 6–8 ...s (15–20 cm). Once very rare, ...puses are now protected by law and ...become more common in some regions.

MAMMALS

Mammals
- 4,150 species
- young feed on mother's milk
- body with fur or hair
- warm-blooded
- most have four limbs

First major subgroup of mammals:

Monotremes
- 3 species, platypus and 2 echidnas
- only mammals that lay eggs
- adults have no teeth
- found only in Australia and New Guinea

MARSUPIAL MAMMALS

MARSUPIALS ARE POUCHED MAMMALS, NAMED FOR THE POUCH OF THE FEMALE. She gives birth to babies that are at a very early stage of development, tiny and helpless. The babies crawl to the pouch, or marsupium, and continue to develop there in safety, feeding on her milk. There are about 120 species of marsupial in Australia, 50 species in New Guinea, and 90 species in South and Central America. One species, the Virginia opossum, has spread through southern North America. The largest marsupials are kangaroos and wallabies. They have big, muscular hind legs and bound along at great speed.

⬥ The marsupial mole has shiny golden fur.

⬥ The Virginia opossum is agile climber and usually in trees. But it has adapted life in towns, clambering fences and scavenging for food in trash cans and du

⬥ The female red kangaroo is smaller than the male, weighing less than 30 kg. The young in the pouch is called a joey.

The babies of marsupial mammals are born tiny and undeveloped. At birth, baby kangaroo is hardly larger than a grape, and its legs have only just be to grow. Even so, it can crawl from the birth opening to its mother's pouch, where its mouth latches onto her nipple, to suck her milk. The baby lives like this for six months. As it grows larger, it begins to leave the pouch for short periods. Meanwhile another tiny, newborn baby arrives. Even when a youngster is more than a year old, it may dash back to the safety of its mother's pouch if danger appears, and still pokes its head in to feed on her milk. Most kangaroos and wallabies eat leaves, stems, and shoots. And the smaller, shorter-legged tree kangaroos really do live in trees!

⬥ The Tasmanian devil has length of about 24 inches (It lives on the Australian isl Tasmania. Its massive teeth jaws easily crunch bones.

THE APPEALING KOALA

The koala is one of the most appealing marsupials, looking like a teddy bear soft toy. In fact it has very sharp claws to cling on to the branches the gum (eucalyptus) trees where it lives. So it can give a deep scratch if threatened. Koalas spend much of their lives either sleeping or munching gum leaves. They get all their nourishment and moisture from these, so they rarely come down to the ground. Another bearlike marsupial is the wombat. It lives in a complex system of burrows and chambers, which it digs using its powerful, large-clawed feet.

⬥ Wombats feed on roots, shoots, and other plant material. They sometimes ra farm crops.

MARSUPIAL VERSIONS

There are many other kinds of marsupial. Some resemble mammals living on other continents. For example, there are marsupial mice and marsupial cats or quolls.

The brushtail possum once lived in forests, but has now spread to Australian suburbs, where it eats food scraps.

There are also marsupial shrews or planigales, rat- and rabbit-like marsupials called bandicoots, and even marsupial moles. The pouches of tunneling marsupials, such as the wombat and marsupial mole, open backward, so they do not fill with soil as the female digs her way through the ground.

One of the smallest marsupials is the honey possum. It is about the same size as a house mouse and lives on nectar and pollen from flowers. The possum licks up its food using its long, bristly, brush-tipped tongue.

MARSUPIAL GLIDERS

Several species of marsupials can swoop [fro]m tree to tree, using winglike flaps of skin [str]etched between the front and rear limbs. These [in]clude various types of gliders, and the pygmy [po]ssum or feathertail glider. The greater glider, [wh]ich weighs 3 pounds (1.4 kg), can travel 300 [fee]t (91 m) in a single "flight."

[Cr]eatures very similar to marsupial gliders are the [col]ugos or flying lemurs. There are only two [sp]ecies, living in the forests of Malaysia and the [Ph]ilippines. They swoop through the air in a [sim]ilar way to marsupial gliders, but with better [fli]ght control, covering more than 500 feet [(15]0 m). However, these animals are not [ma]rsupial mammals, they are placental mammals.

[Ab]out 20 species of Australian marsupials have [be]come extinct during the last 200 years. Dozens [mo]re are threatened, mainly by habitat loss or [co]mpetition from introduced animals. The [ma]hogany glider, however, was believed to be [ex]tinct, but has been rediscovered in the [fo]rests of North Queensland.

The second major subgroup of mammals:

Marsupials
• about 270 species
• tiny young raised in mother's pouch
• live mainly in Australia, New Guinea, South and Central America

Marsupial groups include:

American opossums
• 75 species
Marsupial mice
• 53 species

Kangaroos and wallabies
• 50 species
Bandicoots
• 17 species
Ringtail possums
• 16 species
Brushtail possums and cuscuses
• 14 species
Rat kangaroos
• 10 species
Gliders
• 7 species
Pygmy possums
• 7 species

Shrew (rat) opossums
• 7 species
Wombats
• 3 species
Bilbies
• 2 species
Honey possum
• 1 species
Koala
• 1 species
Marsupial mole
• 1 species
Monito del monte
• 1 species
Numbat
• 1 species

Koalas look peaceful and quiet. But they can defend themselves with their sharp claws, and the bellowing call of the male koala can be heard over a distance of several miles. Koalas are a threatened species and are fully protected.

INSECT EATERS

THE INSECT-EATING MAMMALS, OR
INSECTIVORES, ARE MAINLY SMALL AND VERY
ACTIVE. They include shrews, hedgehogs, and moles,
and also tenrecs, solenodons, moonrats, and desmans.
Most types eat mainly insects, from soft caterpillars and
grubs, to hard-cased beetles and biting ants. But they
consume other small prey too, from juicy worms and
slugs, to spiders and woodlice. Insect-eating mammals are
generally nocturnal (active at night). They sniff and feel for
food with their sensitive noses and whiskers. Some shrews
are so small and busy that their bodies soon run out of
energy and they must eat every few hours to survive.

◪ The common shrew's
small eyes and little
rounded ears are almost
hidden in its fur. Its main
senses are smell and touc

◪ Desert
hedgehog

Many insect-eating mammals
resemble rodents such as
mice or rats. But rodents
have long, chisel-like front
teeth (page 206).
Insectivores have sharp,
pointed teeth, almost like a
miniature cat. They are fierce hunters
and, despite their size, if threatened they leap at
the enemy in a frenzy of bites and squeals.

GOING COLD
The biggest problem faced by tiny and active
mammals such as shrews is that they are
warm-blooded. Being so tiny, the surface
area of the body is very large compared to
the volume of the body. So huge amounts of
body heat are lost through the body surface,
compared to larger mammals. To keep its
body temperature up, a shrew must "burn"
lots of energy, which it gets from food. So it
must eat—or go cold and die.

The pygmy shrew is one of the smallest
mammals, with a head-and-body as small
as your thumb. It hunts for 2–3 hours, has

a short rest, hunts again, and so on. It may
starve to death after 12 hours without food.

PRICKLY BALL
The prickles of a hedgehog are long, thick, extr
sharp hairs. A fully grown European hedgehog
has about 5,000 of them covering its body.

▶ The desman has a long,
flattened tail for
swimming.

▼ The tail-less
tenrec is from
Madagascar.

▼ Tree shrews live in
the forests
of Southeast
Asia. They are not
insectivores, but are similar in
their habits and food, except
that they are perfectly at
home in the trees.

the prickles normally lie flat, but the hedgehog
can raise them by tensing muscles just under its
skin. With its back arched, head and legs tucked
in, and spines pointing out, the hedgehog then
becomes a spiny ball. This deters most predators,
but is no defense against road traffic.

LIVING UNDERGROUND

Moles are well suited to life in the soil. The
cylindrical body, short limbs, and soft, thick fur
allow a mole to slide through the soil, as it digs
tunnels using its flattened, strongly clawed front
paws. Here and there the mole heaves loose soil
to the surface through an upright tunnel, making
a molehill. A mole's tunnel network may stretch
more than 500 feet (150 m). It feeds on animals
like worms that fall in through the sides.

Golden moles are only found in southern and
central Africa. They have shiny fur with a golden
sheen, and their eyes are covered by hairy skin.
Like other moles, they spend most of their lives in
tunnel systems below the ground.

A shrew tackles a lizard almost its own size. Shrews
have poisonous saliva (spit), which helps to paralyze victims
when the shrew bites them.

MORE INSECTIVORES

Tenrecs are another group of African insectivores.
Some resemble large shrews, others have spines
like a hedgehog's. The most unusual tenrecs are
the otter shrews of West Africa. They swim well
and hunt for water insects, small fish, and frogs.
Solenodons are like giant shrews. There are only
two species, both from the West Indies region and
both rare. One is found just on the island of
Cuba. The other lives only on nearby Hispaniola
(Haiti and the Dominican Republic).

The moonrat (top left), with its
striped face, is one of the largest
insect eaters. It has a head and body
16 inches (40 cm) long. It is active at
night and has a hairless, scaly tail
like a rat, hence its name.
The golden mole (near left) often
comes to the surface to feed.
The Cuban solenodon (below left) is
12 inches (30 cm) long. It tackles
animal prey as large as rats.
The pygmy white-toothed shrew
(bottom left) is the smallest
of the insectivores.

Moonrat

Golden mole

Cuban solenodon

The pygmy white-
toothed shrew

The third major subgroup of mammals:

Placentals
• about 3,880 species
• unborn develop in
the womb, nourished by the
placenta (afterbirth)
• worldwide, in all
habitats, mountain
to deep sea

Placentals include:

Insect-eating mammals
(insectivores)
• 345 species
• eat insects, worms, slugs, and
similar small animals
• small and active
• long snout, small eyes and ears

Insect-eating groups include:
Shrews
• 246 species
Tenrecs and otter shrews
• 33 species

Moles and desmans
• 29 species
Golden moles
• 18 species
Hedgehogs and moonrats
• 17 species
Solenodons
• 2 species
Tree shrews
• 18 species
• resemble squirrels
Elephant shrews
• 15 species
• small with pointed shrewlike face
• long nose, almost like an
elephant's trunk in some species

Another group of placentals:

Colugos (flying lemurs)
• cat-sized gliders
• live in Southeast Asian forests

BATS

ABOUT ONE FOURTH OF ALL MAMMAL SPECIES ARE BATS. They are the biggest mammal group, after rodents. About 960 differ[ent] species are found throughout the world, except in the colde[st] regions. Although some mammals can glide, bats are the on[ly] mammals that can truly fly. There are two main kinds of bat[s]. One is the fruit bats and flying foxes. These are mostly large, with a body the size of a small dog and wings about 6 feet (1.8 m) across. They eat fruits, flowers, leaves, and other pl[ant] parts. The other main kind is the insect-eating bats. These [are] much smaller, with a body the size of a mouse or rat. Surprisingly, some insect-eating bats not only eat insec[ts] but also mice, voles, frogs, and fish.

◪ The vampire bat has four razorlike canine teeth and makes only a tiny slit in its victim's skin. It usually chooses a furless or featherless part of the body, such as the ankle. It feeds for about half an hour each night. In some areas vampire bats spread diseases such as rabies.

Most bats are nocturnal, or active at night. Apart from flying foxes, they find their way by a sound-radar system called echolocation. Most smaller bats feed on night-flying insects such as moths. But some bats specialize in finding other foods. The fisherman bat of Central and South America swoops over rivers and lakes, and hooks up fish from just under the surface.

lower arm bone (radius)
first finger (thumb)
claw
second finger
wrist
third finger
fifth finger
fourth finger
wing membrane (patagium)

A BAT'S WING
The wing (arm) of a bat is different from the wing of a bird. It is a thin, skinlike membrane, the patagium, stretched between hugely long arm, hand, and finger bones. The patagium is a thin layer of blood vessels and elastic threads sandwiched between two layers of skin.

◪ The pipistrelle is one of the smallest bats, with a head and body 1.6 inches (4 cm) long and a wingspa[n] of 8 inches (20 cm).

◪ The mouse-eared bat's high-pitched squeaks of sound emerge from its mouth. Some bats emit sounds through the nose.

outgoing pulse of ultrasound

It uses its long, curved claws to spear the fish. Mastiff bats catch bees and wasps. Greater horseshoe bats, named after their horseshoe-shaped noses, dive onto beetles and other ground-dwelling insects. Other bats catch night-flying birds such as nightjars and even small owls.

The huge ears of
g-eared bats can turn and
ivel with great accuracy, like
lar dishes. They catch the
urning echoes of sound,
ich a bat uses to find its way
the dark.

⚠ Resting, or
roosting, bats hang
upside down by their
foot claws. They wrap
their wings around the
body to keep in warmth.

⚠ Flying foxes like the common
long-tongued fruit bat have
dog- or foxlike faces. They roost
by day in trees, often making
chattering noises.

World Watch

In some
parts of the world,
especially the tropics, bats
are among the most
common mammals. In other
areas, such as Europe, they
have become extremely
rare. Modern farming
methods using pesticides
mean that their insect prey
is scarcer now. The old
hollow trees that they roost
in have been felled, or their
caves have been blocked
up. In some countries, such
as Britain, all bat species
are protected by law

LEGEND OF A VAMPIRE

Vampire bats feed on blood. But they are not dangerous to
people, as the legends say. Vampire bats live in Central and South
America, and are quite small, with a head and body length of
only 3 inches (8 cm). They usually feed on the blood of sleeping
cattle, pigs, or horses. The vampire lands near its victim, crawls
over the ground, and makes a small slitlike wound with its sharp
teeth. Then it dribbles spit to stop the blood clotting and licks
up the oozing blood.

Some bats
atch prey in
eir tail
embranes,
hers in their
ot claws.

Many bats roost together in colonies, in caves or hollow
trees, and also inside modern "caves" such as church
towers and mine shafts. In tropical areas bats are active all
year. In temperate lands, most bats hibernate through the
winter, emerging from their deep sleep when the weather
warms up again in spring.

The biggest group of bats is the common or vesper bats.
It includes common European species such as the pipistrelle,
long-eared bat, and noctule. The smallest mammal is a bat –
Kitti's hog-nosed bat from Thailand. Its head and body are
just 1.2 inches (3 cm) long and it weighs 0.07 ounces (1.5 g).
And one of the biggest gatherings of mammals is of bats. Some
colonies of the Mexican free-tailed bat contain up to 10 million
bats, all clustered together in a single cave.

HOW BATS FLY IN THE DARK

returning
echo

Most bats use echolocation to find
their way, even in total darkness. They
emit very high-pitched pulses of sound, called
ultrasound, which are too high for most
humans to hear. The sound pulses bounce back
as echoes off nearby objects. The bat hears the
pattern of echoes and analyzes it to give a
"sound-picture" of the surroundings. Flying foxes
and fruit bats have good eyesight and smell, and fly
mainly at dusk and dawn. Most do use echolocation.

BATS	Some groups of bats:	
• 960 species • the only mammals with true, powered flight • front limbs are wings • most are nocturnal	Flying foxes, fruit bats • 175 species Common or vesper bats • 320 species Spear-nosed bats • 140 species Free-tailed bats • 90 species Horseshoe bats • 70 species Leaf-nosed bats • 60 species	Sheath-tailed bats • 50 species Slit-faced bats • 12 species Ghost-faced bats • 8 species Vampire bats • 3 species Bulldog bats • 2 species Hog-nosed bat • 1 species

ANTEATERS, SLOTHS, AND ARMADILLOS

SOME MAMMALS LIVE AT A SLOW PACE. They include anteaters, armadillos, pangolins, and especially sloths. These creatures share other features too, such as long, sharp claws and very small teeth, or none at all. They feed on soft or tiny food items that do not need much biting or chewing. For defense, armadillos and pangolins have a covering of bands or scales made from tough bone and horn, like a suit of armor. Sloths rely on staying still and unnoticed. Anteaters slash at enemies with their claws.

⬆ A sloth is so well suited to hanging around that it can hardly walk on the ground. It has to drag its body along with its curved claws.

LARGEST...!

The largest armadillo is the giant armadillo of Brazil and Peru, at 5 feet (1.5 m) long. It is endangered by the loss of its dense forest habitat.

⬇ The tongue of the giant anteater is 2 feet (60 cm) long. It can collect hundreds of termites or ants with a single lick. One anteater may eat 20,000 ants in a single day!

An anteater eats not only ants. It also licks up termites and small grubs with its very long, sticky tongue, which emerges from the small mouth at the end of the long snout. The anteater digs out or rips open the ant nest or termite mound with its large front claws, and licks up the milling insects in their hundreds. But it does not eat them all. It soon moves on, leaving the nest to be repaired as a larder for the future.

⬆ The nine-banded armadillo the most common and widespread type. Like the others, it feeds mainly at nig

⬇ The tree pangolin ha gripping or prehensile tai rough, scaleless patch of s on the underside near the helps to give extra g

The giant anteater is the largest of the four anteater species. It is 80 inches (200 cm) long, but much of this is its long, down-curved nose and brushlike tail. It also has a shaggy coat and an awkward, rolling way of walking. Giant anteaters roam forests and scrub in Central and South America. The other three species are smaller and stay mainly in trees, using the strong tail as an extra limb to clasp branches.

Most of the armadillo's body is protected by bony ...tes. However, a predator may succeed in flipping the ...nadillo onto its back, to get at the soft underside.

...OW AS THE SLOTH

...he sloths of South American ...inforests are named for their very ...ow movements. They spend most of ...eir lives hanging upside down from ...ee branches, either munching ...aves, crawling slowly along, or ...aying perfectly still, asleep. A ...oth relies on its stillness and ...mouflage to escape detection. ...he hairs of its fur have furrows ...here microscopic plants (algae) ...ow, giving the animal a ...eenish tinge among the leaves.

...RMORED ARMADILLOS

...he most obvious feature of an ...madillo is the hard, protective ...overing over its back, like armor ...ating. Each plate or band has a ...rd, bony core covered by a tough, ...rny substance (like our fingernails). ...exible skin between the bands allows the ...madillo to hunch up its body and tuck its legs ...derneath when a predator comes near. Some ...madillos can roll up into a tight ball, for greater ...otection. Most armadillos eat ants, termites, ...d similar small animals. Some are also fond of ...uit. They live in South and Central America, ...d the nine-banded armadillo ranges into ...uthern North America.

...pangolin sheds a few of its scales each ...nth, and new ones soon grow. As it ...s up ants with its strap- ...ped tongue, the ...golin closes its eyes ...nostrils so the ...s cannot ...them.

◘ A sloth feeds mainly on fruit and leaves, hanging by its long, hooked claws. Even its digestion works slowly. It can take as long as a month for a meal to pass through its body. Most sloths come down from their trees about once each week, to leave their droppings on the ground. They spend about two thirds of their time asleep!

MAMMAL "PINE CONES"

Pangolins, like armadillos, are protected by hard, bony plates. The plates consist of flat, point-edged scales that overlap like the scales on a pine cone.

Most pangolins lick up ants and termites, using their long tongue in the same way as an anteater.

EDENTATES (SMALL-TOOTHED OR TOOTHLESS MAMMALS)

- 36 species
- slow-moving
- most have long claws
- small simple teeth, or toothless

Groups include:

Armadillos
- 20 species
- South and Central America

Pangolins
- 7 species
- Africa, India, and Southeast Asia

Sloths
- 5 species
- South and Central America

Anteaters
- 4 species
- South and Central America

201

RABBITS, HARES, AND PIKAS

EVER ALERT TO DANGER, RABBITS AND HARES ARE ALWAYS READY TO DASH FOR SAFETY. They live in open, grassy country, and have large eyes and huge ears to look and listen for predators.

◢ The winter fur of Arctic and snowshoe hares is white, for camouflage in snow and ice. It molts in spring. The summer fur is brown.

Their back legs are long and muscular, ideal for running at high speed from danger. Although they resemble rodents such as squirrels and rats, rabbits and hares belong to a different mammal group, the lagomorphs. This name means "leaping shape," which is what these creatures do to survive. The lagomorph group also includes pikas. These are like small, dumpy rabbits with shorter ears and little legs. They also lack the rabbit's bobtail.

◣ The volcano rabbit lives only on grassy mountain slopes in Mexico. It has short ears and a small tail. It is a very rare species, and protected by law.

◣ The hare's prominent eyes allow it to see above and even behind itself, so it can spot predators such as eagles from almost any direction.

There is no exact difference between rabbits and hares. Generally, the larger types with longer legs and longer ears are known as hares, or jackrabbits in North America. The smaller species with shorter ears are usually called rabbits. Hares that live in the far north, such as the Arctic and snowshoe hares, molt into a white coat during the snowy winter season. The numbers of snowshoe hares living in the northern forests of North America vary on a fairly regular cycle.

⚠ "Mad March hares" are usually males battling for a female at breeding time in spring. Or the pawing and boxing may be a jill (female) chasing away an unwanted jack (male).

may have up to 20 babies each year, rabbits have a deserved reputation of increasing numbers very quickly.

HAY FOR WINTER

Pikas look like a combination of rabbit and guinea pig or vole. They live in mountainous country in Asia, with one species also in north west North America. Most pikas prefer rocky slopes. The large-eared pika of the Himalayas and nearby mountains is one of the highest-living mammals, found at heights of more than 20,000 feet (6,000 m). Pikas graze on a range of plants, mostly grasses, flowers, and young stems. In the fall, they pull hay, soft twigs, and other stores of food into their burrows to eat during the long, cold winter.

⚠ The American black-tailed jackrabbit is actually a type of hare. It uses its large ears to listen for danger and also to keep cool in the great heat of summer.

...ey reach a peak roughly every ten years, then ...l again. Why this is so is not clear. But it affects ...populations of lynx, snowy owls, and other ...edators in the same way, since they depend on ...hares for food.

...e large ears of a rabbit or hare not only pick up ...faintest noises, like an elephant's ears; they ...o help to lose body heat into the air ...ring very hot weather. If a rabbit or ...e detects danger, it races away, ...pelled by great leaps of its ...ge back legs. It may thump ...ground first with its rear ...t to warn others nearby, ...d it can zigzag at great ...ed. Some hares sprint ...more than 50 mph ...km/h). However, they do ...have great stamina, and ...dators such as wolves soon ...them out.

...AWING TEETH

...bits and hares have strong teeth ...gnawing grasses, stems, seeds, roots, ...k, and other plant foods. Some rabbits live ...roups or colonies in networks of underground ...nels, called warrens, which they dig in the soil ...edges and banks. Most hares live alone and ...t in the open, in shallow bowl-like areas in the ...ss or scrub, called forms. They also have their ...bies in these forms. For this reason, young hares ...own as leverets) can run and hide almost as ...n as they are born.

...EDING LIKE RABBITS

...y rabbits born in the safety of the breeding ...mber or "stop," are blind and helpless at first. ...ir eyes open at a week old and they venture ...of the nest at three weeks. But at only four ...nths of age they can breed. Since one female

⚠ The running hare kicks off with its long back legs, and cushions its landing on the two front legs with paws held together. Then it thrusts its rear legs forward on either side of the front paws, and makes another leap.

⚠ Most pikas, like the northern pika, are about 8–10 inches (20–25 cm) long.

Rabbits and hares
• 44 species
• large ears
• long back legs
• eyes face sideways
• very short "bob" tail
• slitlike nostrils
• eat plants

Pikas
• 14 species
• rounded ears
• almost tail-less
• eat plants

HYRAXES AND THE AARDVARK

HYRAXES (ALSO CALLED HYRACES) ARE SMALL PLANT-EATING MAMMALS ABOUT THE SIZE OF RABBITS. They also resemble rabbits in appearance, but with shorter ears and legs, and a short, stumpy tail rather than a "bobtail." Hyraxes are found over much of Africa, and also in parts of the Middle East. Most types live in rocky country and sit on boulders or outcrops, sunning themselves as they rest. Rock hyraxes are commonly

△ The tree hyrax climbs nim even on damp, slippery branches. Hyraxes are long-l for fairly small plant-eating mammals. Some survive for more than 12 years, compare to 2–3 years for most rabbits

COUSINS!

Hyraxes look similar to rabbits and hares (lagomorphs), or to rodents such as rats and guinea pigs. But scientific studies show that their closest mammal relatives are elephants! Hyraxes and elephants, and also aardvarks, share similarities in their teeth, jaw bones, muscles, and other internal body parts.

known as dassies, and some types are also called conies. The aardvark is another African mammal, and quite unlike any other — it is the only member of its group, the tubulidents.

△ Rock hyraxes form family groups. The adult male defends territory against neighboring groups of the spe

Hyraxes are stocky, well-built mammals suited for clamberin over rocks or climbing trees. Their small feet have thick, rubbery, moist soles to give a firm grip even on smooth rocks and branches. The feet are also equipped with nail-like hooves rather than proper claws, and are not design for digging burrows or scraping up food. So hyraxes ma their nests in caves or cracks between rocks, under tree roots, or inside hollow trees.

Rock hyraxes make their homes on rocky outcrops or hills known as kopjes (koppies). They usually live in colonies of about 10–30, including adults and young. Rock hyraxes eat a wide variety of plants, especially grasses, even when dry and tough. Bush and tree hyraxes prefer softer leaves and fruits.

◁ A hyrax has a small face and an upturned mouth that always seems to "smile." But this is only our own interpretation, based on human facial expressions.

E "EARTH PIG"

ere is only a single
ecies of aardvark, a
me that means
arth-pig" in the
rikaans language.
is strange animal is
ite unlike any other
ammal, especially its
eth and claws (right).
teeth are covered,
t with hard white
amel as in most
ammals (including
rselves), but with a
ft, grey substance
lled cementum.

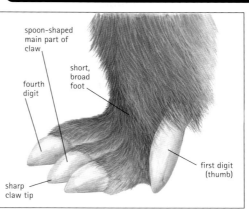

THE AARDVARK'S ODD CLAWS

The aardvark is a very efficient
burrower. If a predator threatens, it
can dig itself into even hard ground in
just a few minutes. It also digs for
food, and it excavates several burrows
around its home territory for shelter
and safety. The main breeding burrow
of the female may be 39 feet (12 m)
long. The aardvark does all this digging
using its powerful feet with their
unusual curved claws. There are four
on each front foot and five on each
rear foot. They jab into the hard soil
even through matted grass roots.

spoon-shaped
main part of
claw

short,
broad
foot

fourth
digit

first digit
(thumb)

sharp
claw tip

The aardvark is also something
a mystery. Although it is the size of a large pig,
is hardly ever seen by day, since it hides in one
its many burrows. At night, it roams in search
its food, ants and termites. But it is extremely
y and secretive, and darts away into the
rkness if it senses danger.

Aardvarks live in open woodland, scrub, and
grassland across much of central and southern
Africa. They find their food by nosing about,
sniffing, and listening. After
digging out the tiny prey, the
aardvark gathers them using
its long, sticky tongue. It may
need to hunt for several
hours each night, covering
9 miles (15 km) or more,
to find food.

he aardvark has a head-and-body
th of about 4 feet (1.2 m), with a
of 20 inches (50 cm). Its head
arrow, with long ears and a
, flexible snout tipped by
glike nose.

Hyraxes
• 11 species
• soft, moist pad on sole of foot
• flattened claws, like tiny hooves
• eat plants

Rock hyraxes (Dassies)
• live among rocks
• Africa, Middle East

Tree hyraxes
• live mainly in forests
• Africa

Bush hyraxes
• live among rocks or
  in hollow trees
• mainly east Africa

Aardvark
• 1 species
• large, piglike
• prefers woodland and scrub
• central and southern Africa

MICE, RATS, AND CAVIES

THE RODENTS OR GNAWING MAMMALS ARE BY FAR THE LARGEST MAMMAL GROUP. The 1,700 species mean that almost one of every two mammals is a rodent. About seventy-five percent of these are types of mice and rats, and their South American relatives, cavies—the best-known being the guinea pig. The rodent's key feature is its four long, sharp, chisel-like incisor teeth at the front of the mouth. These can chew even the hardest foods, such as nuts or tree bark. Some small rodents, including mice, rats, hamsters, gerbils, and guinea pigs, are often kept as pets. (More rodents are described on pages 208 to 211.)

◨ The jerboa has huge bac feet that work like sandsh so it does not sink into the desert surface.

◨ A dormouse may hibernate for up to eight months, depending on the climate of the region.

◨ The cavy group of rodents includes guinea pigs, porcupines, spiny r and mole rats.

Mice and rats range in size from the pygmy mouse, less than 4 inches (10 cm) long including its tail, to rats that reach a total length of 32 inches (80 cm). The harvest mouse is one of the smallest, with a body hardly larger than a thumb. It is a very agile climber and uses its long tail as an extra limb to grasp grass stems. It spread rapidly when people began to plant wheat and similar crops. Bu then it suffered as machines took over harvesting from people. It could n escape from its ball-shaped nest as the combine harvester approached.

Some mice and rats have taken to living near people, especiall in our houses, farms, and food stores. They cause damag and also spread diseases. The fleas that live on certain rats may bite people and spread plague. House mic get into pantries and larders. Brown and roof rat are a nuisance in grain stores.

Lemmings have blunt noses, small ears, round bodies, and thick fur. These features help then stay warm in their cold northern homelands. They live among grasses and bushes on the ground, feeding on roots and shoots. When conditions are good and food is plentiful, lemmings breed so fast that they end up eating all of the available food.

◧ The yellow-necked mouse is common in farm and woods across Europe. It may even come houses in the fall, to escape the cold and loo food. It eats mainly seeds, berries, and ins

nce the food supplies have gone, many
nmings set off on a mass migration to find
w places to live. During these "lemming
ars," they become bold and aggressive. At
st they travel only at night. But soon they
urney by day too. The urge to move on is so
ong that they enter towns and cross streets,
d even dive into rivers or tumble off cliffs.
ese migrations have led to legends that the
nmings really want to die!

G CHEEKS

ne hamster is a familiar pet, yet it is rarely seen
the wild. Its original home was the steppe
asslands of Eastern Europe, but it has now
read into Central Europe too. Hamsters eat
any foods. They carry what they cannot
nsume back to the nest, filling their stretchy
eek pouches. In the wild, many hamsters
bernate during winter. But they wake up every
w days to nibble at their store of nuts, berries,
d other food.

nother group of small rodents is the jerboas.
ney have very long back legs and jump
ceptionally well, using the long tail to balance.

Naked mole rats work together for the good of the
ony, like bees or ants. Only the chief female, or queen,
 have babies. The rest are "workers" and do specific jobs.

boas live in the deserts of North Africa, the
iddle East, and Central Asia. They feed mainly
 seeds and insects. Gerbils are similar to
boas, but they have shorter back legs and
maller ears. Like jerboas, they spend the day in
 their burrows, to avoid predators and also the
intense desert heat.

◀ When lemmings become too
numerous in an area, they have a
strong instinct to set off and look
for less crowded places.

▲ Black or ship rats have spread around the world, from their
original homeland of tropical Asia. They travel on ships, being
agile enough to climb aboard along the mooring ropes.

SLEEPING MICE

Common dormice are about the same size as
house mice. But they have soft, light brown fur
and a furry tail. They are well known for their
long winter sleep or hibernation. The name
"dormouse" comes from the French word *dormir,*
"to sleep." In summer they eat flowers, shoots,
nuts, berries, insects, and spiders.

African naked mole rats have hardly any fur
and live entirely underground,
in large colonies. They
chisel through the soil
with their huge front
teeth. Members of the
colony have different
jobs. Some are diggers, some
gather food, and some
guard against intruders.
Only one female, the
queen, can produce
young. Apart from
certain insects, this type
of colony is unique in
the animal world.

▲ Jumping mice bound along like
miniature kangaroos. They can
cover more than 6 feet (1.8 m) in
a single leap. Fast reactions and
speed help small rodents elude
their many predators.

RODENTS	
• 1,700 species	
• long, sharp gnawing front teeth	Jerboas
• most are small and nocturnal	• 31 species
	Jumping mice and birch mice
Some groups of small rodents:	• 14 species
	Dormice
Old World rats and mice	• 10 species
• 480 species	African mole rats
New World rats and mice	• 9 species
• 365 species	Cane rats
Pocket mice	• 2 species
• 65 species	Chinchilla rats
Spiny rats	• 2 species
• 55 species	Rock rat
	• 1 species

207

LARGE RODENTS

PORCUPINES, BEAVERS, CHINCHILLAS, AND COYPUS ARE ALL LARGE RODENTS, BUT THE BIGGEST OF ALL IS THE CAPYBARA OF SOUTH AMERICA. The size of a sheep, the capybara lives in forests near lakes and rivers, and feeds on waterside vegetation. It has partly webbed toes and spends much of its time wading and swimming. The American beaver is another huge rodent, with a head and body about 3 feet (1 m) long, and webbed feet suited to life in water. The crested porcupine of Africa is large too, with a head and body about 31 inches (80 cm) long. Like other porcupines, it is protected by spines which are thicker, sharper versions of normal mammal fur.

🔼 The tree porcupine has long toe claws and a muscular, curly, prehensile tail, for gripping branches.

🔼 In the wild, chinchillas li... in multi-family groups of about 50–100. They eat alm... any kind of plant food.

🔽 Young capybaras can rur... and swim a few hours after birth. Capybaras live in fam... groups and feed mainly at dusk and dawn. They are preyed on by large cats, especially jaguars, and big snakes such as anacondas.

BEAVERS

Beavers gnaw through trunks to fell trees. They feed on the soft, sap-rich bark. They also use the logs and branches to build a wall or dam across a stream. Then they construct their home or lodge in the pool that forms behind the dam. The lodge gives protection against winter weather and predators such as wolves. Both dam and lodge are strengthened and cemented with stones and mud. The lodge has several tunnels leading from the living quarters down i... the water. It also has a "chimney" leading upwa... for fresh air. In cold weather, the beaver family stays in the lodg... They feed on twigs, bark, and leaves which they have stored in the lodge or jamme... under stones... their poo...

🔽 Inside a beaver's lodge, a mother suckles her young. When they reach two years of age, they will leave and build their own lodges.

◪ Coypus can cause damage because they raid farm crops and dig burrows in the banks of drainage channels.

...he beaver has a unique feature among ...dents—its flat, scaly, paddlelike tail. This has ...o main uses. When the beaver swims with its ...ebbed back feet, the tail is used as a rudder for ...eering. If the beaver senses danger, it slaps its ...il onto the water's surface with a loud splash, ... warn others of its family group.

...RCUPINES

...here are two main groups of porcupines. The ...merican or New World porcupines live mainly ... trees and most have prehensile tails. They feed ... leaves, fruits, and shoots, feeding mostly at ...ght. The Old World porcupines of Europe, ...rica, and Asia are ground-dwellers. At night ...ey grub about in the soil for roots and other ...ant food. They also feed on fruits and berries, ...d can damage crops. By day, they sleep in their burrows.

Porcupines cannot "shoot" their spines, or quills, at enemies. Instead, they rush at an attacker and turn around to jab in the spines. If the spines

◪ The biggest spines on the crested porcupine's back are 12 inches (30 cm) long. This rodent rattles special hollow tail spines as a warning that it may charge backward at an attacker.

◪ The beaver's sharp gnawing teeth, the incisors, can cut down a small tree in a few minutes.

...AIN GROUPS OF LARGER ...ODENTS
...ntinued from page 207):

...orcupines	Pacas
21 species	• 2 species
...avers	Degus
2 species	• 8 species
...ountain	Tuco-tucos
...aver	• 33 species
1 species	Gundis
...ringhare	• 5 species
1 species	Chinchillas
...goutis	• 6 species
13 species	Capybara
...utias	• 1 species
13 species	Coypu
...carana	• 1 species
1 species	

pierce the skin, they come away from the porcupine's body and work into the flesh.

CAVIES
Among the South American cavy group there are several large species. The mara of Argentina has a head and body up to 30 inches (75 cm) long, and very long legs. It grazes in open grassland and can outrun most predators, sprinting at 28 mph (45 km/h). Agoutis are also large cavies. They look like giant, tail-less rats. They feed by day on plants and rest at night in burrows. An agouti can leap over 6 feet (2 m) straight upward to avoid danger.

Another group of cavies is the chinchillas and viscachas. The chinchilla itself is now rare in its natural habitat, the rocky uplands of the Andes mountains. But it is commonly kept as a pet, and some are still farmed for their fur, which is the finest and softest of any mammal. In the wild, this fur keeps the chinchilla warm in the bitter Andean winter, and is kept in good condition by regular dust baths.

The coypu is another large rodent of the cavy group. Swimming, it looks similar to a beaver, but has a rat-like tail. It eats water plants and rests by day in tunnels.

◪ Maras are active by day. They search for any type of plant material to eat, including grass, shoots, leaves, and fruits. They can run almost as fast as a hare, bounding along in a similar manner using their strong back legs.

OLDEST... !
Porcupines are among the longest-lived rodents. The oldest known individual was at least 27 years of age when it died in a zoo. Since porcupines are so well protected by their spines, they may live almost as long in the wild.

SQUIRRELS AND CHIPMUNKS

SQUIRRELS ARE BRIGHT-EYED, PERT-EARED, SHORT-NOSED, BUSHY-TAILED RODENTS THAT LEAP AROU IN TREES AND FEED ON NUTS. Actually, this is true o most squirrels, but not all. Some members of the squirrel family live on the ground and hardly ever venture into t In fact, rather than climb above the surface, they tunnel beneath it and live in underground burrows. These grou squirrels include marmots, chipmunks, prairie dogs, and sousliks. But most squirrels stay high above ground in the branches, and flying squirrels can even glide from tree to tre

▼ European red squirrel

Tree-dwelling squirrels are skilled climbers and leapers. They cling onto the bark with their sharp claws, and use the long, bushy tail as a balance when running along a branch, and as a rudder when leaping to another bough. The claws grip so firmly that a squirrel can race head-first down a tree trunk.

▲ Thirteen-lined ground squ

The familiar gray squirrel lived originally in eastern North America. It has spread to Europe and southe Africa. Like its cousin the European red squirrel, it builds a main nest, or drey, from twigs and leaves. About the size of a soccer ball, the drey is usually anchored high in the fork of a tree branch. It has a s lining of grasses and moss. Smaller dreys are used as temporary shelters. A larger, stronger drey is built t rear the young and as a winter refuge. In cold weather, tree squirrels stay in their dreys and sleep Unlike some ground squirrels, they do not go into the very deep sleep of true hibernation. They emerge from time to time and search for food, especially in mild weather.

▼ The groundhog or woodchuck is one of the largest marmots with a head and body length of 32 inches (80 cm).

◄ Some ground squirrels sleep very deeply, or hibernate, in their nests during the cold season. The Arctic ground squirrel of Alaska and northern Canada is perhaps the record-holder. It hibernates for up to nine months of the year.

Eastern chipmunk

Many squirrels store food, mainly seeds and nuts, when it is plentiful. This happens especially in the fall, as the squirrel prepares for the cold season. Gray squirrels regularly bury acorns or beech mast (nuts) in the soil, returning to dig them up later. But they lose or forget about many of the nuts. However, in doing this, they act as tree planters. This helps to offset the damage that some squirrels do in woodlands and timber plantations. They nibble bark and injure or even kill trees.

Marmots and prairie dogs are stout-bodied, short-tailed or tail-less ground squirrels. Most dwell in underground burrows. In Europe, Alpine marmots scamper over high meadows and rocky slopes. Many family groups live close together, their burrow entrances dotted over the ground. The burrows may go down 10 feet (3 m), ending in a hay-lined sleeping chamber. In the fall, the marmots collect grass, seeds, nuts, fruits, and other plant food. Then they retreat underground, sealing the entrances with soil and hay, and hibernate huddled together. North American prairie dogs live in bigger colonies called townships, some with thousands of members.

◢ The rat-sized European souslik inhabits warm, dry grasslands, where it digs deep tunnels in the soil.

The scaly-tailed squirrels of West African forests are not true squirrels, but they are rodents and have a similar lifestyle. They glide like flying squirrels and feed mainly on fruits and nuts. The pocket gophers of North America are expert diggers, using their large front claws and chisel-like teeth. Both grow about 0.04 inches (1 mm) each day to replace the wear.

Golden-mantled ground squirrel

▼ There are at least 50 species of flying squirrels, most from Asia. They glide on furry flaps of skin stretched between front and back legs.

◗ Prairie dogs are named for their doglike, yapping "barks." Shown right is a black-tailed prairie dog.

MAIN GROUPS OF SQUIRREL-LIKE RODENTS
(continued from page 207):

Squirrels and marmots
• 267 species
includes tree squirrels, ground squirrels such as prairie dogs, chipmunks, marmots, sousliks

Pocket gophers
• 34 species
Scaly-tailed squirrels
• 7 species
Pocket mice
• 65 species

DEER, CAMELS, AND PIGS

MAMMALS WITH HOOVES, RATHER THAN CLAWS, ON THEIR FEET ARE CALLED UNGULATES. There are 203 species, all plant-eaters, in two main groups. The larger group is the even-toed ungulates, with tw or four hoofed toes on each foot. They include deer, cattle, antelopes, giraffes, hippos, pigs, camels and llamas. The odd-toed ungulates have one, three, or five hooves per foot (page 216). All even-toed ungulates, except pigs and peccaries, have a special form of digestion. The stomach is divided into several chambers. Food goes into the first chamber, the rumen, where it is part-digested. Then the animal brings it up and "chews the cud" before swallowing it again for the rest of digestion.

◁ Giraffes live in groups, called troops, of about 6–10. A troop consists of females and their young, and a senior male who defends their territory.

▲ During the breeding season, male de like this elk bellow and threaten rival males for control of the herd. This is called the rut.

Deer are among the most common and widespread hoofed mammals. They live mainly in woods and forests, browsing on leaves. Some, like red and fallow deer, have spread to other habitats, such as moors and parks. Male deer have antlers, which they shed and regrow each year, and which they use to battle with rival males at breeding time. Only in reindeer, or caribou, do females also have antlers. Deer live in herds for safety, have keen senses, and flee danger at great speed.

Most camels today are domesticated, used as pack animals in dry scrub and desert, and to provide meat, milk, skins, and hair. But some wild camels can still be found in the remote grasslands of Mongolia. These are bactrian or two-humped camels. Domestic one-humped or dromedary camels live throughout the Middle East and North Africa.

Some dromedaries were taken to Australia, as pack animals for the inland deserts, and now li wild in the outback.

WOOLLY COUSINS

The llama, alpaca, guanaco, and vicuna of Sout America are close relatives of camels. They live mainly on the slopes of the Andes mountains and hav thick, woolly coats. Llamas and alpacas are domesticated, pack animals an for their fine wo The rare vicuna now a protecte species.

◁ Camels su for days without food weeks without a d They obtain some mois from food, and also n water in their bo because of their specia body chemistry. A ca can gulp 14 gallons (! in a few min

▶ Wild pigs like the warthog use their tusks and strong snouts to grub in the soil for their varied food of roots, bulbs, and small animals.

...iraffes are so tall they ...re easy to spot in their ...omeland of the African savanna (grassland). ...hey use their great height to reach tasty buds, ...aves, and fruits in the tree tops. The okapi is a ...ose relative of the giraffe. This extremely shy ...rest dweller is seldom seen in the wild. It stands ...most 6 feet (1.8 m) tall and has a giraffelike ...ead, neck, and body, although the neck is not quite as long in proportion to the body. It also has striped legs like a zebra.

WILD PIGS

The wild ancestor of our domestic pigs is the wild boar. It has thick fur and a large, powerful head. Wild boars are common in woods and forests in many parts of Europe and Asia. There are another seven species of wild pigs, including the African warthog and the very rare, protected babirusa of Sulawesi in Southeast Asia. Most have tusks formed from their up-curved canine teeth. Peccaries are very similar to wild pigs but have tusks in the upper jaw that grow downward. They live mainly in South and Central America.

▲ Llamas are South American relatives of camels. They eat mainly grass.

The hippopotamus is the largest even-toed ungulate. Hippos live in Africa, in groups of 10–15. They spend the day lazing in rivers, lakes or water holes. They emerge at night to graze waterside plants, moving along regular pathways. The much smaller pygmy hippo is a rare animal of swampy forests in west and central Africa. It is an endangered species, with just a few thousand left.

...A fallow deer youngster, or ...n, feeds on its mother's milk.

...he tusks of a hippo are really large canine teeth. They may ...20 inches (50 cm) long. Male hippos sometimes fight each ...er for females or territory and can inflict nasty wounds with ...r tusks. Hippos are the third largest ...l animals. A big male may reach ...ngth of 13 feet ...) and weigh ... over ...ns.

UNGULATES
• 203 species
• hoofed feet

Even-toed ungulates:

Deer
• 36 species
  including red, fallow, sika, roe, caribou (reindeer), moose (elk), muntjac
Camels and llamas
• 6 species
Giraffe and okapi
• 2 species
Wild pigs
• 8 species
Peccaries
• 3 species
Hippos
• 2 species
Chevrotains
• 4 species
Musk deer
• 3 species

ANTELOPES, WILD CATTLE, AND SHEEP

CATTLE, SHEEP, AND GOATS WERE PROBABLY TAMED FROM ABOUT 9,000 YEARS AGO, MAKING THEM SOME OF THE FIRST DOMESTICATED ANIMALS. The many breeds of cows today are descended from the wild auroch, which roamed the forests of Europe and Asia, but which finally died out in the 17th century. Like antelopes, cattle have horns that grow throughout their lives and are not shed, unlike the antlers of deer. Most antelopes and gazelles are fairly large, long-legged, fast-running grazers and browsers of grasslands and open scrub.

◪ Wild goats live from Greece and Turkey across to India. They are the ancestors of farmyard goats.

The wild cattle group, known as bovids, includes the American buffalo and European bison. Both species became rare due to hunting by humans. American buffalo are now protected in sanctuaries in the open plains and Canadian woodlands. European bison were almost extinct, but now live in several forest sanctuaries, especially in Poland and Russia.

▶ There are two varieties of American buffalo. The wood buffalo is larger and darker than the plains buffalo, which lives farther south.

◪ North American mountain goats live high on snowfields and along edges of glaciers.

The yak is another species of cattle. It lives on the high plains of Tibet, at altitudes of 20,000 feet (6,000 m). Few wild yaks survive, but there are many domesticated yaks, which are kept by local people for their meat, milk, skins, and hair.

Another domesticated species of cattle is the water buffalo, which came originally from India and Southeast Asia. It has the largest horns of any living animal, with a record tip-to-tip spread of more than 13 feet (4 m). Water buffalo have been taken to Africa, South America, and Australia, where some have returned to the wild.

ere are various species of wild sheep and goats,
d some have been domesticated. Wild species
clude the wild goat of eastern Europe and Asia,
e chamois and mouflon of Europe and the
iddle East, and the American bighorn sheep.
amois are very agile and sure-footed, leaping
er high mountain crags. Their hooves have soft
ds with hard edges, to help them grip even on
ooth, slippery, wet rocks. The ibex of eastern
rope, north Africa, and Asia is another
untain dweller, normally found above the
ber line. It climbs to even higher levels to
oid the summer heat, then descends to sheltered
er slopes for the winter.

E LONGEST COAT

sk ox from northern North America look like
d cattle, but they are members of the sheep
d goat group. They stand about 56 inches
4 m) tall at the shoulder and have the longest
r of any wild mammal, reaching 3 feet

⬆ Wild water buffalo survive in a few parts of Africa and Asia,
mainly in swampy areas.

(90 cm) on the neck and flanks. This thick coat
protects them from fierce Arctic storms. Like
most cattle, sheep, goats, antelopes, and gazelles,
they dwell in herds. If danger or bad weather
threatens, the adults huddle together and face
outward to protect the young in the middle.

KEEN SENSES

Antelopes and gazelles are known for
their speed and agility. Keen senses
give them early warning of
predators. Most antelopes live on
the African savanna (grassland).
Several species, such as
springbok, Thomson's gazelles,
and Grant's gazelles, gather in
huge herds. Some antelopes, such
as hartebeest, have short horns.
Others, such as the sable antelope
and gemsbok, have longer horns.
The largest antelope species is the
giant eland of Africa, 10 feet (3 m)
long and 6 feet (1.8 m) at the
shoulder.

ome antelopes and
lles, like springbok, leap
ght up more than 10
(3 m). This is called
king. It shows predators
as lions that they are
nd difficult to catch.

◀ Male cattle,
sheep, goats,
antelopes, and
gazelles use their
horns to battle with
rivals at breeding
time. In Thomson's
gazelles, the male
has much larger,
thicker horns than
the female.

MORE GROUPS OF EVEN-TOED UNGULATES
(continued from page 213):

Cattle
• 23 species, including domestic cattle,
yak, water buffalo, African buffalo,
American and European bison,
kudus, elands, bongo, nyala

Sheep and goats
• 26 species, including saiga, musk ox,
chamois, ibex, markhor, mountain
goat, Barbary sheep, mouflon,
bighorn sheep

Duikers
• 17 species

Gazelles and dwarf antelopes
• 30 species, including Grant's
gazelle, Thomson's gazelle,
dikdik, blackbuck, springbok,
gerenuk

Grazing antelopes
• 24 species, including waterbuck,
wildebeest (gnu), impala, sable
antelope, oryx, lechwe, addax

Pronghorn
• 1 species

HORSES, ZEBRAS, AND RHINOS

THE HOOFED MAMMALS CALLED ODD-TOED UNGULATES ARE A MUCH SMALLER GROUP THAN THE EVEN-TOED UNGULATES (PAGE 212). They include wild horses, asses, and zebras, which are very similar in general body size and shape, and also rhinos and tapirs. Horses and zebras ha long legs for fast running in open country. Like cows and sheep, horses have bee domesticated and there are now many breeds of different sizes and colors. Rhino are huge mammals—the white rhino is the third-largest land animal, after the tw kinds of elephants. Tapirs are smaller, piglike animals of South America, with one species in Southeast Asia.

⬆ An adult tapir
a dark brown c

Horses, donkeys, asses, and zebras are all known as equids. All domestic horses belong to the species *Equus caballus*. They are probably descended from horses that looked very similar to Przewalski's horse, *Equus przewalskii*, of the Mongolian steppe (grassland) in Central Asia. There are no longer any truly wild

⬆ A baby Brazilian tapir is born with spots and stripes, but these fade and disappear when it becomes an adult.

members of this species. It was rescued from extinction by being domesticated by local Mongolian people, and being bred in various wildlife parks. It may be possible to re-establish wild herds of Przewalski's horses in their Mongolian homeland.

There are two species of wild ass, one in Africa and one in Asia. Domestic donkeys are descended from a form of the African wild ass. Asses are smaller than horses and have longer ears, a more uneven mane, and a tufted tail.

STRIPED HORSES
Zebras are "striped horses." The three species live mainly on the plains of east and southern Africa. Like all equids, zebras live in herds.

◀ No one knows why zebras have such vivid stripes. Each zebra's stripe pattern is unique, so perhaps herd members use the markings to recognize each other.

▼ All rhinos are very similar appearance. The white or square-lipped rhino (below) a small hump on its back, jus front of the hips. The exceptionally thick skin of th Indian rhino is creased into c folds at the shoulders and hi Rhinos are usually peaceful b if they are threatened they charge in defense.

◄ Zebras use their speed to flee from large predators such as lions, hunting dogs, and hyaenas.

All equids have just one large hoofed toe on each foot. Rhinoceroses—rhinos for short—have three hoofed toes per foot. They are bulky animals with very thick skin, almost like armor plating. Unlike horses, rhinos generally live alone and have small eyes and poor sight. But their large ears can pick up the faintest sounds and they also have an excellent sense of smell.

Like all odd-toed ungulates, rhinos are plant eaters. They graze on tough grasses and scrubby bushes. Both males and females have horns, but these are not true horn or bone, they are made of very tightly packed hairs. The white rhino reaches 14 feet (4.3 m) in head–body length, stands over 6 feet (1.8 m) tall at the shoulder, and weighs over 3 tons. Smallest of the five species is the Sumatran rhino, at 8 feet (2.5 m) in length.

◄ In many parts of the world, horses have escaped from captivity to run free on plains and hills. They grow up wild, but they can usually be caught and tamed.

World Watch

All rhino species are hunted for their horns. Some people believe that the powdered horn has medicinal or magical powers. Horns are also made into trinkets and traditional dagger handles. White rhinos have increased in recent years in protected areas of southern Africa. But the other four species are all very rare. Most threatened is the small Javan rhino. Just a few dozen survive in one or two forest wildlife reserves.

TAPIR "TRUNK"
Tapirs live deep in the tropical forests and swamps of South America and Southeast Asia. They resemble pigs, but without the flat-ended snout. A tapir has a long, flexible upper lip, which it uses to gather food. The South American tapirs are reddish-brown; the Malayan tapir is black and white. All are about 8 feet (2.5 m) in length.

ODD-TOED UNGULATES
(continued from page 213):

Horses, asses, and zebras
• 7 species, including domestic horse, Przewalski's horse, African ass, Asiatic ass, Grevy's zebra, mountain zebra, plains zebra

Rhinos
• 5 species, including black rhino, white rhino, Indian rhino, Javan rhino, Sumatran rhino

Tapirs
• 4 species, including Malayan tapir, Brazilian tapir, Baird's tapir, mountain tapir

ELEPHANTS

ELEPHANTS ARE THE LARGEST LAND ANIMALS. AFRICAN ELEPHANTS, WITH THEIR HUGE EARS AND LONGER TUSKS, ARE BIGGER THAN ASIAN ELEPHANTS. These great mammals are famed for their size, strength, and stamina, and also for their long lives and complex herd behavior. People have long trained elephants, especially in Asia, for farming, logging, hunting, warfare, and ceremonies. Sadly, people also threaten their survival, especially in Africa, mainly through killing them for their ivory tusks.

ELEPHANTS

- 2 species
- African elephant scattered across central, east and southern Africa, common in a few small areas
- Asian elephant found in India, Sri Lanka, southern China, and Southeast Asia (rare in wild)

🔽 The Asian elephant has a more domed forehead and humped back than the African elephant. It squirts water, mud, or dust over itself to keep cool and to get rid of irritating skin pests.

African elephants live mainly south of the Sahara Desert, in a wide range of habitats including grassland, forests, and dry, thorny scrub. Asian elephants are found mainly in the forests of India, Sri Lanka, and Southeast Asia. Most Asian elephants are kept and trained by people. Fewer than 50,000 live in the wild, in hilly and remote jungle.

In each species, a small family group lives together. They move slowly and steadily, feeding mainly on grasses, bark, leaves, and twigs. They spend up to 18 hours feeding and consume about 330 pounds (180 kg) of food each day. An elephant walks at an average speed of 3 mph (5 km/h). However, if it senses danger, it can sprint away or charge at the attacker at up to 25 mph (40 km/h)—faster than a human.

Elephants keep in touch with their herd members in several ways. They have a simple language of deep growls and rumbles which carry for hundreds of yards in open country. They also sniff the air with their trunks, and they touch other herd members with their trunks too. In fact the elephant's trunk, an extra-long nose with a flexible tip (one lip in Asian elephants, two in African), has many jobs. It is used for grasping food, squirting water or dust, greeting other elephants, and guiding babies or calves

🔼 Elephants sniff and caress each other when they meet, to make sure that they are from the same herd, not intruders.

▶ As drinking holes shrink in the dry season, the herd relies on the long memory of the matriarch (senior female), who may be more than 60 years old. She knows places where there may still be water. The elephants gouge a hole with their tusks and sip the water that collects in it.

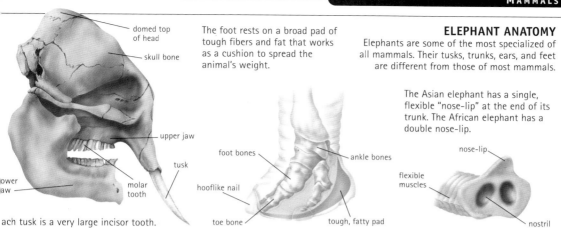

domed top
of head

skull bone

The foot rests on a broad pad of
tough fibers and fat that works
as a cushion to spread the
animal's weight.

ELEPHANT ANATOMY
Elephants are some of the most specialized of
all mammals. Their tusks, trunks, ears, and feet
are different from those of most mammals.

The Asian elephant has a single,
flexible "nose-lip" at the end of its
trunk. The African elephant has a
double nose-lip.

upper jaw

tusk

molar
tooth

ower
aw

foot bones

ankle bones

hooflike nail

nose-lip

flexible
muscles

ach tusk is a very large incisor tooth.

toe bone

tough, fatty pad

nostril

EPING COOL
elephant cannot drink through its trunk. But
ucks water into the trunk and then squirts the
ter into its mouth—or over its back for a cooling
ower." Elephants also keep cool by bathing in
d and flapping their ears. The ears work like
liators to lose excess body heat into the air.

OVERSIZED TEETH
An elephant's tusks are its incisor teeth. They start to
grow at about two years of age, and continue to
grow throughout the animal's life. Both males and
females have them, but usually in female Asian
elephants, they are short and hidden by the trunk
and lower lips.

LARGEST... !
The largest African male
elephants stand 13 feet
(4 m) tall at the shoulder,
measure 33 feet (10 m)
from trunk tip to tail tip,
and weigh over 6 tons. The
tusks can be over
10 feet (3 m) long.

n elephant
is led by
matriarch
ior
ale). She
embers the
tion of
onal
ing places.

CATS

"CARNIVORE" MEANS "MEAT-EATER."
The Carnivora group includes mammals with long,
sharp claws to catch prey, and long, sharp teeth to
rip it up. This group is described over the next ten
pages, starting with the most carnivorous of all—the cats.
Some carnivores scavenge or eat the occasional fruit or
berry. But the cats are active hunters of living prey, with
large eyes to see in the dark, and claws which (except for
the cheetah) can be pulled back into the toes, to keep them sharp. The carnivore
group also includes wolves and wild dogs, hyenas, bears, raccoons, pandas,
civets, genets, weasels, mongooses, and in the sea, seals and sea lions.

◪ The lynx lives in all north
continents. It is similar to
bobcat (opposite, top right),
larger, with bigger ear
cheek tufts. It takes larger
such as hares and young d

◪ The cheetah is the fastest
land animal over short
distances. It can reach speeds
of more than 60 mph (95
km/h). But it gives up after
about 200 yards (180 m) if the
prey seems to be getting away.

◪ A lion pride is led by the
chief male. Females or
lionesses lack the long neck
mane. Cubs lose their spots
as they grow.

Cats are found around
the world in many
habitats, from cold
mountains to moist
tropical forests. They
combine strength and
stealth with speed and
agility, using their
excellent eyesight,
hearing and smell.

Cats are a uniform
group, which means
they are very similar in
overall body shape and
features—and also in
their hunting methods.
Most live alone and
prowl at night. They
stalk their prey quietly,
keeping low near the
ground. Then they

make a quick dash to grab the victim, holding it
down with their hooked claws and biting it with
their long, sharp canine teeth. The large, sharp-
edged cheek teeth or carnassials can shear
through tough skin, sinews, and gristle.

Lions are the only cats
that live and hunt in
groups, called prides.
The large, shaggy-
maned chief male
patrols the pride's
territory, roaring and
leaving scent marks to
warn off other prides.
The lionesses do the
hunting, often as a
team to bring down a
zebra or wildebeest.
One or two lionesses
walk toward the
victim, to drive it
toward the others who
are waiting in ambush.

◪ Ocelots range from southe
North America down to Sout
America. They are expert
swimmers and climbers,
catching birds in the trees an
frogs in the water.

THE DOGLIKE CAT

The cheetah is built more like a greyhound than
cat, with a long, flexible back, long slim legs an
a relatively small head. It hurls its
after its prey with an amazi
burst of speed, rather than
stalking. The serval is a
smaller version of the
cheetah, but has larger ears.
It also lives in Africa, hunts by da
and races after prey such as hares.

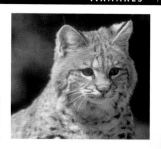

Leopards often drop onto their prey from a branch, then drag the corpse back up to keep it safe from other animals, before indulging in a treetop feast.

The bobcat can climb, but it prefers to hunt on the ground for rats, rabbits, and running gamebirds such as grouse.

Tigers are the biggest cats, and the rare Siberian tiger is the biggest of the tigers. It measures 10 feet (3 m) long and weighs over 650 pounds (300 kg).

[TH]E BLACK "PANTHER"

[Th]e most adaptable of the seven species [of] big cat is the leopard. It has short legs [an]d a muscular body, and swims or [cli]mbs after its prey. It often prowls near [to]wns and villages and may lie on a [br]anch, ready to drop silently on a victim [pa]ssing below. Some leopards are born [wi]th almost black fur, and are called [bla]ck panthers. The snow leopard or [ou]nce is slightly smaller than the [leo]pard and has very thick fur, to keep [ou]t the cold in its Asian mountain [ho]me. It can easily leap across an icy [rav]ine 10 feet (3 m) wide.

[SM]ALLER CATS

[Th]ere are smaller cats on almost every [co]ntinent. Most are about 32–44 inches [(80]–110 cm) long, including the tail. [Th]ey live in trees, using the tail to help them [bal]ance, and hunt birds, snakes, lizards, [squ]irrels, and small monkeys. The pampas cat [of] South America is at home on grassland, [wh]ere it pursues rodents and ground birds.

[HO]ME CATS?

[Th]e many types of domestic cat were probably [bre]d from the African wild cat, beginning in Egypt [so]me 4,000 years ago. These first domestic cats [pro]bably caught mice in grain stores. Pet cats have [the] night-prowling, hunting instincts of their wild [an]cestors. In some areas, they have returned to live [an]d breed in the wild, and are called feral cats.

[Ca]ts (felids)

[Big] cats
[•] [7] species
[• s]harp teeth and claws
[• c]an roar loudly

[Li]on
[•] Africa
[Ti]ger
[• S]outh and East Asia
[Ja]guar
[•] Central and South America
[Le]opard
[•] Africa, South Asia
[Sn]ow leopard
[•] Central Asia

Clouded leopard
• Southeast Asia
Cheetah
• Africa, Middle East

Small cats
• 28 species
• resemble big cats, but smaller
• most cannot roar loudly

Small cats include the cougar (puma or mountain lion, the largest small cat), lynx, bobcat, caracal, ocelot, margay, leopard cat, African wild cat, European wild cat, black-footed cat (the smallest small cat)

221

DOGS, FOXES, AND HYENAS

THE DOG FAMILY INCLUDES WOLVES, FOXES, AND JACKALS, AS WELL AS THE FAMILIAR DOMESTIC DOG, WHICH WAS PROBABLY BRED FROM THE GRAY WOLF. All of these carnivores (page 220) are strong and agile, with long legs for distance running, muscular bodies, powerful sharp-toothed jaws, and keen senses of sight, hearing, and especially smell. They differ from cats mainly in that they have longer muzzles, they cannot pull their cla into their toes, and most live in pairs or larger groups called packs—apart from foxes, which dwell alone. Hyenas are also doglike carnivores, but they are not members of the dog family.

⬧ The fennec fox of No Africa hunts small prey such as termites and ot insects, mainly by soun so it has very large ears

⬧ The coyote, with its mournful howl, may live alone but also gathers in packs to hunt.

Dogs have a different hunting technique from that of cats. Their long, powerful legs enable them to run well for miles. They can track prey over long distances, following the scent with their keen noses, until it tires and is caught.

THE BIGGEST DOG
The gray wolf is the largest of the dog family, with a head–body length of 56 inches (130 cm).

⬧ The gray wolf's strength, stamina, and cunning are fa in myth and legend.

⬧ The arctic fox has thick fur that turns white in winter, matching its snowy surroundings.

It is found in remote scrub, forest, tundra, and mountains—mainly because people have driven it away. Wolves eat a wide range of meat, from deer to mice, voles, and lemmings. They also scavenge, and even take berries and fruits. The coyote is common in par of North America, and resembles a smaller version of the wolf.

⬧ A male, or dog, red fox, and a fem vixen, chase in courtship before mati

The maned wolf lives in tall grassland in parts of South America. It has brown fur and such long, slim legs that it looks like a "wolf on stilts."

The African wild dog is an endangered species. There are y about 5,000 left, mainly in one Tanzanian wildlife reserve. y are the most efficient of all pack hunters.

E DOMESTIC DOG

l domestic dogs, from huge great danes to tiny ihuahuas, belong to one species, *Canis niliaris*. The first dogs were probably tamed m a type of gray wolf, as long as 10,000 years o. The dingo of Australia may once have been even earlier, part-domesticated form of the olf. But dingoes now roam wild across large eas of Australia. The most carnivorous dogs are e African wild dogs, iose teeth are rticularly large d sharp. They d mainly on large mmals brought wn by a pack of to 20 members.

LY CUNNING

ost foxes are agile d stealthy, using a mbination of stalking d running to catch y. The red fox has a endary reputation for cunning. It adapts to most habitats and foods, including those provided by people, so it has become one of the most

The striped hyena has a horselike mane that extends from head to tail. It searches at night for carcasses of large animals already part eaten by big cats.

widespread of all mammals. In spring and summer it feasts on eggs, young birds, and rodents. In the fall it fattens itself on fruits and berries and takes young rabbits and hares. In winter it raids trashcans and dumps. Other foxes have similar wide tastes, ranging from crabs and dead fish along the water's edge, to worms, beetles and snails, berries, and fungi.

Jackals are similar to foxes, although slightly larger, with a head–body length of 28–40 inches (70–100 cm). They eat a great range of foods, too. Unlike foxes jackals live in family groups of 4–6 members. They hunt as a pack to catch small gazelles and antelopes.

THE MASTER SCAVENGERS

Hyenas do not belong to the dog family. But they are similar powerful carnivores. Far from slinking away like cowards, hyenas are very aggressive and successful pack-hunters. The hyena has one of the strongest sets of jaws and teeth in the animal kingdom. It is an expert scavenger, helping vultures to clear the remains of dead animals from the African plains. The hyena eats skin, chews gristle, and cracks bones with ease. Some hyena groups do hunt and kill more than half their victims. Even lions are wary about trying to take a kill from a pack of hyenas.

Most dogs bark, yip, or yelp. But the dingo of the Australian outback rarely makes a sound.

Jackals, like most wild dogs, convey different messages to pack members by the positions of their ears, mouth, legs, and tail.

Dogs (canids)

- large, sharp canine teeth
- long snouts
- claws cannot be pulled into toes
- most can bark or yelp

Larger wild dogs
- 4 species

Grey or timber wolf
- All northern lands
Red wolf
- Southeast North America
Coyote
- North and Central America
Dingo
- Australia, Southeast Asia

Other wild dogs
- 5 species including dhole, African wild dog, maned wolf, raccoon dog, bush dog

Jackals
- 4 species
- Africa, Middle East, India

Foxes
- 21 species
- worldwide

Hyenas
- 4 species
- Africa, Middle East

BEARS, RACCOONS, AND PANDAS

BEARS ARE NOT ESPECIALLY CARNIVOROUS. They catch prey such as deer, birds, and fish. But they also scratch up worms and grubs, raid wild bees' nests for honey, and eat buds, fruits, seeds, and roots. However, like other carnivores, they have sharp teeth and strong jaws. They are big and muscular, with powerful limbs and huge paws. Raccoons are much smaller and look like a combination of bear and dog. They live across North, Central, and South America. The red panda is similar to a raccoon and dwells in eastern Asia. Its cousin is one of the world's rarest yet best-known creatures—the giant panda.

⬥ The tree-dwelling sun bea Southeast Asia is the smalles bear. It has a head–body len of only 4 feet (1.2 m).

⬥ Asian black bear

⬥ Red panda

◀ Brown b feast on sa as they t leap up wate on their wa their spaw places upstr

The giant panda is a member [of] the carnivore group, but it [har]dly ever eats meat. It [con]sumes mainly stems and [lea]ves of bamboos.

Bears may look friendly and cuddly. But the larger species are massive, powerful animals, and sometimes dangerous to people—especially a mother bear protecting her young. If a bear is disturbed, it may charge as its main method of self defense. Bears were once hunted for their fur, to protect farm animals, and for "sport." Today most species are rare and live in remote places. Because of their unpredictable nature, they are best left undisturbed.

◨ The kinkajou lives in Central and northern South America. It rests in a tree hole by day and comes out at night to feed on small animals and fruits. Its tail is prehensile, working like a fifth limb to grasp branches.

The creamy white fur of the polar bear blends in well with its snowy, icy habitat in the far north. This [ca]mouflage helps it to stalk seals on the ice without being detected. As well as [ver]y thick fur, polar bears have a thick layer of fat under their skin to keep out [th]e cold. A polar bear can run fast and even catch young or sick reindeer. Like [oth]er bears, it has poor eyesight and relies mainly on smell. It can scent a seal [or] walrus carcass 2 miles (3 km) away.

[VA]RIABLE BEARS

[Th]e Asian (Himalayan) black bear [ha]s a silky coat with a white [V-]shaped chest mark and large, [rou]nded ears. It is an expert [cli]mber, eats ants and grubs as [we]ll as fruits and nuts, and often [res]ts in the branches. The small [sun] bear lives in the forests of [Sou]theast Asia, where it feeds on [fru]its, termites, small birds, and mammals. [Th]e brown bear species is very variable and [inc]ludes the grizzly, Kodiak, and Alaskan bears. [Th]e smallest variety is the European brown bear, [no]w very rare, found in a few mountainous [reg]ions as far south as Italy and Spain.

◨ The grizzly or brown bear shows its long canine teeth in a warning snarl that few animals will ignore.

[ABO]UT AT NIGHT
[Th]e common raccoon, with its "bandit" face [ma]sk, is a well-known nighttime scavenger in [No]rth America. It eats fish, frogs, small birds and [ma]mmals, eggs, fruits, nuts, seeds—in fact, almost anything. The raccoon group includes coatis, from the forests of South and Central America. The coati's flexible, elongated nose sniffs out insects and similar small prey on the forest floor.

◨ The common raccoon, like the red fox, is adaptable and comes into cities to scavenge in trash. It can climb and swim well, and handles food delicately in its front paws.

The giant panda of China is easily recognized and extremely rare—with perhaps only 1,000 left in the wild. It looks like a bear, but it is not closely related to bears. There is so little goodness in its bamboo food that it eats for up to 15 hours each day. The red panda is related to the giant panda, but is much smaller, fox-like in shape, and with deep red fur.

Bears (Ursids)	Raccoons and pandas
• 7 species	• 17 species
• large head, wide face	• mostly long-bodied, bushy-tailed
• poor sight but keen smell	• alert, agile and adaptable
• bulky, sturdy body	• live mainly in trees
• big paws and claws	• Americas, apart from
• very short tail	2 panda species
Polar bear	
• Arctic Ocean and far north	Main groups of raccoons and
Brown bear	pandas:
• all northern lands, southern	
Europe	Raccoons
American black bear	• 6 species including crab-eating
• North America	raccoon
Asian black bear	Coatis
• Central and South Asia	• 4 species including ringtailed
Sun bear	coati, white-nosed coati
• Southeast Asia	Olingos
Sloth bear	• 2 species
• India, Sri Lanka	Ringtail and cacomistle
Spectacled bear	• 2 species
• South America	Kinkajou
	• 1 species
	Pandas
	• 2 species, giant and red

WEASELS, MONGOOSES, AND CIVETS

THE SMALLEST OF THE MAMMAL CARNIVORES (PAGE 220) ARE WEASELS, STOATS, SKUNKS, BADGERS, MINK, OTTERS, AND THEIR RELATIVES, KNOWN AS MUSTELIDS. They are mostly long and slender, with low-slung bodies and short legs, keen eyes, and sharp teeth. They may be small, but when out hunting they are some of the most fearless and aggressive of all animals. However, they are otherwise shy and secretive, seldom seen in the wild except when they bound across the road. Mongooses, civets, and genets are also small carnivores; mongooses resemble stoats, while civets, genets, and linsangs are catlike animals with bushy tails, found in southern Europe, Africa, and southern and Southeast Asia.

△ The smallest mammal carnivore is the least (dwarf) weasel of North America, a variety of common weasel. It is less than 8 inches (20 cm) long, including the tail.

△ The spray from the striped skunk's glands at the base of its tail is so foul-smelling, it can stop the enemy breathing.

Each type of mustelid takes different prey, according to its size. Weasels are specialist hunters of mice and voles, but they occasionally eat birds, frogs, and baby rabbits. The weasel's small head and narrow body allow it to follow mice into their burrows. Stoats are larger, have a black tail tip, and hunt rats and rabbits. Pine martens are bigger still, and such skilled climbers that they can catch squirrels. The sable of Siberian forests has a head–body length of 16 inches (40 cm) and very thick, soft fur. It stays mainly on the ground, eats hares and similar animals, and also fruits and berries.

△ The sea otter of north and east Pacific coasts floats on its back to prepare food.

Wolverines are the largest members of the weasel family. They live in northern forests and tundra, and move quickly over loose snow with their broad feet. They scavenge on carrion, but also kill prey as large as reindeer, covering up to 25 miles (40 km) in search of food.

△ The wolverine or "glutton" lives in all northern lands, but is rare in many areas. Incredibly strong, it can drag prey as large as a deer for several miles.

◧ Meerkats often stand upright near their burrows to peer across the African grassland and bush, watching for danger.

▷ The common genet is indeed common in some areas, but shy and nocturnal, so rarely seen.

The black-footed ferret of North America is one of the world's rarest mammals. It became extinct in the wild in the late 1980s, but has been bred in captivity, and may become reestablished in its habitat.

dgers are mainly nocturnal and eat many foods—worms, insects, small mmals, roots, seeds, and fruits. Eurasian badgers live in family groups, extensive burrows called setts. American badgers are fiercer and live in stern North America.

HOME IN THE WATER

ters are beautifully adapted to swimming the water's surface and below it. They ddle with their webbed feet, and swim er by swaying the whole body and tail m side to side. Otter fur is waterproofed plentiful oil made in the skin. The thick underfur ps tiny bubbles of air. These prevent waterlogging and keep the otter warm. The giant otter of South America s a head–body length of up to 5 feet (1.5 m).

unks live only in the Americas. The 13 species are all very ilar, with black and white fur and bushy tails. They feed insects, lizards, fruits, and berries. They are known for aying a horrible-smelling liquid if disturbed.

HELPFUL MONGOOSE

Mongooses live mainly in dry country, hunting a variety of mice, insects, and other small animals, and occasionally eating fruit. Some species may tackle rats and even poisonous snakes. For this reason, people allow them to stay around towns and may even feed them. Most live alone, but banded mongooses and meerkats live in large family groups. Meerkats post sentries who stand upright looking out for enemies.

vets, genets and linsangs are catlike in build and bits. They stealthily hunt small animals at night, nouflaged by their spots and stripes. Most species e in Africa, India, or Southeast Asia, with a few in thern Europe. Civets produce a powerful musky-elling substance that was once collected for perfumes.

WEASELS AND STOATS
(MUSTELIDS)
• 67 species
• small to medium size
• long, slim, flexible body
• short legs, medium tail
• very active predators
• all regions except Australia, Madagascar

Groups include:

Weasels, stoats and martens
• 33 species, including:
Common weasel (North America, Europe, Africa, Asia)
Stoat (North America, Europe, Asia, New Zealand)

Other species include American, pine and stone martens, fisher, polecat, grison, mink, sable, zorilla, wolverine (largest), black-footed ferret (rarest)

Skunks
• 13 species, including:
Striped skunk (North America)
Spotted skunk (North, Central America)

Otters
• 12 species, including:
Eurasian otter (Europe, Asia, Africa)
Cape clawless otter (Africa)
Giant otter (South America)

Badgers
• 9 species, including:
Eurasian badger (Europe to China)
American badger (North America)
Honey badger or ratel (Africa to India)

Mongooses, civets, and genets
• 66 species
• long, flexible body
• active, agile predators

Mongooses
• 31 species
• Africa, southern Asia
• resemble weasels or stoats
Species include Egyptian mongoose, banded mongoose, meerkat (suricate), cusimanse

Civets and genets
• 35 species
• Europe, Africa, southern Asia
• catlike
• large eyes and ears
• bushy tail
Species include African civet, common genet, African linsang, binturong, fanalouc, fossa

◧ A mongoose avoids a snake's deadly bite by its agility and lightning-quick reactions.

SEALS, SEA LIONS, AND SEA COWS

SEALS, SEA LIONS, AND THE WALRUS ARE
SUPERBLY ADAPTED TO LIFE IN THE WATER. Unlike
whales and dolphins, however, they rarely venture
into the open ocean. They usually stay near land because they must
come ashore to breed, typically on rocky, isolated coasts or on ice.
These mammals are all meat-eaters, taking prey such as fish and squid.
Sea cows are large, slow-moving mammals that graze on water plant

▲ Like all sea mamm
the manatee must com
the surface to brea

▲ A seal swims by bending its
body and pushing with its rear
flippers, like a fish uses its tail.
The front flippers are held by its
sides or used to steer and brake.

Seals, sea lions, and sea cows are all
marine mammals—they live in the
oceans. They all have limbs that are
paddle-shaped for rowing themselves
through the water. True or earless
seals form the largest group, with 19
species. They do have ears, but these
lack ear flaps and so are not
noticeable on the outside. On land,
seals are clumsy and can only slide
or hump along slowly. Their rear

flippers trail uselessly behind. But
water, few animals can match the
speed and grace.

NO CRABS TO EAT
The most abundant seal by far, a
one of the world's most numerou
large wild mammals, is the
crabeater seal. Some 20 million li
on and around the pack ice of
Antarctica. But it does not eat cra

▲ A Galapagos sea lion mother prepares to
her youngster. Baby seals are called

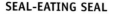

Crabs do not live in this habitat. Instead, the crabeater, like the great whales, feeds mainly on shrimplike krill.

SEAL-EATING SEAL

Three other seals in the same region are the Weddell seal, the smaller Ross seal, and the larger leopard seal. The first two dive to great depths, the Weddell seal descending to 1,500 feet [50 m] after fish and squid. The leopard seal, in ntrast, is a sleek, fast, and fierce surface edator. It grows to 11 feet (3.5 m) long and rsues mainly penguins, but it will eat large fish d even kill other seals.

he baby harp seal is one of the most appealing of all animals. radually loses its fluffy baby fur and develops the dark head, k side stripes and pale gray background color of the adult.

ONT FLIPPER POWER

e eared seals have much more noticeable ear ps on the sides of the head. They include fur ls and sea lions. They have torpedo-shaped dies like true seals, but their rear flippers are ger and more mobile, and their front ones ger and more powerful. They swim mainly by owing" with these long front flippers. On land, y can shuffle about by tucking their rear ppers under the body and propping themselves on their front pair. They rest and breed on d at traditional sites called rookeries.

E SEAL WITH TUSKS

e huge walrus is more than 10 feet m) long. It has a very fat, bbery body and ra-long

The Mediterranean monk seal is one of the rarest seals, with st a few hundred left. They live in remote sea caves in scattered colonies, in the Mediterranean Sea and Atlantic Ocean.

The male dugong munches sea grass, its body scarred from fights with male rivals at breeding time. A dugong has notched tail flukes like a whale; the manatee's tail is rounded.

upper canine teeth known as tusks. Both males and females have tusks, which can grow to 2 feet (60 cm) in length. They use the tusks for grubbing in the sea bed for shellfish and other food, and to help pull themselves out from the water.

GENTLE PLANT EATERS

Manatees and dugongs are sometimes called sea cows, because they are peaceful, slow plant-eaters, like cows on land. They graze on water plants in shallow tropical seas and estuaries. The dugong lives in the southwest Pacific Ocean, one species of manatee lives near the Amazon River, another around the West Indies, and a third off the coast of West Africa. These bulky animals grow to 10–13 feet (3–4 m) long. Sea cows bobbing, half-seen through ocean mists, may have given rise to sailors' legends about mermaids.

The crabeater seal has few enemies, apart from killer whales and its larger cousin, the leopard seal.

Sea lions and seals *(pinnipeds)*
• 34 species
• smooth, streamlined head and bulky body
• paddlelike limbs
• sharp teeth

True or earless seals
• 19 species
• no visible or external ear flaps
• cannot tuck rear flippers under body
• inshore waters of all seas and oceans but less common in tropics
• include gray seal, common (harbor) seal, harp seal, northern elephant seal, leopard seal, Mediterranean monk seal

Eared seals (fur seals and sea lions)
• 14 species
• ear flaps (may be hidden in fur)
• can tuck rear flippers under body
• inshore waters of most seas and oceans, ice floes
• include northern fur seal, Californian sea lion, Galapagos fur seal

Walrus
• 1 species
• long tusks
• Arctic and northern oceans

Manatees and dugong *(sea cows)*
• 4 species
• plant eaters
• include Amazonian manatee, West Indian manatee, West African manatee, dugong

Walruses live all around the s and oceans of the far th. A layer of fatty blubber er skin which is 1.7 inches m) thick, protects against intense cold.

GREAT WHALES

WHALES AND DOLPHINS ARE PERFECTLY ADAPTED TO LIFE AT SEA. In fact, they never come ashore—unless beached by accident, when they usually die. Great whales differ from toothed whales such as dolphins and porpoises (page 232) because they have comblike baleen in their mouths, for filter-feeding. Great whales were once hunted in huge numbers for their meat, fat, oil, and baleen (whalebone). The slaughter drove some species almost to extinction. Laws now prevent them from being killed in large numbers, and most whale populations are slowly recovering. Great whales show complicated behavior and communicate with a wide variety of sounds and calls.

🔺 Blue whale

World Watch

World Watch

For centuries, small numbers of great whales were hunted with spearlike harpoons from sailing or rowing boats. But in the 19th century, whaling ships were equipped with steam engines. Then came faster diesel engines and explosive harpoons. The whales could not escape. Thousands were killed yearly. By the 1950s their numbers had plummeted. In the mid-1980s mass whaling ceased at last.

Baleen whales have huge and very unusual mouths. Their jaws lack teeth. Instead, the mouth contains rows of baleen plates. These are straplike or curtainlike structures that hang down from the roof of the mouth. They have fringed edges like brushes or combs. They work as filters to sieve the small animals of the plankton from the water.

🔻 Humpback whales open their vast mouths and swim up to the surface, trapping small creatures inside.

HOW GREAT WHALES FEED

These vast animals feed in different ways. Right whales cruise along with their mouths open at the surface. Blue and humpback whales take a massive mouthful of sea water, then press the huge tongue upward inside the mouth to force the water out through the baleen plates. The gray whale grubs in the mud the seabed and does the same. In all of these whales, food items such as krill and small fish get trapped in the combs or bristles of the baleen, which are tough and springy, like plastic. The whale then licks the food off the baleen plates and swallows it.

◁ The gray whale feeds on small creatures in the mud, leaving great holes and furrows in the seabed.

ray whales feed mainly in the shallow ▷astal waters of the Arctic, between North ▷merica and Asia. They dive down to 300 ▷et (90 m) and scoop up a rich mixture of ▷ud, to filter the small animals living in it. ▷hen the whale has a mouthful of food it ▷rfaces to strain off the water, swallows ▷ meal, and dives for another load.

◫ Over millions of years of evolution, a whale's front legs have become flippers, used for swimming slowly and steering in the water. The rear legs have disappeared, while the tail has developed wide flukes. These swish up and down to drive the mammal through the water with the power of a racing car engine.

Most whales feed and travel in loose groups called pods. Members keep in touch using an amazing variety of sounds, many too low or ▷h for us to hear. Blue and fin whales emit ear- ▷litting, low-pitched grunts that are the loudest ▷ises made by any animal. Such sounds ▷vel for hundreds of miles ▷rough the seas.

made by gray whales in the eastern Pacific. They travel each year from the breeding lagoons off the Californian and Mexican coasts, to feed in the rich waters of the Bering Sea, and then back again—a distance of some 9,000 miles (15,000 km). Humpbacks are also great travelers. Some spend the winter in the Caribbean and the summer near Greenland and Iceland.

▷E SONG OF THE ▷MPBACK WHALE
▷en more extraordinary are the songs ▷ the humpback whale. These eerie, ▷intive sounds plunge from high squeaks ▷ deep wails, in a sequence that lasts half an ▷ur or more, making it the longest, most ▷mplicated song of any animal. Usually, the ▷ger is a male trying to attract a female at ▷eeding time. Humpbacks also make acrobatic ▷ps almost right out of the water, then splash ▷ck in with an enormous crash.

▷ALE MIGRATIONS
▷any whales travel or migrate long distances ▷tween their main feeding places and the waters ▷ere the females give birth to their young, ▷own as calves. Most great whales tend to feed ▷ in polar waters during the brief Arctic ▷ or Antarctic summer, then return ▷ near to the tropics for ▷ winter. The longest ▷ migrations are

Great whale calves stay with their mothers for up to a year. Like all mammals, they feed at first on her rich milk, but gradually they learn to filter-feed for themselves. A newborn blue whale calf weighs 3 tons and measures 23 feet (7 m) long. Each day it drinks 56 gallons (200 l) of milk. Female great whales usually have only one calf every two years—one reason why their numbers take so long to recover.

◫ Minke whales are the smallest great whales, at 32–36 feet (10–11 m) in length.

Dolphins and whales (Cetaceans)	Rorquals
• 76 species • entirely aquatic, most in the sea • long, submarine-shaped body • front limbs are flippers • tail flukes The largest whales: Baleen or great whales • 10 species • comblike baleen in mouth • worldwide, mainly colder oceans	• 6 species including blue whale (largest living animal), fin whale, humpback whale, minke whale, sei whale, Bryde's whale Gray whale • 1 species Right whales • 3 species including right whale, pygmy right whale, and bowhead

DOLPHINS AND PORPOISES

TOOTHED WHALES INCLUDE MANY KINDS OF PORPOISES AND DOLPHINS, AND ALSO SPERM WHALES, BEAKED WHALES, AND TWO WHITE WHALES—THE NARWHAL AND BELUGA. These all have more normal mouths and teeth than great whales (page 230). However, unlike land carnivores, a toothed whale's teeth are all similar in size and shape, designed to grasp slippery fish and squid. The largest species of toothed whale is the sperm whale. Males or bulls are up to 66 feet (20 m) long and weigh 50 tons—the largest carnivores on Earth.

ON GUARD! !

The narwhal grows to 16 feet (5 m) long, with mottled brown coloring. It also has a long tusk! Only the male has a tusk—a greatly lengthened upper left incisor tooth with a twisted spiral surface pattern. It grows up to 8 feet (2.5 m) long. Rival males "fence" with their tusks at breeding time.

☑ The common or har[bor] porpoise finds its prey of f[ish] such as herring or macke[rel] using a sonar syst[em] of sound clicks a[nd] listening to [the] echo[es]

Dolphins range in length from only 4 feet (1.2 m) in Heaviside's dolphin, to 23 feet (7 m) or more in the huge and powerful killer whale, or orca. Killer whales are among the fiercest predators of the sea, though they rarely pose a threat to people. With immense speed and power, they pursue their prey of fish, seals, seabirds, dolphins, and even larger whales. They hunt in groups and sometimes work together to herd a school of fish into shallow water, to feed at their leisure.

⬆ Narwhal

Like the other dolphins, killer whales are regarded as "intelligent" animals. This is partly because they can be taught to do tricks. But in the wild they also show great curiosity and

adaptable behavior, working out how to eat new and unfamiliar foods.

All of the dolphins are active, even playful creatures. They are sleek, powerful swimmers, a[nd] sometimes follow ships—perhaps to fe[ed] on any leftove[rs] thrown over t[he] side, or to save energy by swimming i[n] the ship's wake. Most dolphins live in groups and communicate with each other using a great variety of squeals, buzzes, clicks, a[nd] grunts. They also use these sounds for echolocation or sonar, like bats (page 198) but underwater, to find prey and navigate through cloudy water. Like all whales, they breathe through their nostrils, which are joined together on the top of the head as the blowhole.

SNUB-NOSED WHALES

A dolphin has a protruding beaklike snout and a curving sickle-shaped back fin. Porpoises are similar, but lack the dolphin's bea[k] and have a snub nose instead. They are also generally smaller than dolphins, growing to abo[ut] 6 feet (2 m) in length. Most species are dark gra[y] and feed, like dolphins, on fish and squid.

☑ River dolph[in]

◀ The killer whale is the largest dolphin. It feeds mainly on seals and other sea mammals, as well as penguins and fish. It is a very fast swimmer, reaching 35 mph (55 km/h).

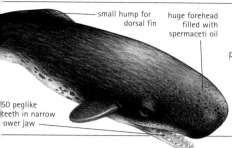

small hump for
dorsal fin

huge forehead
filled with
spermaceti oil

50 peglike
teeth in narrow
lower jaw

GIANT CARNIVORE
The massive sperm whale is
the largest predator on the
planet, and also the deepest-
diving of all mammals. It
reaches depths of 2 miles
(3 km) in search of its prey,
which includes the
fearsome giant squid.

so are seen much less often than
other whales. They eat mainly
squid. The largest is Baird's beaked
whale, about 43 feet (13 m) long.

The two kinds of white whales are
the narwhal and beluga. The
narwhal's swordlike tusk may have
inspired legends about the mythical
unicorn. The beluga is tuskless
and is pure white when
adult. It also has a flexible
neck, so it can turn its
head to each side. Belugas
live in all Arctic and
northern seas. They make such loud
chirps, trills, and squeaks that these
can be heard above the water, earning
them the nickname of "sea canary."

River dolphins live in fresh water and estuaries.
Their echolocation is very sensitive, helping them
find their way in muddy water. They include the
very rare whitefin dolphin. There are perhaps only
150–200 left, in the Yangtze
river in China.

porpoises tend to stay inshore, usually in small
groups of about 10 or 15, and seldom
leap clear of the water.

BIGGEST TOOTHED WHALES
Sperm whales feed mainly on
large squid, which they
catch deep in the ocean.
The sperm whale is gigantic,
but the dwarf sperm whale is
more dolphin-sized, at about
8 feet (2.6 m) long. These whales
are named for the waxy, oily
substance, spermaceti, that takes
up most of their
bulging
foreheads.
It may help
the whale to
dive very deep and
also to focus the sound
waves it uses for echolocation.

◢ The northern
bottlenose whale is
a toothed whale—
but it only has two
teeth. These are in
the lower jaw, and
they may never grow
above the gum.

BEAKED WHALES
The beaked whales are mysterious
creatures that resemble overgrown
dolphins. There are 18 species, but they spend
most of their time diving to immense depths and

continued from page 231:

dolphins and other toothed whales
• 66 species
• mostly smaller than great whales
• short, sharp teeth

groups include:

dolphins
• 32 species
• worldwide, mainly offshore in
warm seas
• beaklike snout
• includes common, bottlenose and
spinner dolphins, melon-headed
whale, pilot whales, killer whale
(orca)

porpoises
• 6 species
• coastal waters of northern
hemisphere
• lack dolphin's "beak"
• includes common and Dall's

porpoises

River dolphins
• 5 species
• fresh water
• Amazon, La Plata, Indus, Ganges,
and whitefin dolphins

Sperm whales
• 3 species
• blunt forehead
• includes sperm and pygmy sperm
whales

Beaked whales
• 18 species
• resemble large dolphins with
beaklike snout
• includes northern bottlenose
whale and Cuvier's beaked whale

White whales
• 2 species
• whitish color
• narwhal and beluga

◢ Many dolphins,
like these
bottlenoses, make
spectacular leaps into
the air, sometimes up to
10 feet (3 m) clear of the
sea. One species, the
spinner dolphin, leaps high
into the air and spins like a
top at the same time.

233

LEMURS AND BUSHBABIES

ALONG WITH MONKEYS AND APES, THE LEMURS AND BUSHBABIES BELONG TO A GROUP OF MAMMALS KNOWN AS PRIMATES. The main primate features include a relatively large brain for the size of the body, well-developed hands with thumbs that can grasp and manipulate small items, and large, forward-facing eyes. The lemurs and bushbabies, plus the pottos, lorises, and tarsiers, are prosimians, which means "early-monkeys." They resemble animals that appeared on Earth before the later primates, the monkeys and apes.

△ The potto can grasp twigs between its fingers and thumb, and also between its big toe and other toes. It has a head–body lengt about 14 inches (35 cm).

△ Ring-tailed lemur mother and baby

▶ Bushbabies have such precise hearing and fast reactions that they can hear a moth flutter past, and reach out and grab it, all in total darkness.

Lemurs are found only in Madagascar. They resemble a combination of monkey and squirrel, and range in size from lesser mouse-lemurs smaller than your fist, to the large indri with a head–body length of 28 inches (70 cm). Most lemurs feed mainly at night on fruits, seeds, flowers, and leaves, which they gather as they move through the trees. They see and hear well at night wi their large eyes and ears. Most species have long tails for balancin

The ring-tailed lemur's tail is brightly patterned with alternate rings of black and white. This species is active by day. It wipes its large tail on scent glands under its arms and chin, then waves the tail aloft to send sight and smell signa to its troop members. However, most lemur species are much less noticeable, as they hide by day and creep through the shadowy trees at night.

▶ Mouse lemurs are the smallest lemurs, and also the smallest primates. Yet they are long-lived for such small mammals. Some have survived 12–15 years in captivity.

▶ The slow loris is well named, sinc hardly seems to move as it cre through the thickest rainforest. It grip a twig and hang by just one f

PRIMATES

- 180 species
- large, forward-facing eyes
- manipulative hands
- mostly tree-dwelling

Prosimians
- 36 species
- mostly smaller than monkeys
- simple teeth with few points (cusps)

Main groups of prosimians:

Lemurs
- 10 species
- Madagascar only

Sifakas
- 4 species
- Madagascar only
- resemble large lemurs

Dwarf lemurs and mouse lemur
- 8 species
- Madagascar only

Aye-aye
- 1 species
- Madagascar only

- long, thin middle finger

Bushbabies
- 6 species
- Africa
- enormous eyes

Lorises and pottos
- 4 species
- Africa and Asia

Tarsiers
- 3 species
- Southeast Asia (Borneo, Sumatra, Philippines)

The aye-aye of Madagascar has batlike ears, large front teeth, and an extraordinary long middle finger to pick grubs out of wood. It is an endangered species.

ushbabies live mainly in East Africa. Like murs, they prefer dense forests. They are small d agile, and find insects at night with their huge es and keen hearing. The tail-less lorises and ottos of Africa and Asia are much more slow-oving than bushbabies. They creep slowly ong branches as they feed on a range of ems, from fruits and tree sap, to insects d snails, even a small bird or shrew. uge-eyed tarsiers watch the forest oor from a low bough. hen a lizard or insect mbles past, they pounce.

he indri he largest e of lemur. It has a ad and body up to 2 feet) cm) long, and weighs as much as 22 unds (10 kg). It also lacks the typical ur's long tail, having a short stump.

The tarsier leaps extremely well using its muscular back legs and long, strong rear feet. It keeps its body upright as it springs from one branch to another.

235

AFRICAN MONKEYS

ABOUT 40 SPECIES OF MONKEYS LIVE IN AFRICA, IN HABITATS RANGING FROM DENSE TROPICAL FOREST, TO OPEN WOODLAND AND SAVANNA, TO DRY ROCKY SCRUB. Most common are the guenons, with long tails. They inhabit mainly forests, traveling and feeding in groups. One of the most abundant and widespread guenons is the vervet monkey, equally at home on the ground or in trees. When feeding on the ground, vervets are

◤ White-cheeked mangabey

always wary, and quickly rush to safety in the trees if danger threatens. Many of these African monkeys have colorful markings with different patterns of red, brown, gray, black, and white, especially around the face. These colors change to show the sex and age of each troop member.

◀ Colobus monkeys have four fingers on each hand. Their thumbs are tiny or missing.

◤ Olive baboons live in troops of 100 or more. The troop ha social order with leading males and females. Young males pa the edges and act as scouts to check for danc

Colobuses are some of the most beautiful and graceful of all monkeys, with their long, glossy coats and sweeping, tufted tails. They stay mainly in trees along the forest edge, and rarely come down to the ground except to feast on fallen fruits. Unfortunately, many colobus monkeys are killed for their fur, and several species are now rare or endangered. Another great threat to all monkeys is habitat loss—the clearance of their forest homes for farmland, buildings, and roads.

LARGEST... !
The mandrill and drill are the largest monkeys. Males reach 3 feet (90 cm) tall and weigh 110 pounds (50 kg).

The adult male mandrill has a [bri]ght red nose, with bright or [pal]e blue patches at each side, [an]d yellow-orange fur on the [chi]n. Mandrills live in troops of [20]–40 in West African forests. [Th]ey sleep in trees, but feed [m]ainly on the ground.

[DO]G-FACED MONKEYS
[Ba]boons are large, [m]ainly ground-dwelling [m]onkeys. They have [do]glike faces and sharp [te]eth. They are [po]werfully built, with [m]uscular shoulders and [ar]ms, and they can run [an]d clamber with great [sk]ill. This group includes the forest-living mandrill [wi]th its vividly colored face, and the drill with its [eq]ually colorful rear end.

[M]ost baboons live in large groups called troops, [an]d have close-knit social behavior. Olive baboons [liv]e in extended family groups within the larger [tro]op. Each family usually includes offspring and [al]so the offspring's offspring as well. The family [te]nds to stay together and help each other if one is [sic]k or injured. Some species of baboon even live [in] desert habitats with hardly any trees. [C]hacma baboons, a shaggy, dark gray variety [of] the savanna or common baboon species, [ca]n survive even in the almost waterless [wa]stes of the Namib Desert, in [so]uthern Africa.

[M]angabeys are closely related to [ba]boons. They too have strong [ja]ws and especially powerful [in]cisor teeth, to crack open [to]ugh nuts and seeds. They [al]so eat fruits, leaves, [fu]ngi, insects, lizards, and [ba]by birds. They are [mo]re lightly built than

Vervet monkeys can run, climb, and swim well, and eat most kinds of food.

baboons, with tails longer than their bodies, to help balance in the treetops. Since they live among dense forest foliage, they communicate not by visual signs, like baboons, but by loud whoops and cries, like most other monkeys. Mangabeys are mainly black, gray, or brownish.

PRIMATES
(continued from page 235):

Old World monkeys
• 133 species
• forward-facing eyes
• nostrils close together
• manipulating hands
• most have long tails

Groups of African monkeys:

Guenons
• 17 species
• slender body
• several are colorful
• mainly forests

Colobus monkeys
• 9 species
• graceful and agile
• black and white or red-brown
• woodland and forest

Baboons
• 5 species
• mainly African
• heavy body, doglike face
• some have short tails
• spend time on the ground

Mangabeys
• 4 species
• medium-sized
• graceful and agile
• forests

237

ASIAN MONKEYS

THE LARGEST GROUP OF ASIAN MONKEYS IS THE
LEAF MONKEYS AND LANGURS. They are found
mainly in southern Asia, but some live in North Africa
and others in China. This group contains many species
that dwell in forests, like most other monkeys. But there
are also some which survive high in mountains, where it is
snowy and treeless. The Hanuman (or common) langur is one of the
most adaptable, ranging from gardens and towns to remote, rocky
uplands. It is regarded as sacred in the Hindu faith. Even though it
often raids crops, it is seldom harmed. Most leaf monkey
and langurs feed on leaves, fruits, nuts, buds, and
flowers. They rarely drink, obtaining
most of the water they need from
their juicy food. Due to loss of
their forest home, some
of these monkeys a
rare and a few a
on the official
"Red Lists" of
threatened
species.

▶ Hanuman langurs are bold monkeys and soon become used to people. They sometimes raid picnic sites, shops, and houses to look for food.

WAAAH! !

In some langurs, a young monkey is cared for by "baby-sitters" as well as by its own mother. These other females may even give their own milk to the baby. However, they may also simply put it down and walk off! The abandoned baby cries out, and its mother soon comes back.

▶ Most primates only enter water if they must, to escape danger. Proboscis monkeys are the best swimmers in the group. They often cross rivers, even diving below the surface.

▼ Many macaques have hairless faces, with red skin.

▼ Like m
monkeys and o
primates, rhe
macaques groom e
other and their young.
monkey searches through
fur with its nimble fingers for
of dirt, and for pests like fleas ;
lice, that it pops into its mou
This mutual grooming helps
strengthen relationships wit
the family and the tro

Macaques are the most widespread monkeys,
found from North Africa across the Middle East
and Asia, including the Philippines and Indonesia.
The habitats they occupy are equally varied,
including rainforests, mangrove swamps, scrub,
and even buildings such as shrines and temples.
The rhesus and Japanese macaques can survive
winter snow and ice, feeding on roots and tree sap.

he crab-eating macaque was named because
rly scientific observers watched it eat crabs.
t like many monkeys, it has a mixed diet of
sects and similar small animals, eggs, fruit,
ds, leaves, and almost anything else.

UB-NOSED MONKEYS

ese large monkeys take their name from the
t, short nose, set back from the rounded
uzzle. They also have strong arms which are
most as long as their legs. They are found
ainly in forests and bamboo jungles in China,
bet, and Southeast Asia, some species
habiting the cloud forests high on mountain
opes. At least two species are rare or
dangered, with populations of just a few
ndred. They can survive only if their forest
bitats are protected.

OBOSCIS MONKEYS

e proboscis monkey is named for the male's
ominent, protruding nose, which droops down
over the mouth. The
female has a shorter,

he snub-nosed monkeys of
na migrate in spring up the
untain slopes, and come back
n as cold autumn mists
k the uppermost forests.

more normal
monkey
nose, as do
both sexes of
the related
pig-tailed
monkey. Both of
these species are
rare and live in
restricted areas.

The proboscis monkey
lives in Borneo, and the
pig-tailed monkey on
the Mentawai Islands
off Sumatra.

The favorite habitats of
the proboscis monkey
are mangrove
swamps along the
coast, where they
feed mainly on the
young shoots and
leaves of mangroves
and the fruits of other
trees, such as pedadas.
Occasionally they swim
across stretches of
water and even dive
from heights of 50 feet (15 m) into the sea to
avoid danger. The proboscis monkey's leafy food
is poor in nutrients, so it must eat large amounts.
After a good meal, about half of the monkey's
body weight of 30–44 pounds (15–20 kg) is the
leaves in its enormous stomach.

⬆ Japanese macaques live high
in mountains, where it becomes
cold and icy in winter. They
sometimes warm themselves by
bathing in natural hot springs.

⬇ Old World monkeys differ from
New World or American species
in various ways, including
their nostrils being
close together.

LD WORLD MONKEYS
ontinued from page 237)

sian groups include:

eaf monkeys and langurs
20 species
India, China, Southeast Asia
long limbs and tail
some have crestlike hairs on
head
various habitats

lacaques
15 species
mostly Asian
bulky, sturdy build
often live on the ground

ub-nosed monkeys
6 species
China and Southeast Asia
broad face with snub nose
forest and bamboo groves

oboscis monkeys
2 species
Borneo, Sumatra
bulky, rotund body
prominent floppy nose
rainforest and mangroves

239

AMERICAN MONKEYS

NEW WORLD OR AMERICAN MONKEYS ARE FOUND MAINLY IN TROPICAL FORESTS. Most are agile and acrobatic, leaping easily through the treetops, but they are difficult to study and little is known about some species. There are two main groups, the small tamarins and marmosets, and the larger howler and wooly monkeys. They may be hard to see, but they can certainly be heard since they communicate by very loud calls. Their howls, hoots, and whoops are some of the most characteristic rainforest noises.

Howler monkeys live mainly in the Amazon region, in small troops of up to ten. Their large throats work as resonance chambers to make their calls extremely loud.

Howler monkeys live in forests, from the steamy trop lowlands to the slopes about 3,000 feet (900 m) above. The species feed mainly on fruits and young leaves. As their na suggests, they are very noisy animals. Their howling c carry for hundreds of yards through the forest. Mos the howling happens as dawn breaks, and for the sa reason that birds sing their dawn chorus. The sou allow rival howler troops to tell each other wh they are, and that their home areas or territo are occupied. This helps to avoid direct fig

SHAGGY SA

Saki monkeys have shaggy fur coats, the males tend to have bright marki around the face. Their main foo fruits, berries, and seeds, gathere they move in small groups thro the forest canopy. Some type sakis eat small animals like l chicks, mice, and bats, as we eggs and the honey of wild b

The owl monkey, or douroucouli, is the only monkey which is active during darkness. Its large eyes are adapted for night vision.

Squirrel monkeys are lively an bold, and sometimes raid fields o crops. They live in groups of 30– and move in the branches with g ease. Like other monkeys they us long, thin tail as a balancing aid.

...DERS IN THE TREES

...der monkeys are the most expert climbers of all
...nkeys. They are named for their long furry legs
...d grasping tail, which stick out at all angles,
...king them look like hairy five-legged spiders.
...ne species can even pick up small objects with
... tail. They dangle in the highest branches, run
...d leap with breathtaking skill, and also swing
...ng using their hands as hooks, like gibbons.
...ey feed on ripe fruits.

...RTLY PREHENSILE

...puchin monkeys are medium sized, with a head
...d body 12–14 inches (30–35 cm) long and a tail
...ip to 20 inches (50 cm). They are found in
...st parts of Central and South America, in a
wide range of forest
types. They have arms
shorter than their legs,
and the tail is less
grasping or prehensile
than most other
American monkeys.
Their varied diet
includes insects and
frogs, as well as fruits
and leaves. Capuchins
often come down to the
ground to feed—which
is another unusual
feature of the New
World monkeys.

...e tail of the spider monkey
... muscular and grasping that
...n hold the creature's entire
... weight, leaving the hands
...feet free to gather food.

SMALL FAMILIES

Titi monkeys are small,
with long, bushy fur.
Unlike most other
American monkeys,
...y live in small family groups rather than large
...ps. Sitting side by side on a branch, they
...netimes twist their dangling tails together for
...a support and security. They are usually quiet,
...make loud dawn calls that last for several
...utes, to defend their territory.

...LY COATS

...oly monkeys live mainly in the Amazon region.
...e spider monkeys, they have a long, strong
...hensile tail, which they use to hang from forest
...ches. They are large monkeys with a head
... body length of 2 feet (60 cm) and a tail even
...ger. They have thick, dense fur and feed mainly
...ruits and leaves.

...red uakari is one of the oddest looking of all
...keys. Its fur is white or chestnut, but its face
...forehead are bald and the pale skin goes
bright red in sunlight,
almost as if sunburned.
This monkey also has a
relatively short tail.
Uakaris prefer damp
lowland forests, clamber
rather than leap through
the branches, and feed
mainly on fruit.

SMALL AND SQUIRREL-LIKE

Tamarins and
marmosets are small,
squirrel-like monkeys,
found mostly in the
Amazon region.
Tamarins are generally
bright in color, and
some have long
"whiskers" or a ruff of hair around the face.
They eat mainly fruit and insects. Marmosets are
slightly smaller than tamarins, and less brightly
patterned. They use their large front teeth to bite
small holes in the bark of certain forest trees.
They then feed on the nutritious, sugary sap or
gum that oozes out.

▲ The wooly spider monkey, or
muriqui, is the symbol of Brazil's
conservation movement. This is
the largest American monkey
species, and also one of the
rarest. Just a few hundred are
left in the country's southeast
coastal forests.

IN GRAVE DANGER

Several species of tamarin and marmoset are in
danger of extinction, often because they are
restricted to a particular kind of forest with
certain tree species. The lion tamarin, with its
golden mane of silky fur, has almost disappeared
from the wild. Several zoos
around the world are
trying to save this
species.

▶ The chief male of the
brown capuchin troop
follows just behind the
younger males as they
forage. In this position, he
receives plenty of food,
but he is also safe since
those in front are
more likely to
encounter any
predators.

NEW WORLD MONKEYS	
• about 50 species • nostrils far apart • many have prehensile tails Howler monkeys and spider monkeys • 29 species • flat faces • most live in forests • incudes howler monkeys (6 species), saki monkeys (6), spider monkeys (5), capuchin monkeys (4), titi monkeys (3), wooly monkeys (2), uakaris (2), night monkey (1), squirrel monkey (1)	Tamarins and marmosets • 21 species • most live in forests of Amazon area • small and squirrel-like • long, furry tail • thumb and fingers cannot hold or manipulate items as well as larger monkeys • feed on fruit, sap, and insects • includes tamarins (12 species), marmosets (9)

GIBBONS

APES ARE LARGER THAN MONKEYS, HAVE ARMS THAT ARE LONGER THAN THEIR LEGS, AND LACK TAILS. They also have large heads and strong jaws with big teeth. The ape group includes gibbons or lesser apes, and orangs, gorillas, and chimp known as great apes. There are nine species of gibbon, all in th forests of Southeast Asia. They are incredibly agile climbers, using their hooklike hands and long, muscular arms to swing around. They also leap with great ease and walk upright on their back legs, even along narrow branches, holding their arms out for balance.

◤ The lar gibbon is also known as the common or white-handed gibbon. Its main coat color varies according to where it lives. Almost black individuals are from the Thailand region (see map opposite).

Like many tree-dwelling primates, gibbons are almost entirely vegetarian. Their favorite food is ripe fruit, which accounts for about two thirds of their diet, and which they travel great distances to find. They also eat flowers, buds, shoots, and leaves, and the occasional insect or other small animal. Fruit provides most of the water they need, but they also lick raindrops or dew from leaves. In a typical day, a gibbon spends about three hours searching for food, some four hours eating, and the rest of the time resting, sleeping, grooming, playing, and calling.

ARMS AND SHOULDERS

The gibbon's main method of moving is almost unique among primates. Most forest monkeys have long tails to help them balance and perhaps to grasp branches. But the gibbon is tail-less. Instead, it has long, muscular arms and very broad shoulders. It uses these to hang from branches and swing hand-over-hand with amazing speed and skill. This way of moving is called brachiation.

▣ On Sumatra and the Malay peninsula, most lar gibbons have brownish fur. These two sites are color-coded blue and red on the map (opposite), while the Thai area is coded green.

◤ Siamangs make their calls louder by inflating their throat pouches like balloons.

The gibbon's shoulder and arm joints are very flexible, and a gibbon can hang by one arm an turn its body in a complete circle.

GIBBON DUETS

Gibbons are also famed for their loud, sometin musical calls. These echo throug the forest, especially during the dawn chorus. Gibbons use these calls to communicate with each oth and with neighboring groups. Usually the female starts the call. Her mate th adds his own cries in the gaps betwee her sounds, so the result is a duet. Th song of a gibbon usually follows a regu pattern. It begins with a "tuning up" perio where the pair practice and loosen their throats and mouths. The next stage cons of alternating sequences, as the female male take turns. Then comes the mair part—the "great call" of the female.

WHERE GIBBONS LIVE

Each species of gibbon lives in a different region of Southeast Asia. This is called geographic separation. It means that they do not compete for food, since all species have similar diets. The exception is the siamang, which is considerably larger than the other species and takes larger food items.

1 Hoolock gibbon
2 Lar gibbon
3 Concolor gibbon
4 Pileated gibbon
5 Agile gibbon
6 Lar gibbon
7 Kloss gibbon
8 Siamang
9 Moloch gibbon
10 Muller's gibbon

...ING SOLO

...one species, the kloss gibbon, male and female ...g separately rather than together. The male ...oduces a loud and musical solo in the morning, ...: as long as two hours. The female's song is ...ually shorter, but even more impressive. Every ...ee or four days she climbs to the top of a tree ...perform. Her song has some 20 different ...rases, each lasting about half a minute, with ...g notes rising and falling. She ends with a flourish and her "great call"—during which she launches herself into the air, then rushes about tearing off leaves and snapping twigs.

...APES

• 13 species
• resemble large, tail-less monkeys
• Africa and Southeast Asia

Gibbons (lesser apes)
• 9 species
Agile gibbon
• Malaya, Sumatra, Borneo
Concolor gibbon
• Laos, Vietnam, S. China
Hoolock gibbon
• Assam, Bangladesh, Burma
Kloss gibbon
• Mentawai Islands (Sumatra)
Lar gibbon
• Thailand, Malaya, Sumatra
Moloch gibbon
• Java
Muller's gibbon
• Borneo
Pileated gibbon
• Thailand, Cambodia
Siamang
• Malaya, Sumatra

▶ Gibbons, along with the orang, have the longest arms in relation to their body size, of any primate. The largest gibbon, the siamang, has an "armspan" of more than 5 feet (1.5 m). Yet its head and body are only about 32 inches (80 cm) long.

PARTNERS FOR LIFE

The duet of a female and male gibbon helps to maintain their partnership, because they pair for life. They live as a small family group with their two or three young. Baby gibbons are born about every two years, and they cling tightly to their mother's fur even as she swings at speed through the trees. In some species, such as the siamang, the male takes over the care of the older offspring, until they are perhaps five years old. Gibbons are long-lived animals for their size, reaching about 40 years of age in the wild.

▶ Compared to other mammals, baby apes are cared for by their mothers for a long time. The young lar gibbon feeds on its mother's milk for up to two years.

243

ORANGS AND GORILLAS

THE ORANG, GORILLA, CHIMP, AND PYGMY CHIMP ARE THE FOUR KINDS OF GREAT APES, AND THE LARGEST OF THE PRIMATES. They are also the closest living relatives of ourselves, the human species. The mysterious orangs live deep in the forests of Borneo and Sumatra, in Southeast Asia. They are difficult to spot because they are rare, very shy, and live mainly on their own rather than in family groups or troops. Gorillas, the largest apes, dwell in a few restricted areas of West and Central Africa. They live in small groups. They are massive, muscular and powerful animals, yet also peaceful and gentle—unless threatened.

🔼 The female gorilla is pregnant for just over nine months. When the baby is born, it cannot walk or climb, but only cling to her fur. By about three months of age the youngster is sitting up, and by six months old, it is able to climb and walk. The mother feeds it on her milk for up to 18 months.

The name "orangutan" means "man of the woods." This second-largest ape has bright reddish-brown fur, which is long and shaggy. Despite their size and weight, orangs are skilled at clambering around in the trees, spreading their weight using all four limbs. They are very fond of fruit and spend many hours feasting on a tree of ripe figs or mangoes. They also eat leaves and shoots. Their big teeth and strong jaws help them to tear open even hard nuts, and pull off strips of bark to get at the sap-laden soft wood beneath. Orangs also eat insects and the occasional egg, chick, small bird, lizard, or mouse.

World Watch

Gorillas are the largest primates. A mature male is 6 feet (1.8 m) tall and weighs up 400 pounds (180 kg). Bu their size and power have r helped them survive. Rathe it has partly led to their plight. Gorillas have been shot for "sport." Their han and feet are cut off for "trophies." They are amon the most endangered of al animals, especially the mountain gorilla. Human conflicts where they live ha not helped.

LARGEST... !

The orangutan is the largest tree-living mammal. Males grow to 5 feet (1.5 m) tall and weigh 200 pounds (90 kg).

▶ The massive head, neck, shoulders, and arms of the gorilla make it the strongest primate. Large males weigh up to 400 pounds (180 kg).

◄ Gorillas usually sleep in nests that they make by bending and interlocking twigs and branches. Babies sleep with their mothers up to the age of about three years. These are mountain gorillas, with longer fur than the two lowland varieties.

► The lowland gorillas have shorter, less shaggy fur than the rarer mountain gorillas.

THE LONG CALL

Orangs live in similar lowland rainforest habitats to gibbons (page 242). And like gibbons, orangs make loud calls to communicate with each other. However, it is only the male orang that does this, uttering what is known as his "long call," which lasts for a minute or two. The call starts with a series of roars, getting louder, then dying away to end with bubbling sounds. The call is not to keep in touch with family members, since orangs live solitary lives, except for a mother with her baby. The male probably makes the call to attract a female, and to warn rival males off his territory.

Gorillas are very heavily built, with a broad chest, long arms, and a large, tall-domed head (especially in adult males) with massive jaws and teeth. The nose is black, leathery, and flattened. The fur and skin is mostly black, except in older adult males, which develop a silvery-white patch on the back and flanks, giving them the name of silverbacks.

platforms where they sleep at night. Younger gorillas spend part of the day in trees too. They weigh much less than the adults and so find climbing easier— and there are more branches that will bear their weight. But most older members of the gorilla group prefer to feed and travel on the ground. They amble along on all fours, using the soles of the feet and the bent knuckles of their hands.

Gorillas live in groups of about 5–35 animals. A typical group consists of one silverback male, one or two junior males, and several females with their offspring. Unlike most other monkeys and apes, gorillas are mostly silent, except when rival adult males meet. Then they may threaten each other. They beat their chests, thrash branches, and make barking, roaring, and hooting calls.

▲ Orangs seem to make no distinction between their arms and legs, using all of them for both climbing and feeding.

THE MOST VEGETARIAN APE

Gorillas are strong and muscular enough to overpower any animal in their dense forest habitat. Yet they are almost entirely vegetarian. They feed mainly on leaves, shoots, stems, and ferns, and occasionally ripe fruits. Their main feeding periods are early morning and mid-afternoon, with long rests in between.

In the early evening, gorillas climb into trees to weave nest

► Old male orangs develop long, shaggy fur especially over the shoulders and back, and loose, wrinkled skin on the chest and belly. They are also bigger and heavier, with larger cheek flaps than the females.

APES (continued from page 243):	Western lowland gorilla (Cameroon, Central African Republic, Congo, Gabon, Equatorial Guinea)
Great apes	Eastern lowland gorilla (eastern Congo)
• 4 species	Mountain gorilla (Congo, Rwanda, Uganda)
• largest primates	• eats plant material, berries, fruits
• tail-less	
• fingers and thumb can manipulate small items	Orang (orangutan)
Gorilla	• 1 species
• 1 species	• tropical rainforests
• tropical rainforests	• Sumatra and Borneo
• 3 varieties or subspecies:	

CHIMPANZEES

CHIMPANZEES HAVE THE MOST COMPLICATED SOCIAL LIVES OF ALL THE APES. They have a huge range of facial expressions, body postures, gestures, signs, and sounds. They can work out how to solve simple problems, in the wild and in captivity. They make and use simple tools. In many ways, they seem to be a link between the world of animals and our human world. Their body structure and genes, their behavior and intelligence, and their evolution as shown by fossils, mean that chimps are our closest relatives.

▲ The pygmy chimp, or bonobo, is only slightly smaller than the common chimp, with a head–body length of 22–26 inches (55–65 cm).

There are two species of chimpanzee. These are the chimp or common chimpanzee, and the bonobo or pygmy chimpanzee. The chimp is covered with black or gray hair, except for the ears, face, hands, and feet. The face is usually pink, turning darker brown or black with age. The pygmy chimp is slightly smaller, with a lighter build and smaller teeth, and a darker face. It also has sideways tufts of hair over its ears.

Both species of chimps are long lived. Some reach 50 years of age. More than any other animals, they show degrees of humanlike attributes. These include care for their kin, teamwork during hunting, sharing out food, long-lasting bonds or "friendships," the ability to learn through their lives as they acquire skills, use tools and work out problems, with a good long term memory for individuals, places, and events. A chimp also shows self-awareness. Unlike other animals, it recognizes that the reflection in a mirror is itself, not another chimp.

▲ A mother chimp cares for her youngster for up to three years.

THE TWO CHIMPS
There are several differences between the common chimp and the pygmy chimp. But these are quite minor, even in overall size. Some experts suggest that the two chimps are really varieties, or subspecies, of the same species.

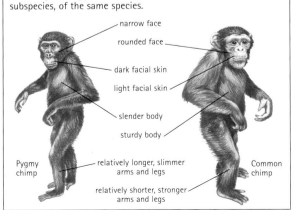

narrow face
rounded face
dark facial skin
light facial skin
slender body
sturdy body
Pygmy chimp
relatively longer, slimmer arms and legs
Common chimp
relatively shorter, stronger arms and legs

However, chimps can also show aggression and violence that is not directed toward catching food or in self-defense against rivals, as it is in other animals. In humans, this type of aggression might be called "mindless."

THE CHIMP'S DAY
Chimpanzees are mainly active during the day. They rise at dawn to search for food, and spend time feeding and resting.

▲ Chimps spend many hours grooming others in their family or group. They remove old hair, bits of dirt, and pests such as fleas from each other's fur and skin. Apart from improving hygiene, this mutual grooming helps to strengthen the relationships within the troop.

MAKING FACES

Chimpanzees use a kind of language to tell each other important information about their surroundings and intentions. They use many facial expressions, and utter various shouts and grunts. Tame chimps have learned our own sign language, using their hands to communicate with people.

Thoughtful

Pleased

Angry

...hen they move on, they travel (like gorillas) ...ainly on the ground rather than in trees, ...uckle-walking on all fours. At night, each adult ...akes itself a nest platform, like the gorilla's. The ...imp bends and weaves together branches, twigs, ...d leaves, and rests and sleeps until the morning.

...E CHIMP'S HABITAT

...eal chimp habitat includes areas with fruit trees, ...ce fruit is their major food and they eat it for ...least 4–5 hours each day. Other favored foods ...e young, freshly sprouted leaves, seeds, and also ...t bark, sap, juicy pith wood, and flowers. They ...metimes use rocks to smash open hard-cased ...its and nuts, such as those of oil palms.

Chimps also eat termites, ants, and caterpillars. A chimp may use a stick to probe inside a termite mound. The insects crawl onto the twig, and the chimp pulls it out and licks them off. Groups of chimps occasionally work together to catch and eat young pigs, monkeys, and antelopes.

An adult male chimp is far stronger than an adult human, with a broad chest and very muscular arms. Male chimps, especially, get into fights or territorial disputes. They pick up and hurl large boulders or branches with great ease. Most chimp troops number about 20–50 individuals, with one or two large, leading males, various younger males, and females with their young.

Chimp numbers have fallen rapidly in recent years. The main causes are habitat destruction and illegal trapping. Many of the remaining populations are small and separated, and so at risk of extinction.

APES (continued from page 245):

Chimpanzees
• 2 species

Common chimpanzee
• West and Central Africa, from Senegal to Tanzania, mainly in Congo, Gabon, Cameroon
• forest, patchy woodland
• fruits, seeds, soft bark and other plant parts, also insects, eggs, small mammals

Pygmy chimpanzee (bonobo)
• Central Africa, only in Congo
• rainforest
• fruits, shoots, leaves, buds

...Many facial expressions made by chimps ...k similar to our own. However, we ...st be very careful about assuming ...t a chimp's expression that looks ...e our own, means the same as ...r version. A chimp who appears ...be in a good mood and ...ghing (right) is really fearful, ...ing its teeth in defense to ...hreat. Chimps learn ...ch during their ...g "childhood."

GLOSSARY

Abdomen The region of an animal's body that contains mainly the parts or organs for digestion, reproduction, and excretion (getting rid of waste products).

Antenna A "feeler," a long and thin part, usually on or near the head, that detects touch—and perhaps smells and tastes as well.

Arthropod An invertebrate animal that has a hard outer body casing (exoskeleton) and jointed limbs, such as an insect, crab, spider, centipede, or millipede.

Asexual reproduction Producing offspring without sex (see Sexual reproduction). For example, some simple animals simply split in two (fission). Some grow "buds" that detach to form new individuals (vegetative reproduction). Some female animals produce eggs that develop into young without being fertilized by the sperm from a male (parthenogenesis).

Camouflage When an animal is shaped, colored, and patterned to blend in with its surroundings, so that it is less likely to be noticed, especially by its predators or prey.

Canine teeth Long, sharp teeth, like spears or daggers, near the front of the mouth of a mammal. They are well developed in meat-eaters such as dogs and cats.

Carapace A large, hard, shieldlike covering over an animal's body. The upper part of the shell of a turtle is a carapace. So is the top part of the shell of a crab.

Carnivore An animal that eats the meat or flesh of other animals. Most carnivores are predators.

Carrion "Dead meat"—the dead and dying bodies or carcasses of animals, which are usually eaten by scavengers.

Cilia Microscopic hairlike parts that coat many outer surfaces and inner linings of animals and their body parts, such as the body surface of a tiny worm or the inside of the intestine. Cilia wave to-and-fro like tiny oars to cause movement.

Compound eye An eye made up of many separate light-detecting units, like a mosaic, rather than one larger unit, like our own eye. Insects have compound eyes.

Courtship behavior The movements, actions, sounds, and scents made by a male and/or female animal of the same species, when they come together to mate.

Detritivore An animal that feeds on detritus—the dead, dying, and rotting bits of animals, plants, and other once-living things.

Digestion Breaking down bits of food into tiny pieces by squeezing and squashing them, and pouring powerful chemical juices onto them. The pieces or nutrients are small enough to be taken into body tissues for growth and life processes.

Digit A toe, finger, or similar part on the end of a limb.

Dorsal On the top, upper side, or back of an animal, like a fish's dorsal fin.

Echolocation A system of sending out sounds, listening to the echoes that bounce back, and working out the position of nearby objects. Bats, dolphins, shrews, and some birds use echolocation.

Egg A single living cell produced by a female animal for reproduction. Some eggs are microscopic. Birds' eggs are large and enclosed in a hard shell.

Endoskeleton A strong supporting framework on the inside of the body, such as our own bones.

Evolution The changes in living things through time, due to changing conditions. New species appear, and existing species that are not suited or adapted to the conditions, and which cannot change or evolve, die out or become extinct.

Exoskeleton A strong supporting framework on the outside of the body, such as an insect's body casing.

Extinction When all the members of a particular group of living thing, usually a species, die out so that the species disappears forever.

Eye A body part that detects light rays and produces nerve signals that go to the animal's brain. (See also Compound eye.)

Filter-feeding When an animal feeds by filtering or sieving lots of tiny particles, usually from water, using body parts shaped like combs, brushes, or feathers.

Flagellum A long, whiplike part sticking out from a microscopic cell. It lashes to-and-fro to cause movement.

Food chain and web The links between different living things, according to how they obtain their food. A simple food chain is when a rabbit eats some grass, and a fox eats the rabbit:
Grass > Rabbit > Fox
 In nature, many animals eat a variety of foods, so the food chains link into a complex network known as a food web.

Genes Instructions or blueprints to make living things, in the form of chemical codes of the substance DNA (deoxyribonucleic acid), found inside cells. A livin thing develops in shape, and color, and carries ou digestion and other body processes, according to t genes it is born with.

Gills Body parts specializ for absorbing oxygen dissolved in water. They a usually delicate and featl

Gland A body part that makes a certain product, usually a liquid, for use b the animal. A salivary gla for example, makes saliva (spit), a venom gland ma poison, and a mucus glar makes slimy mucus.

Habitat A type of natura place with characteristic plants and animals, such pond, an oak wood, or a rocky seashore. Some animals, such as penguin live only in one habitat. Others, such as the red f range across many habita

Herbivore An animal tha eats mainly plants or the parts and products, such leaves, fruits, or roots.

Hermaphrodite An anim that has both female and male sex organs, which a it to produce both eggs a sperm for reproduction.

Hibernation When a wa blooded animal goes into "deep sleep" during adve conditions. Its body temperature falls drastica and its heartbeat, breathi and other body processes almost stop.

Incisor tooth Long, shar edged, chisel-like teeth a the front of the mouth o mammal. They are well developed in rodents (gnawing animals) such a mice, rats, and beavers.

ctivore An animal that
s mainly insects, especially
s or termites, and often
er small prey items too,
n as worms, spiders, slugs,
snails.

rtebrate An animal
hout a backbone or, more
urately, without a
ebral column (see
ebrate). The vast majority
nimals, both in numbers
ndividuals and numbers of
ies, are invertebrates (eg
cts, starfish, and worms).

jdom One of the five
n groups of living things.
nals make up the biggest
dom, Animalia.

a The active growing and
ing stage in the lives of
ain animals. It usually
ows the egg stage. A larva
s not look like its parent.

gs Body parts specialized
absorbing oxygen from air.

amorphosis When an
al changes its body
e dramatically as it
vs. For example, a
erfly begins life as an
hatches into a caterpillar
a), then turns into a
salis (pupa), and finally
the adult butterfly.

ration A long journey to
food or more suitable
ditions. Some migrations
regular, to-and-fro along
same route, at the same
each year. Others are
sional, as when lemmings
out of food and set off in
ost any direction.

ar teeth Wide, flat teeth
e back of the mouth of a
mal, for chewing. They
well developed in
ivores such as zebras,
lopes, and elephants.

us A slimy, usually sticky
tance made by many
als, for uses such as
ection, trapping bits of
, deterring enemies, or
ng movement.

Muscle A body part of an animal specialized to get shorter, or contract. Muscles make movements.

New World Term used for the continents and nearby islands of North and South America. They are separated from the Old World by the Atlantic and Pacific Oceans.

Nutrients Substances such as minerals that a living thing takes in as food, so it can grow, maintain, and repair its body, and use energy for life processes.

Old World Term used for the continents and main islands of Europe, Africa, Asia, and Australia. They are separated from the New World by the Atlantic and Pacific Oceans.

Omnivore An animal that eats many kinds of food, including meat and plants.

Oxygen An invisible gas, with no taste or smell, that makes up one fifth of the air around us. Oxygen is needed by living things because it is a vital part of the chemical process which breaks down food to get energy. Most animals obtain oxygen through their gills or lungs, or by absorbing it through the body's surface.

Parasite A living thing that exists on or in another living thing, known as the host. The parasite gains something, such as shelter or food, and usually causes harm to the host it lives off.

Parthenogenesis See Asexual reproduction.

Pheromone A chemical substance, like a scent, that an animal releases into the air or spreads on the ground. Each pheromone causes a certain reaction in others of its species, such as getting ready to breed, or following the pheromone trail to food.

Predator An animal that hunts or actively pursues other, usually smaller, creatures—its prey—for food.

Prehensile A body part that is flexible and muscular, and which can be used for grasping and holding. Some monkeys have prehensile tails for gripping branches.

Prey Any animal that is pursued or hunted as food, by a predator.

Proboscis A movable stalklike part on the head of an animal, usually with the mouth on it or near it.

Pupa The seemingly inactive, resting stage in the lives of certain animals, such as insects. It usually follows the larva stage and is sometimes called a chrysalis or cocoon.

Sexual reproduction When a sperm cell joins with an egg cell to make a fertilized egg, which develops into a new individual. This usually involves a female and male of the same species mating (having sex). (See Asexual reproduction.)

Species A kind or type of living thing, such as the tiger, the golden eagle, the African elephant or the common octopus. Members of a species can breed with each other, but not with members of another species.

Sperm A single living cell, usually shaped like a microscopic tadpole, produced by a male animal for reproduction. (See Sexual reproduction.)

Symbiosis When two different kinds or species of living things exist closely together and benefit each other in some way, such as giving protection to the other creature from potential predators or sharing food. Sea anemones and clownfish have a symbiotic relationship.

The fish's thick coating of slime protects it against the anemone's stings.

Territory An area that an animal occupies and defends against rivals of its species. Some territories are for feeding, some are for breeding, and some are for both. A tiger's territory covers dozens of square miles of forest. A limpet's territory is just a few square feet of seashore rock.

Thorax The region of an animal's body that contains mainly the parts for moving, such as legs or wings, and often those for breathing and pumping blood (the heart). In the human body it is called the chest.

Torpor When a cold-blooded animal becomes inactive, usually because the temperature falls, as at night or in winter.

Vegetative reproduction See Asexual reproduction.

Ventral On the underside or belly of an animal, like a fish's ventral fin.

Vertebrate An animal with a backbone or, more accurately, a vertebral column—a row of bones or cartilages called vertebrae. The main groups of vertebrates are fish, am hibians, reptiles, birds, and mammals.

Viviparous When a female animal gives birth to babies ("live young"), rather than laying eggs.

Warning colors Bright colors and patterns on an animal's body, which warn others that it is dangerous or harmful in some way. It may have a sting, or a poison bite, or a horrible taste. Red and black or yellow and black are common warning colors, found on bees, wasps, beetles, frogs, snakes, and various other animals.

INDEX

ACKNOWLEDGMENTS

The publishers wish to thank the following artists who have contributed to this publication:

Janet Baker (Julian Baker Illustrations), Andy Beckett (Illustration), John Butler, Kuo Kang Chen, Wayne Ford, Chris Forsey, Roger Gorringe (Illustration), Ron Hayward, Roger Kent (Illustration), Stuart Lafford (Linden Artists), Mick Loates (Linden Artists), Alan Male (Linden Artists), Matt Nicholas (David Lewis Agency), Jane Pickering (Linden Artists), Terry Riley, Mike Saunders, Sarah Smith (Linden Artists), Christian Webb (Temple Rogers), David Webb (Linden Artists), Martin Wilcock (Illustration).

The publishers wish to thank the following photographic sources for the use of their photographs in this publication:
OSF = Oxford Scientific Films; NHPA = Natural History Photographic Agency

Page 12/13 (C) Peter Parks/OSF; 14 (C/L) Peter Parks/OSF; 17 (B/R) Karen Gowlett-Holmes/OSF; 16 (C/L) Harold Taylor/OSF; 18 (L) Peter Parks/OSF; 18/19 (C) M.I. Walker/NHPA; 22 (B) Richard Herrmann/OSF; 26 (B) Frederik Ehrenstrom/OSF; 29 (T/R) A.N.T./NHPA; 30/31 (C) Peter Parks/OSF; 34 (B/L) Norbert Wu/NHPA; 37 (T/R) A.N.T./NHPA; 38 (B) David B. Fleetham/OSF; 45 (T/L) David Fox/OSF, (B) Rodger Jackman/OSF; 46/47 (B) G.I. Bernard/NHPA; 49 (C/B) London Scientific Films/OSF; 50/51 (C) London Scientific Films/OSF; 52/53 (C) Image Quest/NHPA; 55 (C/R) Peter Parks/OSF; 56 (T/L) Colin Milkins/OSF; 56 (T/R) Rudie H.Kuiter/OSF; 58 (C/R) H.L. Fox/OSF; 62 (B/R) Norbert Wu/NHPA; 67 (T/L) Peter Parks/OSF; 68 (B/L) Frederik Ehrenstrom/OSF; 69 (T/L) Pam & Willy Kemp/OSF; 75 (L/T) Kjell B. Sandved/OSF; 76 (B/R) London Scientific Films/OSF; 79 (B/L) D.M. Shale/OSF; 82 (B/L) Bob Fredrick/OSF; 84 (T/L) Colin Milkins/OSF; 86 (B) Alastair Shay/OSF; 88 (B) Alastair Macewan/OSF; 91 (C) Jan Aldenhoven/OSF; 93 (R) J.A.L. Cooke/OSF; 95 (B/L) A.N.T./NHPA; 96 (B/L) Peter Parks/OSF; 99 (T) Michael Fogden/OSF; 106/107 (T/C) Hellio & Van Ingen/NHPA; 108/109 (C) Kathy Tyrrell/OSF; 110 (B/R) Agence Nature/NHPA, (T/L) Peter Parks/OSF; 112 (B) D. Heuclin/NHPA; 115 (B) B. Jones & M. Shimlock/NHPA; 117 (R) David B.Fleetham/OSF; 118 (B) Richard Herrmann/OSF; 119 (B/L) Kathie Atkinson/OSF, (T/L) Max Gibbs/OSF; 120/121 (C) NHPA; 122 (B) Tobias Bernhard/OSF; 122 (T/L) G.I. Bernard/NHPA; 125 (B/R) A.N.T./ NHPA; 128/9 (B/C) Dr. Ivan Polunin/NHPA; 135 (B/L) Robert Erwin/NHPA; 136 (B/R) G.I. Bernard/NHPA; 136 (B/L) Stephen Dalton/NHPA; 139 (T/R) Martin Harvey/NHPA; 143 (B) Jany Sauvanet/NHPA; 145 (T/L) Daniel Heuclin/NHPA; 146-147 (T/C) Stan Osolinski/OSF; 148/149 (B) Stephen Dalton/NHPA; 149 (T/L) Stephen Dalton/NHPA; 151 (T/R) Haroldo Palo Jr./NHPA; 155 (T/L) Jany Sauvanet/NHPA; 156 (B) Daniel Heuclin/NHPA; 158/159 (B) Stephen Dalton/NHPA; 163 (R) Tui de Roy/OSF; 168-169 (B) David C. Fritts/Animals Animals/OSF; 173 (B) Roger Tidman/NHPA; 174/175 (C) L. Hugh Newman/NHPA: 176 (B) Martyn Chillmaid/OSF; 180 (T/R) Robert Tyrrell/OSF; 183 (B/R) Michael Morcombe/NHPA; 185 (B) Maurice Tibbs/Survival Anglia/OSF; 187 (R) Ralph & Daphne Keller/NHPA; 193 (R) A.N.T./NHPA; 197 (T/R) Raymond A. Mendez/Animals Animals/OSF; 198 (T/L) Richard la Val/Animals Animals/OSF; 199 (C) Stephen Dalton/NHPA; 201 (T/R) Michael Fogden/OSF; 203 (C/R) Manfred Danegger/NHPA; 204 (B/L) Survival Anglia/OSF; 206 (B/L) Andrew Thomson; 207 (C/L) Raymond A. Mendez/Animals Animals/OSF; 211 (T/R) Nick Bergkessel/Photo Researchers/OSF; 215 (C) Anthony Bannister/NHPA; 223 (T/L) Peter Pickford/NHPA; 226/227 (B) Daniel Heuclin/NHPA; 229 (T/R) A.N.T./NHPA; 233 (B) Konrad Wothe/OSF; 236 (B/C) Brian Hawkes/NHPA; 238 (C) Norbert Wu/NHPA; 240 (L) Stephen Dalton/NHPA; 242 (C/R) Martin Harvey/NHPA; 245 (T/C) Martin Harvey/NHPA; 246 (C/R) Martyn Colbeck/OSF.